The Marina Handbook

Washington Edition

Information collected - fall & winter 1995, spring 1996

Canadian Cataloguing in Publication Data

Fox, Duane, 1963-
The Marina Handbook, 1996

ISBN 0-9699288-1-5

1. Marinas--Washington (State)--Guidebooks. 2. Boats and boating--Washington (State)--Guidebooks. 3. Washington (State)--Guidebooks. I. Title
GV776.W2F69 1996   797.1'09797   C95-911225-1

Published by FOXPACIFIC Marine Publications - Nanaimo

Distributed in Canada by
Gordon Soules Book Publishers Limited
1352-B Marine Drive
West Vancouver, B.C.
Canada V7T 1B5

Printed and bound in Canada
Best Book Manufacturers - Toronto

FOXPACIFIC Marine Publications
The Marina Handbook ©
The Marina Handbook - Washington Edition
Edition 1

Written by - Ann Marie Whiteaker & Duane Fox

Production:

Cover design by Duane Fox
Layout & Typeset by Duane Fox
Maps & Charts by Duane Fox
Data Collection & Creative Inspiration by:
>Ann Marie Whiteaker
>Lloyd Folland
>Duane Fox
>George Kelly
>Karen Kelly
>Randi Fox

Edited by: Ann Marie Whiteaker
               Lloyd Folland

Credits:

Department Of Transportation - United States Coast Guard
Canadian Coast Guard; Safe Boaters Guide.
Canadian Tourism Commission
Department of the Treasury, U.S. Customs Service.
Revenue Canada Customs and Excise; Customs & GST Information.
Washington State Parks and Recreation Commission
Aerial photography:
>Boston Harbor Marina
>Cheadle Photography
>Department of Fisheries & Oceans
>Donna Fox
>City of Des Moines
>Eagle Harbor
>Hans Hofmaier
>Jarrel's Cove
>Johnny's Dock
>Lake Bay Marina
>Port of Allyn
>Rest-a-While Marina
>Skipanon Marina
>Snug Harbor
>Suldan's Boatworks
>US Army Corps of Engineers

Special thanks go out to all of the marinas that took the time to participate in this collection of information, and who's continued support will ensure that *The Marina Handbook* contains only the most up to date information.

Acknowledgment

It was raining at the marina in the Bay, a hard rain, Hardy Bay.

January 1990, each day we awoke to hot coffee and the weather channel with the hope that today the weather would break. Having had only a handful of attempts at docking this our first vessel, and with a wealth of advice pried out of Hurricane George, we set out. With the Westerlies on our stern we started down the Queen Charlotte Strait. In only a few hours we had passed a half a dozen marinas and the same questions came up as many times. What marina is that? Can we get lunch there? Is there a gas dock? This was the point in time that the idea came to life: "The Marina Handbook". This adventure has taken me to some of the most beautiful areas on this earth and sometimes through very hazardous situations. To my family and friends that participated in this undertaking I thank you. This handbook is the sum of all the labor, ideas and support generated. From untying at Port Hardy with my trusting crew Doug and Brenda, to finding my partner and friend Ann Marie at the Dinghy Dock, to the countless excursions with my brother Randi; to all you people that put your faith in the creaking timbers of the M.V. Sylva Queen and her fearless captains,

Lets do it again!

M.V. SYLVA QUEEN
48'
BOEING AIRCRAFT 1937

There is no playground on earth equal to the Pacific Northwest. I hope your boating adventures are as interesting as mine have been.

See you on the water.
Duane Fox

The FOXPACIFIC Storefront

⚓ **To Purchase the latest edition of The Marina Handbook**
⚓ **To have your marina included in The Marina Handbook**
⚓ **To be included on one of our lists**
⚓ **To inquire about advertising in The Marina Handbook**
⚓ **To inquire about retailing The Marina Handbook**

Contact FOXPACIFIC Marine Publications in writing
Box 955 Nanaimo, B.C. Canada V9R 5N2
or email fox@island.net
Tel (604) 753-9593 Fax (604) 753-3835

All retail book orders prepaid. Send $13.95 US
$15.95 Cdn cheque or money order
(taxes & shipping included)

The
Marina Handbook

Washington Edition

In gathering this information, we at FOXPACIFIC have attempted to put forth the most comprehensive and up to date marina guide available. At the same time we have made this large amount of information easily accessible, affordable and user friendly. This type of information changes from year to year and so will *The Marina Handbook*. As well as annually updating the marina information, we will be adding more marinas and services. We are open to any and all suggestions in reference to additions and changes that would make this a more complete and easier to use marina guide.

For an up to date listing of British Columbia marinas ask your retailer for *The Marina Handbook S. W. British Columbia Edition.*

TABLE OF CONTENTS

HOW TO USE THE MARINA HANDBOOK

To Find Information

Consistent Format. For ease of use, the *Marina Handbook* has been designed with a consistent format from page to page. This allows the user to quickly access information. Look to fig. 1-1 to familiarize yourself with the different parts of the page. See fig. 1-2 for indexing information.

Marina Page Breakdown

Location: Town, Island, Bay etc.

Location Information: Name, Address, Telephone, Fax and VHF. Approximate Coordinates and a Chart #.

General Information: Summer & Winter Dock Master Office Hours, Moorage Rates, and General On the Dock Services.

Public Services: Services located at or near the Marina. Within walking distance can include walk-on ferry or shuttle service.

Fuel Float Information: Name of fuel company (or operator if independent). Hours of operation, Phone number and Fuel types. (If marina does not have a fuel float this area will be greyed)

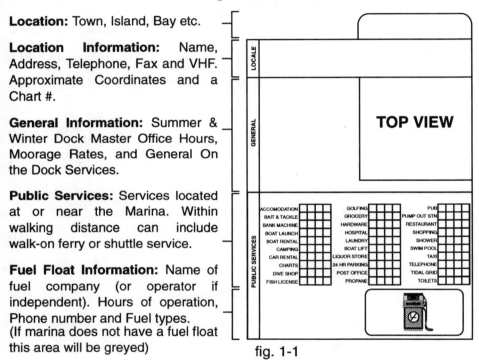

fig. 1-1

Top View: This area contains a graphic image of the associated marina. Due to a square crop our aerial photos may contain part or all of adjacent marinas. In these cases the featured marina is centered in the crop. Marina photos are intended to give the user a general idea of the marina layout. Prior knowledge of the dock layout can substantially reduce the use of reverse.

Important: Any information designated by an (*) should be verified by contacting its associated marina. Some information may be generalized, averaged or was simply unavailable. Lat. / long. coordinates are approximate.

Most of the information contained within the Marina Handbook has been volunteered by each of the marinas . We have transferred this information just as it was submitted. If boxes have been left blank it only means that we did not receive this information.

HOW TO USE THE MARINA HANDBOOK

To Locate A Specific Marina

In this book the term _marina_ is used loosely, from here on in it is understood that the term _marina_ refers to any wharf or float that is intended for boats to tie-up at; State, Commercial, Public or Private.

To Locate A Marina By Name: Go to the alphabetical index at the back of the book and look up the Marina.

To Locate A Marina By Area: If you know where the marina is located (Town, Island, Bay etc.) but do not know its name, flip through the book reading the prominent headings until the area you require is found. All Marina pages have been placed in alphabetical order by location then name giving the reader the ability to quickly access an area and subsequently all of that area's associated marinas.

To Locate A Marina By Map: If you can identify where a marina is located on a chart but do not know its name. Look to pages 3 through 6 where you will find map indexes pinpointing the individual marinas. Look to page 191 to see a map index of State Marine Parks.

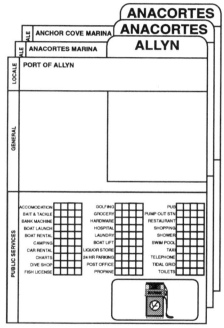

fig. 1-2

All information contained within the _Marina Handbook_ was obtained in writing directly from the marinas or in person by a FOXPACIFIC representative. This information is subject to; change without our knowledge, misinterpretation, misrepresentation and human error. This information is given without guarantee and in no way are the facilities mentioned in this publication obligated to honor the rates or services listed.

Any person that finds incorrect information or knows of marinas not mentioned in the _Marina Handbook_ is invited to contact FOXPACIFIC Marine Publications in writing at Box 955 Nanaimo, B.C. V9R 5N2 or fox@island.net

Attention: The information, pictures, maps, coordinates and distance tables contained within the _Marina Handbook_ are not intended for navigation.

MAP INDEX
WASHINGTON

All of the marinas that have a page & photo in this book are shown geographically on the map index and its insets.

See *Map Indexes* showing fuel floats, and marine parks.

(#) = **Marina's page number (as indicated on map)**
(M) = Marina (no listing)

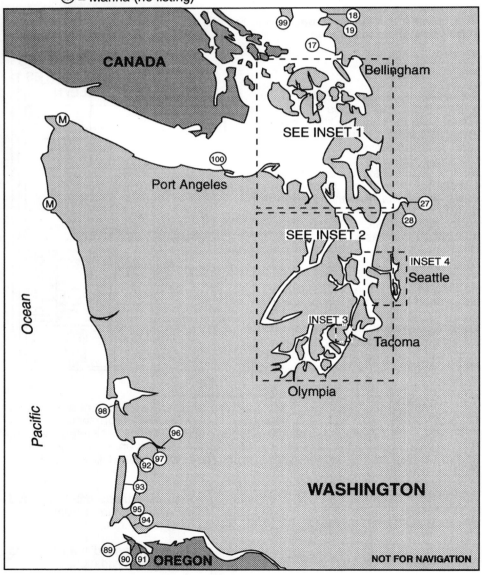

NOT FOR NAVIGATION

MAP INSET 1
SAN JUANS to PORT LUDLOW

(#) = **Marina's page number (as indicated on map)**
(M) = Marina (no listing)

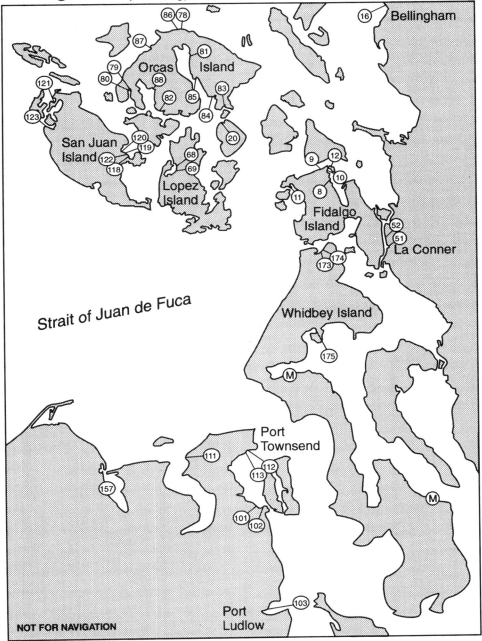

NOT FOR NAVIGATION

4

MAP INSET 2
PUGET SOUND & HOOD CANAL

(#) = Marina's page number (as indicated on map)

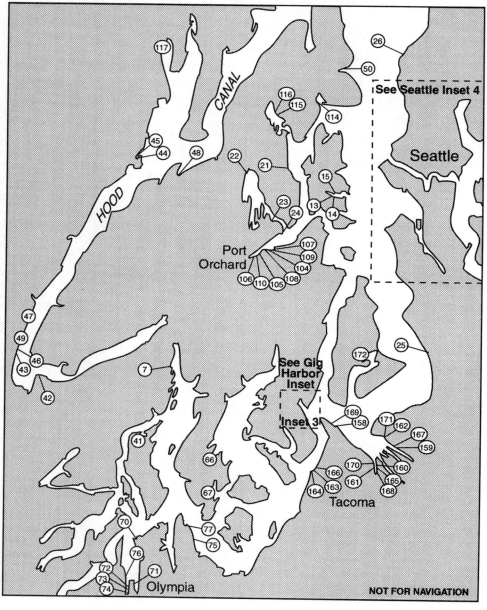

NOT FOR NAVIGATION

MAP INSETS 3 & 4
GIG HARBOR & SEATTLE

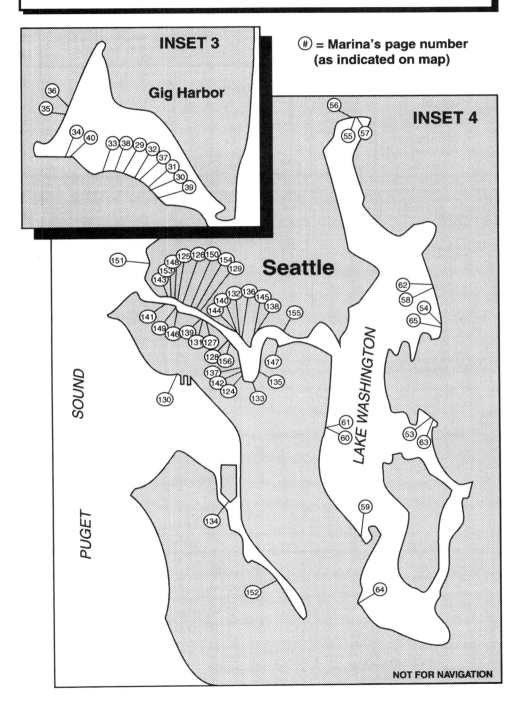

INSET 3

Gig Harbor

(#) = Marina's page number
(as indicated on map)

INSET 4

Seattle

SOUND

PUGET

LAKE WASHINGTON

NOT FOR NAVIGATION

ALLYN

PORT OF ALLYN
VHF:
TEL: 275-2346
FAX:
Washington Area Codes 206, 360 & 509

CHART # 18445
N 47 22 W 122 49

PO BOX 686
BELFAIR, WA.
98528

LOCALE

GENERAL

OFFICE HOURS

SUMMER:	NO OFFICE
WINTER:	

DAILY MOORAGE

SUMMER:	W / PERMISSION
WINTER:	$.25 PER FT

MONTHLY MOORAGE

SUMMER:	$1.13/FT/WK.
WINTER:	$1.50/FT/MTH

VISA | MasterCard | DISCOVER

ON THE DOCK SERVICES

POWER		LIGHTING	✓
30 AMP		CABLE	
WATER		PHONE	
GARBAGE	✓	DERRICK	
WASTE OIL		LIVE ABRD	

WHARVES\FLOATS   150 FT

Note: All marina information is subject to; change without notice, misinterpretation, misrepresentation and human error. In no way are the facilities mentioned in this book obligated to honor the rates and services listed. All information is given without guarantee. No part of this book is intended for navigation.

PUBLIC SERVICES

A: Located at Marina   B: Within Walking   C: Within 20 Miles   D: Not Available

	A	B	C	D
ACCOMMODATION			✓	
BAIT & TACKLE		✓		
BANK MACHINE		✓		
BOAT CHARTER				✓
BOAT LAUNCH	✓			
BOAT RENTAL				✓
CAMPING			✓	
CAR RENTAL				✓
CHARTS			✓	
DIVE SHOP			✓	
FISH LICENSE	✓			

	A	B	C	D
GOLFING		✓		
GROCERY		✓		
HARDWARE			✓	
HOSPITAL				✓
ICE	✓			
LAUNDRY			✓	
BOAT LIFT				✓
LIQUOR STORE			✓	
24 HR PARKING	✓			
POST OFFICE	✓			
PROPANE	✓			

	A	B	C	D
PUB		✓		
PUMPOUT STN				✓
RESTAURANT		✓		
RV FACILITIES			✓	
SHOPS / MALL		✓		
SHOWER			✓	
SWIM POOL				✓
TAXI				✓
TELEPHONE		✓		
TIDAL GRID				✓
TOILETS	✓			

HOURS SUMMER	NO FUEL FLOAT	DIESEL	
		GASOLINE	
HOURS WINTER		STOVE OIL	
		PROPANE	
TEL		AVIATION	

PORTABLE WATER AT TOP OF DOCK.

LOW WATER HAZARD - USE CAUTION.

ANACORTES

LOCALE

ANACORTES MARINA
VHF:
TEL: 293-4543   CHART # 18423
FAX: N 48 30 W 122 36
Washington Area Codes 206, 360 & 509

2415 T AVE.
PO BOX 846
ANACORTES, WA.
98221

GENERAL

OFFICE HOURS
SUMMER:	8AM-5PM M - SAT
WINTER:	SAME

DAILY MOORAGE
SUMMER:	PRIVATE
WINTER:	

MONTHLY MOORAGE
SUMMER:	PRIVATE
WINTER:	

VISA YES   MasterCard YES

DISCOVER

ON THE DOCK SERVICES
POWER	✓	LIGHTING	✓
30 AMP	✓	CABLE	✓
WATER	✓	PHONE	✓
GARBAGE	✓	DERRICK	
WASTE OIL	✓	LIVE ABRD	✓

WHARVES\FLOATS   32-60 FT

Note: All marina information is subject to; change without notice, misinterpretation, misrepresentation and human error. In no way are the facilities mentioned in this book obligated to honor the rates and services listed. All information is given without guarantee. No part of this book is intended for navigation.

PUBLIC SERVICES

A: Located at Marina   B: Within Walking   C: Within 20 Miles   D: Not Available

	A	B	C	D
ACCOMMODATION		✓		
BAIT & TACKLE		✓		
BANK MACHINE		✓		
BOAT CHARTER	✓			
BOAT LAUNCH	✓			
BOAT RENTAL			✓	
CAMPING			✓	
CAR RENTAL		✓		
CHARTS	✓			
DIVE SHOP		✓		
FISH LICENSE	✓			

	A	B	C	D
GOLFING			✓	
GROCERY		✓		
HARDWARE	✓			
HOSPITAL			✓	
ICE	✓			
LAUNDRY	✓			
BOAT LIFT	✓			
LIQUOR STORE		✓		
24 HR PARKING	✓			
POST OFFICE			✓	
PROPANE			✓	

	A	B	C	D
PUB		✓		
PUMPOUT STN	✓			
RESTAURANT		✓		
RV FACILITIES		✓		
SHOPS / MALL		✓		
SHOWER	✓			
SWIM POOL		✓		
TAXI	✓			
TELEPHONE	✓			
TIDAL GRID		✓		
TOILETS	✓			

NO TRANSIENT MOORAGE.
ANACORTES YACHT CHARTER - LARGEST ON
THE COAST, LOCATED AT FACILITY.

CHEVRON

HOURS SUMMER
8-5 M-TH 8-8 F-S

HOURS WINTER
8AM-5PM

TEL   293-8200

MARINE

DIESEL	✓
GASOLINE	✓
STOVE OIL	
PROPANE	
AVIATION	

ANACORTES

ANCHOR COVE MARINA
VHF:
TEL: 293-7033
FAX:
Washington Area Codes 206, 360 & 509

CHART # 18423
N 48 31 W 122 37

1600 5TH ST.
ANACORTES, WA.
98221

LOCALE

GENERAL

OFFICE HOURS
SUMMER:
WINTER:

DAILY MOORAGE
SUMMER: PRIVATE
WINTER:

MONTHLY MOORAGE
SUMMER: PRIVATE
WINTER:

VISA   MasterCard
        DISCOVER

ON THE DOCK SERVICES

POWER	✓	LIGHTING	✓
30 AMP		CABLE	
WATER	✓	PHONE	
GARBAGE	✓	DERRICK	
WASTE OIL		LIVE ABRD	

Note: All marina information is subject to; change without notice, misinterpretation, misrepresentation and human error. In no way are the facilities mentioned in this book obligated to honor the rates and services listed. All information is given without guarantee. No part of this book is intended for navigation.

PUBLIC SERVICES

A: Located at Marina   B: Within Walking   C: Within 20 Miles   D: Not Available

	A	B	C	D
ACCOMMODATION				
BAIT & TACKLE				
BANK MACHINE				
BOAT CHARTER				
BOAT LAUNCH				
BOAT RENTAL				
CAMPING				
CAR RENTAL				
CHARTS				
DIVE SHOP				
FISH LICENSE				

	A	B	C	D
GOLFING				
GROCERY				
HARDWARE				
HOSPITAL				
ICE				
LAUNDRY	✓			
BOAT LIFT				
LIQUOR STORE				
24 HR PARKING				
POST OFFICE				
PROPANE				

	A	B	C	D
PUB				
PUMPOUT STN				
RESTAURANT				
RV FACILITIES				
SHOPS / MALL				
SHOWER	✓			
SWIM POOL				
TAXI				
TELEPHONE	✓			
TIDAL GRID				
TOILETS	✓			

HOURS SUMMER

HOURS WINTER

TEL

NO FUEL FLOAT

DIESEL	
GASOLINE	
STOVE OIL	
PROPANE	
AVIATION	

NO TRANSIENT MOORAGE.
VISITORS ARE THE RESPONSIBILITY OF SLIP OWNERS!
INSURANCE REQUIRED $300,000 LIABILITY.
NO BBQ'S ON DOCK PERMITTED.
PETS MUST BE ON A LEASH AND OWNERS MUST CLEAN AFTER THEM.
NO PASSENGER DROP OFF FOR FERRY ALLOWED.

LOCALE

CAP SANTE BOAT HAVEN

VHF: 66A CB: 5
TEL: 293-0694
FAX: 299-0998
CHART # 18423
N 48 30.70 W 122 36.18
Washington Area Codes 206, 360 & 509

P.O. BOX 297
ANACORTES, WA.
98221

GENERAL

OFFICE HOURS

SUMMER:	7AM-7PM DAILY
WINTER:	8AM-5PM DAILY

DAILY MOORAGE

SUMMER:	$.55 PER FT
WINTER:	$.45 PER FT

MONTHLY MOORAGE

SUMMER:	$3.15 PER FT
WINTER:	SAME

VISA YES
MasterCard YES
DISCOVER

ON THE DOCK SERVICES

POWER	✓	LIGHTING	✓
30 AMP	✓	CABLE	
WATER	✓	PHONE	
GARBAGE	✓	DERRICK	
WASTE OIL	✓	LIVE ABRD	

WHARVES\FLOATS   UP TO 80 FT

Note: All marina information is subject to; change without notice, misinterpretation, misrepresentation and human error. In no way are the facilities mentioned in this book obligated to honor the rates and services listed. All information is given without guarantee. No part of this book is intended for navigation.

PUBLIC SERVICES

A: Located at Marina   B: Within Walking   C: Within 20 Miles   D: Not Available

	A	B	C	D		A	B	C	D		A	B	C	D
ACCOMMODATION		✓			GOLFING			✓		PUB		✓		
BAIT & TACKLE	✓				GROCERY		✓			PUMPOUT STN	✓			
BANK MACHINE		✓			HARDWARE	✓				RESTAURANT	✓			
BOAT CHARTER			✓		HOSPITAL			✓		RV FACILITIES	✓			
BOAT LAUNCH	✓				ICE	✓				SHOPS / MALL		✓		
BOAT RENTAL			✓		LAUNDRY	✓				SHOWER	✓			
CAMPING			✓		BOAT LIFT	✓				SWIM POOL		✓		
CAR RENTAL		✓			LIQUOR STORE			✓		TAXI	✓			
CHARTS	✓				24 HR PARKING	✓				TELEPHONE	✓			
DIVE SHOP	✓				POST OFFICE			✓		TIDAL GRID	✓			
FISH LICENSE	✓				PROPANE	✓				TOILETS	✓			

CALL FOR BERTH ASSIGNMENT AND RESERVATIONS. FREE PUMP OUT AND ALSO FREE TRANSPORTATION TO BINGO/CASINO AND TO ANACORTES AND CONNECTING TO MT. VERNON.

SHELL

HOURS SUMMER

8-6 M-TH, 7-7 F-SU

HOURS WINTER

8AM-5PM

TEL   293-3145

MARINE

DIESEL	✓
GASOLINE	✓
STOVE OIL	
PROPANE	✓
AVIATION	

ANACORTES

SKYLINE MARINA
VHF: 16
TEL: 293-5134
FAX: 293-2427
CHART # 18423
N 48 29 W 122 41
Washington Area Codes 206, 360 & 509

2011 SKYLINE WAY
ANACORTES, WA.
98221

OFFICE HOURS

SUMMER:	8-5 M-TH 8-7 F-SU
WINTER:	9AM - 5PM

DAILY MOORAGE

SUMMER:	$.60 PER FT
WINTER:	SAME

MONTHLY MOORAGE

SUMMER:	VARIES
WINTER:	

VISA YES   MasterCard YES
[ ]   DISCOVER [ ]

ON THE DOCK SERVICES

POWER	✓	LIGHTING	✓
30 AMP	✓	CABLE	
WATER	✓	PHONE	
GARBAGE	✓	DERRICK	
WASTE OIL	✓	LIVE ABRD	✓

WHARVES\FLOATS 20-60 FT

Note: All marina information is subject to; change without notice, misinterpretation, misrepresentation and human error. In no way are the facilities mentioned in this book obligated to honor the rates and services listed. All information is given without guarantee. No part of this book is intended for navigation.

A: Located at Marina   B: Within Walking   C: Within 20 Miles   D: Not Available

	A	B	C	D
ACCOMMODATION		✓		
BAIT & TACKLE	✓			
BANK MACHINE			✓	
BOAT CHARTER	✓			
BOAT LAUNCH	✓			
BOAT RENTAL	✓			
CAMPING		✓		
CAR RENTAL				
CHARTS	✓			
DIVE SHOP			✓	
FISH LICENSE	✓			

	A	B	C	D
GOLFING			✓	
GROCERY	✓			
HARDWARE	✓			
HOSPITAL			✓	
ICE	✓			
LAUNDRY	✓			
BOAT LIFT	✓			
LIQUOR STORE			✓	
24 HR PARKING	✓			
POST OFFICE	✓			
PROPANE	✓			

	A	B	C	D
PUB	✓			
PUMPOUT STN	✓			
RESTAURANT	✓			
RV FACILITIES	✓			
SHOPS / MALL			✓	
SHOWER	✓			
SWIM POOL			✓	
TAXI	✓			
TELEPHONE	✓			
TIDAL GRID			✓	
TOILETS	✓			

UNOCAL 76

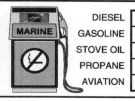

HOURS SUMMER
AS ABOVE
HOURS WINTER
SAME
TEL 293-5134

DIESEL	✓
GASOLINE	✓
STOVE OIL	
PROPANE	✓
AVIATION	

FULL SERVICE MARINA, SHOP AND BOAT YARD FACILITY, AND YACHT CHARTER COMPANY ON SITE.
CNG AVAILABLE AT FUEL FLOAT.

SEE HAUL OUT SECTION OF THIS BOOK.

LOCALE

WYMAN'S MARINA
VHF:
TEL: 293-4606   CHART # 18423
FAX: 293-1055   N 48 31.50 W 122 36
Washington Area Codes 206, 360 & 509

202 U AVE.
PO BOX 349
ANACORTES, WA.
98221

GENERAL

OFFICE HOURS

SUMMER:	VARIES
WINTER:	SAME

DAILY MOORAGE

SUMMER:	INQUIRE
WINTER:	

MONTHLY MOORAGE

SUMMER:	INQUIRE
WINTER:	

VISA	YES	MasterCard	YES
		DISCOVER	

ON THE DOCK SERVICES

POWER		LIGHTING	
30 AMP		CABLE	
WATER	✓	PHONE	
GARBAGE		DERRICK	
WASTE OIL		LIVE ABRD	

Note: All marina information is subject to; change without notice, misinterpretation, misrepresentation and human error. In no way are the facilities mentioned in this book obligated to honor the rates and services listed. All information is given without guarantee. No part of this book is intended for navigation.

PUBLIC SERVICES

A: Located at Marina   B: Within Walking   C: Within 20 Miles   D: Not Available

	A	B	C	D
ACCOMMODATION		✓		
BAIT & TACKLE			✓	
BANK MACHINE		✓		
BOAT CHARTER			✓	
BOAT LAUNCH	✓			
BOAT RENTAL			✓	
CAMPING			✓	
CAR RENTAL		✓		
CHARTS	✓			
DIVE SHOP		✓		
FISH LICENSE		✓		

	A	B	C	D
GOLFING			✓	
GROCERY		✓		
HARDWARE		✓		
HOSPITAL		✓		
ICE	✓			
LAUNDRY		✓		
BOAT LIFT	✓			
LIQUOR STORE		✓		
24 HR PARKING		✓		
POST OFFICE		✓		
PROPANE	✓			

	A	B	C	D
PUB	✓			
PUMPOUT STN			✓	
RESTAURANT	✓			
RV FACILITIES		✓		
SHOPS / MALL		✓		
SHOWER	✓			
SWIM POOL		✓		
TAXI	✓			
TELEPHONE	✓			
TIDAL GRID		✓		
TOILETS	✓			

INDEPENDENT

HOURS SUMMER
8-5 M-F 9-5 SAT
HOURS WINTER
SAME
TEL   293-4606

DIESEL	✓
GASOLINE	✓
STOVE OIL	
PROPANE	✓
AVIATION	

BAINBRIDGE ISLAND

LOCALE

EAGLE HARBOR MARINA
VHF:
TEL: 842-4003
FAX:
Washington Area Codes 206, 360 & 509

CHART # 18445
N 47 37 W 122 30

5834 WARD AVE. N.E.
BAINBRIDGE ISLAND, WA.
98110

GENERAL

OFFICE HOURS
SUMMER:	T-SUN 9AM-5PM
WINTER:	SAME

DAILY MOORAGE
SUMMER:	$.40/FT & PWR
WINTER:	SAME

MONTHLY MOORAGE
SUMMER:	$4.25 - $4.75 /FT
WINTER:	SAME

VISA — MasterCard — DISCOVER

ON THE DOCK SERVICES
POWER	✓	LIGHTING	✓
30 AMP	✓	CABLE	✓
WATER	✓	PHONE	✓
GARBAGE	✓	DERRICK	
WASTE OIL	✓	LIVE ABRD	✓

WHARVES\FLOATS   107 SLIPS

Note: All marina information is subject to; change without notice, misrepresentation, misrepresentation and human error. In no way are the facilities mentioned in this book obligated to honor the rates and services listed. All information is given without guarantee. No part of this book is intended for navigation.

PUBLIC SERVICES

A: Located at Marina   B: Within Walking   C: Within 20 Miles   D: Not Available

	A	B	C	D		A	B	C	D		A	B	C	D
ACCOMMODATION		✓			GOLFING			✓		PUB			✓	
BAIT & TACKLE			✓		GROCERY			✓		PUMPOUT STN	✓			
BANK MACHINE			✓		HARDWARE			✓		RESTAURANT			✓	
BOAT CHARTER			✓		HOSPITAL			✓		RV FACILITIES			✓	
BOAT LAUNCH			✓		ICE	✓				SHOPS / MALL			✓	
BOAT RENTAL				✓	LAUNDRY	✓				SHOWER	✓			
CAMPING			✓		BOAT LIFT			✓		SWIM POOL				✓
CAR RENTAL			✓		LIQUOR STORE			✓		TAXI	✓			
CHARTS			✓		24 HR PARKING	✓				TELEPHONE	✓			
DIVE SHOP			✓		POST OFFICE	✓				TIDAL GRID				✓
FISH LICENSE			✓		PROPANE			✓		TOILETS	✓			

		DIESEL	
HOURS SUMMER	NO	GASOLINE	
	FUEL	STOVE OIL	
HOURS WINTER	FLOAT	PROPANE	
TEL		AVIATION	

SECLUDED YET ONLY 5 MINUTES TO TOWN BY BOAT OR SEATTLE FERRY.
CLUBHOUSE, STORAGE AND WORKSHOPS ON-SITE.

BAINBRIDGE ISLAND

LOCALE

EAGLEDALE MOORINGS
VHF:
TEL: 842-7751   CHART # 18445
FAX: N 47 37 W 122 30
Washington Area Codes 206, 360 & 509

5842 WARD AVE N.E.
BAINBRIDGE ISLAND, WA.
98110

GENERAL

OFFICE HOURS
SUMMER:	N/A
WINTER:	N/A

DAILY MOORAGE
SUMMER:	INQUIRE
WINTER:	SAME

MONTHLY MOORAGE
SUMMER:	INQUIRE
WINTER:	SAME

VISA   MasterCard   DISCOVER

ON THE DOCK SERVICES
POWER	✓	LIGHTING	✓
30 AMP	✓	CABLE	
WATER	✓	PHONE	✓
GARBAGE	✓	DERRICK	
WASTE OIL		LIVE ABRD	✓

WHARVES\FLOATS   UP TO 35 FT

Note: All marina information is subject to; change without notice, misinterpretation, misrepresentation and human error. In no way are the facilities mentioned in this book obligated to honor the rates and services listed. All information is given without guarantee. No part of this book is intended for navigation.

PUBLIC SERVICES

A: Located at Marina   B: Within Walking   C: Within 20 Miles   D: Not Available

	A	B	C	D
ACCOMMODATION		✓		
BAIT & TACKLE			✓	
BANK MACHINE			✓	
BOAT CHARTER			✓	
BOAT LAUNCH			✓	
BOAT RENTAL				✓
CAMPING			✓	
CAR RENTAL			✓	
CHARTS			✓	
DIVE SHOP			✓	
FISH LICENSE			✓	

	A	B	C	D
GOLFING			✓	
GROCERY			✓	
HARDWARE			✓	
HOSPITAL			✓	
ICE	✓			
LAUNDRY			✓	
BOAT LIFT			✓	
LIQUOR STORE			✓	
24 HR PARKING	✓			
POST OFFICE			✓	
PROPANE			✓	

	A	B	C	D
PUB			✓	
PUMPOUT STN		✓		
RESTAURANT			✓	
RV FACILITIES			✓	
SHOPS / MALL			✓	
SHOWER		✓		
SWIM POOL				✓
SWIM POOL				✓
TAXI		✓		
TELEPHONE		✓		
TIDAL GRID				✓
TOILETS		✓		

HOURS SUMMER
HOURS WINTER
TEL

NO FUEL FLOAT

DIESEL
GASOLINE
STOVE OIL
PROPANE
AVIATION

14

BAINBRIDGE ISLAND

LOCALE

WINSLOW WHARF MARINA

VHF: 9

TEL: 842-4202 CHART # 18445

FAX: N 47 37 W 122 30

Washington Area Codes 206, 360 & 509

141 PARFITT WAY S.W.
PO BOX 10297
BAINBRIDGE ISLAND, WA.
98110

GENERAL

OFFICE HOURS

SUMMER:	9AM - 5PM 7 DAYS
WINTER:	9AM - 5PM M-F

DAILY MOORAGE

SUMMER:	NO TRANSIENT
WINTER:	SAME

MONTHLY MOORAGE

SUMMER:	CONDOMINIUM
WINTER:	MOORAGE

VISA	YES	MasterCard	YES
(card)		DISCOVER	

ON THE DOCK SERVICES

POWER	✓	LIGHTING	✓
30 AMP	✓	CABLE	
WATER	✓	PHONE	✓
GARBAGE	✓	DERRICK	
WASTE OIL		LIVE ABRD	✓

WHARVES\FLOATS 24' - 45'

Note: All marina information is subject to; change without notice, misinterpretation, misrepresentation and human error. In no way are the facilities mentioned in this book obligated to honor the rates and services listed. All information is given without guarantee. No part of this book is intended for navigation.

PUBLIC SERVICES

A: Located at Marina   B: Within Walking   C: Within 20 Miles   D: Not Available

	A	B	C	D
ACCOMMODATION		✓		
BAIT & TACKLE		✓		
BANK MACHINE		✓		
BOAT CHARTER				
BOAT LAUNCH			✓	
BOAT RENTAL				
CAMPING			✓	
CAR RENTAL				✓
CHARTS	✓			
DIVE SHOP			✓	
FISH LICENSE	✓			

	A	B	C	D
GOLFING			✓	
GROCERY		✓		
HARDWARE	✓			
HOSPITAL			✓	
ICE	✓			
LAUNDRY	✓			
BOAT LIFT		✓		
LIQUOR STORE		✓		
24 HR PARKING	✓			
POST OFFICE		✓		
PROPANE			✓	

	A	B	C	D
PUB		✓		
PUMPOUT STN	✓			
RESTAURANT		✓		
RV FACILITIES			✓	
SHOPS / MALL	✓			
SHOWER	✓			
SWIM POOL				✓
TAXI	✓			
TELEPHONE	✓			
TIDAL GRID				✓
TOILETS	✓			

HOURS SUMMER	NO FUEL FLOAT	DIESEL
		GASOLINE
HOURS WINTER		STOVE OIL
		PROPANE
TEL		AVIATION

EASY ACCESS TO TOWN.
TRANSIENT SLIPS AVAILABLE ON TENANT
LEAVING. RESERVATIONS ACCEPTED.
UP TO 30' - 40' SLIPS AVAILABLE ON HOLIDAYS.
SHOPS ETC. LOCATED AT MARINA.

BELLINGHAM

LOCALE

PORT OF BELLINGHAM
VHF: 16
TEL: 360-676-25   CHART # 18423
FAX: 360-671-61   N 48 45 W 122 30.5
Washington Area Codes 206, 360 & 509

SQUALICUM MALL # 22
BELLINGHAM, WA.
98225

GENERAL

OFFICE HOURS

SUMMER:	24 HOURS
WINTER:	SAME

DAILY MOORAGE

SUMMER:	$.25 PER FT
WINTER:	SAME

MONTHLY MOORAGE

SUMMER:	$3.10 PER FT
WINTER:	SAME

VISA YES   MasterCard YES
-o-   DISCOVER

ON THE DOCK SERVICES

POWER	✓	LIGHTING	✓
30 AMP		CABLE	
WATER	✓	PHONE	✓
GARBAGE	✓	DERRICK	
WASTE OIL	✓	LIVE ABRD	✓

WHARVES\FLOATS   1800 SLIPS

Note: All marina information is subject to; change without notice, misinterpretation, misrepresentation and human error. In no way are the facilities mentioned in this book obligated to honor the rates and services listed. All information is given without guarantee. No part of this book is intended for navigation.

PUBLIC SERVICES

A: Located at Marina   B: Within Walking   C: Within 20 Miles   D: Not Available

	A	B	C	D		A	B	C	D		A	B	C	D
ACCOMMODATION			✓		GOLFING			✓		PUB	✓			
BAIT & TACKLE	✓				GROCERY			✓		PUMPOUT STN	✓			
BANK MACHINE			✓		HARDWARE	✓				RESTAURANT	✓			
BOAT CHARTER	✓				HOSPITAL			✓		RV FACILITIES			✓	
BOAT LAUNCH	✓				ICE	✓				SHOPS / MALL			✓	
BOAT RENTAL				✓	LAUNDRY	✓				SHOWER	✓			
CAMPING			✓		BOAT LIFT		✓			SWIM POOL			✓	
CAR RENTAL			✓		LIQUOR STORE			✓		TAXI	✓			
CHARTS	✓				24 HR PARKING	✓				TELEPHONE	✓			
DIVE SHOP			✓		POST OFFICE			✓		TIDAL GRID				✓
FISH LICENSE	✓				PROPANE	✓				TOILETS	✓			

SHELL

HOURS SUMMER	MARINE	DIESEL	✓
		GASOLINE	✓
HOURS WINTER		STOVE OIL	
		PROPANE	
TEL 734-1710		AVIATION	

BELLINGHAM

LOCALE

SANDY POINT MARINA
VHF:
TEL: 384-5963
FAX:
Washington Area Codes 206, 360 & 509

CHART # 18423
N 48 47 W 122 43

4323 SALTSPRING DR.
BELLINGHAM, WA.

GENERAL

OFFICE HOURS
SUMMER:	2-7 M-F 8-11AM S,S
WINTER:	SAME

DAILY MOORAGE
SUMMER:	MEMBERS ONLY
WINTER:	SAME

MONTHLY MOORAGE
SUMMER:	MEMBERS ONLY
WINTER:	SAME

VISA   MasterCard   DISCOVER

ON THE DOCK SERVICES
POWER	✓	LIGHTING	✓
30 AMP		CABLE	
WATER	✓	PHONE	
GARBAGE	✓	DERRICK	
WASTE OIL		LIVE ABRD	

Note: All marina information is subject to; change without notice, misinterpretation, misrepresentation and human error. In no way are the facilities mentioned in this book obligated to honor the rates and services listed. All information is given without guarantee. No part of this book is intended for navigation.

PUBLIC SERVICES

A: Located at Marina   B: Within Walking   C: Within 20 Miles   D: Not Available

	A	B	C	D
ACCOMMODATION			✓	
BAIT & TACKLE			✓	
BANK MACHINE			✓	
BOAT CHARTER				✓
BOAT LAUNCH	✓			
BOAT RENTAL				✓
CAMPING			✓	
CAR RENTAL			✓	
CHARTS			✓	
DIVE SHOP			✓	
FISH LICENSE			✓	

	A	B	C	D
GOLFING			✓	
GROCERY			✓	
HARDWARE			✓	
HOSPITAL			✓	
ICE			✓	
LAUNDRY			✓	
BOAT LIFT			✓	
LIQUOR STORE			✓	
24 HR PARKING	✓			
POST OFFICE			✓	
PROPANE			✓	

	A	B	C	D
PUB			✓	
PUMPOUT STN			✓	
RESTAURANT			✓	
RV FACILITIES			✓	
SHOPS / MALL			✓	
SHOWER			✓	
SWIM POOL				✓
TAXI			✓	
TELEPHONE				
TIDAL GRID				✓
TOILETS	✓			

UNBRANDED

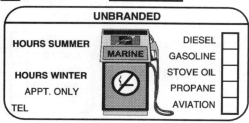

HOURS SUMMER		DIESEL	
	MARINE	GASOLINE	
HOURS WINTER		STOVE OIL	
APPT. ONLY		PROPANE	
TEL		AVIATION	

BLAINE

LOCALE

BLAINE HARBOR
VHF:
TEL: 332-8037
FAX:
Washington Area Codes 206, 360 & 509

CHART # 18421
N 48 59.30 W 122 46

275 PEACE PORTAL
P.O. BOX 1245
BLAINE, WA.
98231

GENERAL

OFFICE HOURS
SUMMER:	8 AM - 4:30 PM
WINTER:	8 AM - 4:30 PM

DAILY MOORAGE
SUMMER:	$.25 PER FT
WINTER:	SAME

MONTHLY MOORAGE
SUMMER:	$3.10 PER FT *
WINTER:	SAME

VISA YES   MasterCard YES

ON THE DOCK SERVICES
POWER	✓	LIGHTING	✓
30 AMP		CABLE	
WATER	✓	PHONE	
GARBAGE	✓	DERRICK	
WASTE OIL	✓	LIVE ABRD	

Note: All marina information is subject to; change without notice, misrepresentation, misrepresentation and human error. In no way are the facilities mentioned in this book obligated to honor the rates and services listed. All information is given without guarantee. No part of this book is intended for navigation.

PUBLIC SERVICES

A: Located at Marina   B: Within Walking   C: Within 20 Miles   D: Not Available

	A	B	C	D
ACCOMMODATION		✓		
BAIT & TACKLE		✓		
BANK MACHINE		✓		
BOAT CHARTER				
BOAT LAUNCH				
BOAT RENTAL				
CAMPING			✓	
CAR RENTAL			✓	
CHARTS		✓		
DIVE SHOP			✓	
FISH LICENSE		✓		

	A	B	C	D
GOLFING			✓	
GROCERY		✓		
HARDWARE			✓	
HOSPITAL			✓	
ICE	✓			
LAUNDRY	✓			
BOAT LIFT	✓			
LIQUOR STORE		✓		
24 HR PARKING	✓			
POST OFFICE		✓		
PROPANE			✓	

	A	B	C	D
PUB	✓			
PUMPOUT STN	✓			
RESTAURANT	✓			
RV FACILITIES			✓	
SHOPS / MALL		✓		
SHOWER	✓			
SWIM POOL				✓
TAXI	✓			
TELEPHONE	✓			
TIDAL GRID				✓
TOILETS	✓			

PLEASE NOTE THAT MONTHLY MOORAGE RATES VARY BY CITIZENSHIP. U.S. RATES HAVE BEEN LISTED, NON U.S. CITIZENS WILL PAY A SLIGHTLY HIGHER FEE.

BLAINE MARINA

HOURS SUMMER
8-5:30 M-F, 9-5 SAT
HOURS WINTER
CLOSED SUNDAY
TEL   332-8425

DIESEL	✓
GASOLINE	✓
STOVE OIL	✓
PROPANE	
AVIATION	

BLAINE

LOCALE

SEMIAHMOO MARINA
VHF:
TEL: 371-5700
FAX:
Washington Area Codes 206, 360 & 509

CHART # 18421
N 48 59.30 W 122 46

9540 SEMIAHMOO PARKWAY
BLAINE, WA.
98230

GENERAL

OFFICE HOURS

SUMMER:	8:30AM - 5PM DAILY
WINTER:	SAME

DAILY MOORAGE

SUMMER:	$.60 PER FT
WINTER:	SAME

MONTHLY MOORAGE

SUMMER:	$4.50 PER FT
WINTER:	SAME

VISA MasterCard DISCOVER

ON THE DOCK SERVICES

POWER	✓	LIGHTING	✓
30 AMP	✓	CABLE	
WATER	✓	PHONE	✓
GARBAGE	✓	DERRICK	
WASTE OIL	✓	LIVE ABRD	✓

Note: All marina information is subject to; change without notice, misinterpretation, misrepresentation and human error. In no way are the facilities mentioned in this book obligated to honor the rates and services listed. All information is given without guarantee. No part of this book is intended for navigation.

PUBLIC SERVICES

A: Located at Marina   B: Within Walking   C: Within 20 Miles   D: Not Available

	A	B	C	D
ACCOMMODATION	✓			
BAIT & TACKLE	✓			
BANK MACHINE				
BOAT CHARTER	✓			
BOAT LAUNCH				
BOAT RENTAL				
CAMPING				
CAR RENTAL				
CHARTS	✓			
DIVE SHOP				
FISH LICENSE	✓			

	A	B	C	D
GOLFING				
GROCERY	✓			
HARDWARE	✓			
HOSPITAL				
ICE	✓			
LAUNDRY	✓			
BOAT LIFT				
LIQUOR STORE				
24 HR PARKING	✓			
POST OFFICE				
PROPANE				

	A	B	C	D
PUB	✓			
PUMPOUT STN	✓			
RESTAURANT	✓			
RV FACILITIES				
SHOPS / MALL				
SHOWER	✓			
SWIM POOL	✓			
TAXI				
TELEPHONE	✓			
TIDAL GRID				
TOILETS	✓			

HOURS SUMMER	NO FUEL FLOAT	DIESEL	
		GASOLINE	
HOURS WINTER		STOVE OIL	
		PROPANE	
TEL		AVIATION	

LOCALE

BLAKELY ISLAND GEN. STORE & MARINA
VHF:
TEL: 375-6121   CHART # 18423
FAX: 375-6141   N 48 35.15 W 122 49
Washington Area Codes 206, 360 & 509

1 MARINE DRIVE
BLAKELY ISLAND, WA.
98222

GENERAL

OFFICE HOURS
SUMMER:	8AM - 8 PM DAILY
WINTER:	11AM- 5PM W- SUN*

DAILY MOORAGE
SUMMER:	$.75 PER FT.
WINTER:	$15.00 PER NIGHT

MONTHLY MOORAGE
SUMMER:	$6.00 PER FT.
WINTER:	$6.00 PER FT.

VISA ☐   MasterCard ☐
☐   DISCOVER ☐

ON THE DOCK SERVICES
POWER	✓	LIGHTING	✓
30 AMP	✓	CABLE	
WATER	✓	PHONE	
GARBAGE	✓	DERRICK	
WASTE OIL		LIVE ABRD	

WHARVES\FLOATS   24', 46' & 80' SLIPS

Note: All marina information is subject to; change without notice, misinterpretation, misrepresentation and human error. In no way are the facilities mentioned in this book obligated to honor the rates and services listed. All information is given without guarantee. No part of this book is intended for navigation.

PUBLIC SERVICES

A: Located at Marina   B: Within Walking   C: Within 20 Miles   D: Not Available

	A	B	C	D
ACCOMMODATION				✓
BAIT & TACKLE	✓			
BANK MACHINE				✓
BOAT CHARTER				✓
BOAT LAUNCH	✓			
BOAT RENTAL				✓
CAMPING				✓
CAR RENTAL				✓
CHARTS	✓			
DIVE SHOP				✓
FISH LICENSE	✓			

	A	B	C	D
GOLFING				✓
GROCERY	✓			
HARDWARE	✓			
HOSPITAL				✓
ICE	✓			
LAUNDRY	✓			
BOAT LIFT				✓
LIQUOR STORE				✓
24 HR PARKING	✓			
POST OFFICE	✓			
PROPANE				✓

	A	B	C	D
PUB				✓
PUMPOUT STN				✓
RESTAURANT	✓			
RV FACILITIES				✓
SHOPS / MALL	✓			
SHOWER	✓			
SWIM POOL				✓
TAXI				✓
TELEPHONE	✓			
TIDAL GRID				✓
TOILETS	✓			

PLEASE NOTE CLOSED JANUARY 1ST
THROUGH TILL FEBRUARY 12.

SHELTERED PICNIC AREA FOR GROUPS.
REFRIGERATOR & COOKING FACILITIES
AVAILABLE.

INDEPENDENT

HOURS SUMMER
8 AM - 8 PM DAILY

HOURS WINTER
11AM--5PM W-SUN

TEL 375-6121

MARINE

DIESEL	✓
GASOLINE	✓
STOVE OIL	
PROPANE	
AVIATION	

BREMERTON

PORT OF BROWNSVILLE

LOCALE

VHF: 16
TEL: 692-5498
FAX: 698-8023
CHART # 18445
N 47 39.10 W 122 36.50
Washington Area Codes 206, 360 & 509

9790 OGLE ROAD N.E.
BREMERTON, WA.
98311- 9398

GENERAL

OFFICE HOURS
SUMMER:	8 - 7 JUN - SEPT
WINTER:	8 AM - 5 PM

DAILY MOORAGE
SUMMER:	$.30 PER FT
WINTER:	SAME

MONTHLY MOORAGE
SUMMER:	$2.60 PER FT
WINTER:	SAME

 YES   YES

YES YES

ON THE DOCK SERVICES
POWER	✓	LIGHTING	✓
30 AMP	✓	CABLE	✓
WATER	✓	PHONE	✓
GARBAGE	✓	DERRICK	✓
WASTE OIL		LIVE ABRD	✓

Note: All marina information is subject to; change without notice, misinterpretation, misrepresentation and human error. In no way are the facilities mentioned in this book obligated to honor the rates and services listed. All information is given without guarantee. No part of this book is intended for navigation.

PUBLIC SERVICES

A: Located at Marina   B: Within Walking   C: Within 20 Miles   D: Not Available

	A	B	C	D
ACCOMMODATION			✓	
BAIT & TACKLE	✓			
BANK MACHINE			✓	
BOAT CHARTER			✓	
BOAT LAUNCH	✓			
BOAT RENTAL				✓
CAMPING			✓	
CAR RENTAL			✓	
CHARTS			✓	
DIVE SHOP			✓	
FISH LICENSE		✓		

	A	B	C	D
GOLFING			✓	
GROCERY	✓			
HARDWARE	✓			
HOSPITAL			✓	
ICE	✓			
LAUNDRY	✓			
BOAT LIFT			✓	
LIQUOR STORE			✓	
24 HR PARKING	✓			
POST OFFICE	✓			
PROPANE	✓			

	A	B	C	D
PUB			✓	
PUMPOUT STN	✓			
RESTAURANT	✓			
RV FACILITIES			✓	
SHOPS / MALL			✓	
SHOWER	✓			
SWIM POOL			✓	
TAXI	✓			
TELEPHONE	✓			
TIDAL GRID				✓
TOILETS	✓			

TEXACO

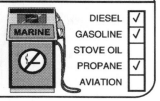

HOURS SUMMER
7AM-7PM
HOURS WINTER
9AM-5PM
TEL   692-5498

DIESEL	✓
GASOLINE	✓
STOVE OIL	
PROPANE	✓
AVIATION	

GROUP TRANSPORTATION AVAILABLE.
UNDERSEA MUSEUM AND PARKS WITH BBQ'S
AND PICNIC TABLES NEARBY.

BREMERTON

LOCALE

PORT OF SILVERDALE
VHF:
TEL: 698-4918   CHART # 18445
FAX: N 47 38 W 122 42
Washington Area Codes 206, 360 & 509

P.O. BOX 310
FOOT OF WASHINGTON AVE.
SILVERDALE, WA.
98383

GENERAL

OFFICE HOURS
SUMMER:	UNATTENDED
WINTER:	

DAILY MOORAGE
SUMMER:	$3.00 < 28 FT
WINTER:	$5.00 > 28 FT

MONTHLY MOORAGE
SUMMER:	N/A
WINTER:	

VISA   MasterCard   DISCOVER

ON THE DOCK SERVICES
POWER		LIGHTING	✓
30 AMP		CABLE	
WATER	✓	PHONE	
GARBAGE	✓	DERRICK	
WASTE OIL		LIVE ABRD	

Note: All marina information is subject to; change without notice, misinterpretation, misrepresentation and human error. In no way are the facilities mentioned in this book obligated to honor the rates and services listed. All information is given without guarantee. No part of this book is intended for navigation.

PUBLIC SERVICES

A: Located at Marina   B: Within Walking   C: Within 20 Miles   D: Not Available

	A	B	C	D
ACCOMMODATION		✓		
BAIT & TACKLE			✓	
BANK MACHINE		✓		
BOAT CHARTER			✓	
BOAT LAUNCH	✓			
BOAT RENTAL			✓	
CAMPING			✓	
CAR RENTAL			✓	
CHARTS				
DIVE SHOP				
FISH LICENSE				

	A	B	C	D
GOLFING			✓	
GROCERY		✓		
HARDWARE			✓	
HOSPITAL			✓	
ICE		✓		
LAUNDRY		✓		
BOAT LIFT			✓	
LIQUOR STORE		✓		
24 HR PARKING	✓			
POST OFFICE			✓	
PROPANE			✓	

	A	B	C	D
PUB	✓			
PUMPOUT STN			✓	
RESTAURANT	✓			
RV FACILITIES			✓	
SHOPS / MALL	✓			
SHOWER			✓	
SWIM POOL			✓	
TAXI	✓			
TELEPHONE	✓			
TIDAL GRID				✓
TOILETS	✓			

THREE NIGHT MAX. LENGTH OF STAY.
LOCATED IN PARK WITH PICNIC PAVILIONS.

WARNING!!! SUDDEN AND SEVERE DOCK MOVEMENT DURING STORMS AND HIGH WINDS CAN BE HAZARDOUS. USE DOCKS AT OWN RISK.

HOURS SUMMER
HOURS WINTER
TEL

NO FUEL FLOAT

DIESEL
GASOLINE
STOVE OIL
PROPANE
AVIATION

22

BREMERTON

LOCALE

PORT WASHINGTON MARINA
VHF:
TEL: 479-3037   CHART # 18445
FAX: N 47 33 W 122 36
Washington Area Codes 206, 360 & 509

1805 THOMPSON DRIVE
BREMERTON, WA.
98337

GENERAL

OFFICE HOURS
SUMMER:	9-5 W-F 10-6 S-S
WINTER:	SAME

DAILY MOORAGE
SUMMER:	$15.00 PER DAY
WINTER:	SAME

MONTHLY MOORAGE
SUMMER:	$3.50/FT SLIP/BOAT
WINTER:	WHICHEVER >

VISA   MasterCard   DISCOVER

ON THE DOCK SERVICES
POWER	✓	LIGHTING	✓
30 AMP	✓	CABLE	
WATER	✓	PHONE	✓
GARBAGE	✓	DERRICK	
WASTE OIL		LIVE ABRD	✓

WHARVES\FLOATS   630 FT

Note: All marina information is subject to; change without notice, misinterpretation, misrepresentation and human error. In no way are the facilities mentioned in this book obligated to honor the rates and services listed. All information is given without guarantee. No part of this book is intended for navigation.

PUBLIC SERVICES

A: Located at Marina   B: Within Walking   C: Within 20 Miles   D: Not Available

	A	B	C	D
ACCOMMODATION		✓		
BAIT & TACKLE		✓		
BANK MACHINE		✓		
BOAT CHARTER	✓			
BOAT LAUNCH			✓	
BOAT RENTAL				
CAMPING			✓	
CAR RENTAL		✓		
CHARTS		✓		
DIVE SHOP		✓		
FISH LICENSE		✓		

	A	B	C	D
GOLFING			✓	
GROCERY		✓		
HARDWARE			✓	
HOSPITAL			✓	
ICE		✓		
LAUNDRY	✓			
BOAT LIFT			✓	
LIQUOR STORE		✓		
24 HR PARKING	✓			
POST OFFICE	✓			
PROPANE			✓	

	A	B	C	D
PUB		✓		
PUMPOUT STN	✓			
RESTAURANT		✓		
RV FACILITIES				✓
SHOPS / MALL		✓		
SHOWER	✓			
SWIM POOL		✓		
TAXI		✓		
TELEPHONE	✓			
TIDAL GRID				✓
TOILETS	✓			

HOURS SUMMER   **NO FUEL FLOAT**   DIESEL / GASOLINE / STOVE OIL / PROPANE / AVIATION
HOURS WINTER
TEL

COMPUTER MONITORS AMERICA ON LINE
CYPRUS ONE.
LIVE-ABOARDS ENCOURAGED.
SECURE MARINA AND PARKING.

23

BREMERTON

THE BREMERTON MARINA VHF: TEL: 373-1035 CHART # 18445 FAX: N 47 32 W 122 38 Washington Area Codes 206, 360 & 509	102 WASHINGTON STREET 8850 SW STATE HWY 3 PORT ORCHARD, WA. 98366

LOCALE

GENERAL

OFFICE HOURS
SUMMER:	8AM - 5PM
WINTER:	SAME

DAILY MOORAGE
SUMMER:	$.25 PER FT
WINTER:	SAME

MONTHLY MOORAGE
SUMMER:	NONE
WINTER:	NONE

VISA MasterCard DISCOVER

ON THE DOCK SERVICES
POWER	✓	LIGHTING	✓
30 AMP	✓	CABLE	
WATER	✓	PHONE	
GARBAGE	✓	DERRICK	
WASTE OIL		LIVE ABRD	

WHARVES\FLOATS 570 FT 40' & 32'

Note: All marina information is subject to; change without notice, misinterpretation, misrepresentation and human error. In no way are the facilities mentioned in this book obligated to honor the rates and services listed. All information is given without guarantee. No part of this book is intended for navigation.

PUBLIC SERVICES

A: Located at Marina B: Within Walking C: Within 20 Miles D: Not Available

	A	B	C	D
ACCOMMODATION			✓	
BAIT & TACKLE			✓	
BANK MACHINE		✓		
BOAT CHARTER				✓
BOAT LAUNCH			✓	
BOAT RENTAL				✓
CAMPING			✓	
CAR RENTAL			✓	
CHARTS			✓	
DIVE SHOP			✓	
FISH LICENSE			✓	

	A	B	C	D
GOLFING			✓	
GROCERY		✓		
HARDWARE			✓	
HOSPITAL			✓	
ICE		✓		
LAUNDRY	✓			
BOAT LIFT			✓	
LIQUOR STORE			✓	
24 HR PARKING		✓		
POST OFFICE		✓		
PROPANE			✓	

	A	B	C	D
PUB		✓		
PUMPOUT STN	✓			
RESTAURANT		✓		
RV FACILITIES			✓	
SHOPS / MALL		✓		
SHOWER	✓			
SWIM POOL			✓	
TAXI		✓		
TELEPHONE	✓			
TIDAL GRID				✓
TOILETS	✓			

RIGHT IN DOWNTOWN BREMERTON. BOARDWALK ADJOINS MARINA. HISTORIC SHIP "USS TURNER JOY DD556" ADJACENT TO MARINA AND OPEN FOR TOURS. SUNDAY FARMERS MARKET MAY THROUGH OCTOBER. FUEL AVAILABLE AT PORT ORCHARD MARINA ONE MILE AWAY. KEY PAD SECURITY.

HOURS SUMMER NO FUEL FLOAT DIESEL
HOURS WINTER GASOLINE STOVE OIL PROPANE
TEL AVIATION

DES MOINES

CITY OF DES MOINES MARINA
VHF: 16
TEL: 824-5700
FAX: 878-5940
Washington Area Codes 206, 360 & 509

CHART # 18445
N 47 24 W 122 20

22307 DOCK AVE. S.
DES MOINES, WA.
98198 - 4627

GENERAL

OFFICE HOURS
SUMMER:	8 AM - 5 PM
WINTER:	8 AM - 5 PM

DAILY MOORAGE
SUMMER:	VARIES BY
WINTER:	BOAT LENGTH

MONTHLY MOORAGE
SUMMER:	VARIES BY
WINTER:	SLIP LENGTH

 YES
 YES
 YES

ON THE DOCK SERVICES
POWER	✓	LIGHTING	✓
30 AMP	✓	CABLE	
WATER	✓	PHONE	✓
GARBAGE	✓	DERRICK	
WASTE OIL	✓	LIVE ABRD	✓

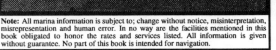

Note: All marina information is subject to; change without notice, misrepresentation, and human error. In no way are the facilities mentioned in this book obligated to honor the rates and services listed. All information is given without guarantee. No part of this book is intended for navigation.

PUBLIC SERVICES

A: Located at Marina   B: Within Walking   C: Within 20 Miles   D: Not Available

	A	B	C	D
ACCOMMODATION		✓		
BAIT & TACKLE	✓			
BANK MACHINE		✓		
BOAT CHARTER	✓			
BOAT LAUNCH	✓			
BOAT RENTAL				✓
CAMPING			✓	
CAR RENTAL			✓	
CHARTS	✓			
DIVE SHOP			✓	
FISH LICENSE			✓	

	A	B	C	D
GOLFING			✓	
GROCERY	✓			
HARDWARE		✓		
HOSPITAL			✓	
ICE	✓			
LAUNDRY		✓		
BOAT LIFT	✓			
LIQUOR STORE			✓	
24 HR PARKING	✓			
POST OFFICE		✓		
PROPANE	✓			

	A	B	C	D
PUB	✓			
PUMPOUT STN	✓			
RESTAURANT	✓			
RV FACILITIES			✓	
SHOPS / MALL		✓		
SHOWER	✓			
SWIM POOL			✓	
TAXI	✓			
TELEPHONE	✓			
TIDAL GRID	✓			
TOILETS	✓			

TEXACO

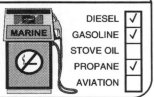

HOURS SUMMER
6 AM - 9 PM
HOURS WINTER
8 AM - 5 PM
TEL   824-5700

DIESEL	✓
GASOLINE	✓
STOVE OIL	
PROPANE	✓
AVIATION	

ONLY MARINA BETWEEN SEATTLE AND TACOMA.
24 HOUR FISHING PIER.
ANNUAL WATERLAND FESTIVAL DURING LAST WEEK OF JULY.
CITY PARK IS ADJACENT TO MARINA.

EDMONDS

PORT OF EDMONDS
VHF: 69
TEL: 774-0549
FAX: 774-7837
Washington Area Codes 206, 360 & 509

CHART # 18445
N 47 48.5 W 122 23.4

336 ADMIRAL WAY
EDMONDS, WA.
98020

LOCALE

GENERAL

OFFICE HOURS

SUMMER:	DAWN TO DUSK
WINTER:	7 AM - 5 PM

DAILY MOORAGE

SUMMER:	$.40 PER FT
WINTER:	

MONTHLY MOORAGE

SUMMER:	VARIES BY LENGTH
WINTER:	

VISA	YES	MasterCard	YES
		DISCOVER	YES

ON THE DOCK SERVICES

POWER	✓	LIGHTING	✓
30 AMP	✓	CABLE	
WATER	✓	PHONE	
GARBAGE	✓	DERRICK	
WASTE OIL	✓	LIVE ABRD	✓

WHARVES\FLOATS   1050 FT GUEST

Note: All marina information is subject to; change without notice, misinterpretation, misrepresentation and human error. In no way are the facilities mentioned in this book obligated to honor the rates and services listed. All information is given without guarantee. No part of this book is intended for navigation.

A: Located at Marina   B: Within Walking   C: Within 20 Miles   D: Not Available

PUBLIC SERVICES

	A	B	C	D
ACCOMMODATION		✓		
BAIT & TACKLE	✓			
BANK MACHINE			✓	
BOAT CHARTER	✓			
BOAT LAUNCH	✓			
BOAT RENTAL				✓
CAMPING				✓
CAR RENTAL			✓	
CHARTS			✓	
DIVE SHOP		✓		
FISH LICENSE	✓			

	A	B	C	D
GOLFING			✓	
GROCERY			✓	
HARDWARE			✓	
HOSPITAL			✓	
ICE	✓			
LAUNDRY		✓		
BOAT LIFT	✓			
LIQUOR STORE			✓	
24 HR PARKING	✓			
POST OFFICE			✓	
PROPANE			✓	

	A	B	C	D
PUB		✓		
PUMPOUT STN	✓			
RESTAURANT	✓			
RV FACILITIES				✓
SHOPS / MALL		✓		
SHOWER	✓			
SWIM POOL			✓	
TAXI	✓			
TELEPHONE	✓			
TIDAL GRID				✓
TOILETS	✓			

LOAN - A - SLIP PROGRAM ENHANCES GUEST MOORAGE AVAILABILITY.

SEE HAUL OUT SECTION OF THIS BOOK

UNOCAL 76

HOURS SUMMER
DUSK TO DAWN
HOURS WINTER
7 AM - 4:30 PM
TEL   775-4588

MARINE

DIESEL	✓
GASOLINE	✓
STOVE OIL	
PROPANE	
AVIATION	

EVERETT

DAGMARS MARINA

VHF:
TEL: 259-6124
FAX: 259-7160
Washington Area Codes 206, 360 & 509

CHART # 18423
N 47 59 W 122 14.1

1871 ROSS AVE.
EVERETT, WA.
98205

LOCALE

GENERAL

OFFICE HOURS

SUMMER:	8 AM - 5 PM
WINTER:	7 DAYS A WEEK

DAILY MOORAGE

SUMMER:	$10.00 PER NIGHT
WINTER:	

MONTHLY MOORAGE

SUMMER:	DRY STORAGE
WINTER:	RATES VARY

VISA	YES	MasterCard	YES
		DISCOVER	

ON THE DOCK SERVICES

POWER	✓	LIGHTING	✓
30 AMP	✓	CABLE	
WATER	✓	PHONE	
GARBAGE	✓	DERRICK	
WASTE OIL	✓	LIVE ABRD	

Note: All marina information is subject to; change without notice, misinterpretation, misrepresentation and human error. In no way are the facilities mentioned in this book obligated to honor the rates and services listed. All information is given without guarantee. No part of this book is intended for navigation.

A: Located at Marina   B: Within Walking   C: Within 20 Miles   D: Not Available

PUBLIC SERVICES

	A	B	C	D		A	B	C	D		A	B	C	D
ACCOMMODATION			✓		GOLFING			✓		PUB			✓	
BAIT & TACKLE	✓				GROCERY			✓		PUMPOUT STN	✓			
BANK MACHINE			✓		HARDWARE	✓				RESTAURANT			✓	
BOAT CHARTER				✓	HOSPITAL			✓		RV FACILITIES			✓	
BOAT LAUNCH	✓				ICE	✓				SHOPS / MALL			✓	
BOAT RENTAL				✓	LAUNDRY			✓		SHOWER			✓	
CAMPING			✓		BOAT LIFT	✓				SWIM POOL			✓	
CAR RENTAL			✓		LIQUOR STORE			✓		TAXI	✓			
CHARTS			✓		24 HR PARKING	✓				TELEPHONE	✓			
DIVE SHOP			✓		POST OFFICE			✓		TIDAL GRID				✓
FISH LICENSE			✓		PROPANE			✓		TOILETS	✓			

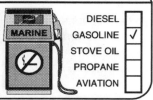

CHEVRON

HOURS SUMMER

MARINA TENANTS

HOURS WINTER

MARINA TENANTS

TEL   259-6124

DIESEL	
GASOLINE	✓
STOVE OIL	
PROPANE	
AVIATION	

PUMP OUT IS FOR PORT-A-POTTIES.
FUEL FLOAT IS FOR MARINA TENANTS ONLY.
MULTIPLE BOAT LAUNCH RAMPS.

EVERETT

LOCALE

PORT OF EVERETT MARINA
VHF: 16
TEL: 259-6001   CHART # 18423
FAX: N 47 59 W 122 14.1
Washington Area Codes 206, 360 & 509

1720 W. MARINE VIEW DRIVE
EVERETT, WA.
98206

GENERAL

OFFICE HOURS
SUMMER:	8AM - 4PM DAILY
WINTER:	8AM - 4PM 6 DAYS

DAILY MOORAGE
SUMMER:	$.35 PER FT
WINTER:	SEE COMMENTS*

MONTHLY MOORAGE
SUMMER:	$2.89 -$5.55*
WINTER:	SAME

VISA MasterCard DISCOVER

ON THE DOCK SERVICES
POWER	✓	LIGHTING	✓
30 AMP	✓	CABLE	✓
WATER	✓	PHONE	✓
GARBAGE	✓	DERRICK	✓
WASTE OIL	✓	LIVE ABRD	✓

Note: All marina information is subject to; change without notice, misinterpretation, misrepresentation and human error. In no way are the facilities mentioned in this book obligated to honor the rates and services listed. All information is given without guarantee. No part of this book is intended for navigation.

PUBLIC SERVICES

A: Located at Marina   B: Within Walking   C: Within 20 Miles   D: Not Available

	A	B	C	D
ACCOMMODATION	✓			
BAIT & TACKLE	✓			
BANK MACHINE			✓	
BOAT CHARTER	✓			
BOAT LAUNCH	✓			
BOAT RENTAL				✓
CAMPING				✓
CAR RENTAL			✓	
CHARTS	✓			
DIVE SHOP				
FISH LICENSE	✓			

	A	B	C	D
GOLFING			✓	
GROCERY	✓			
HARDWARE	✓			
HOSPITAL			✓	
ICE	✓			
LAUNDRY	✓			
BOAT LIFT	✓			
LIQUOR STORE			✓	
24 HR PARKING	✓			
POST OFFICE			✓	
PROPANE	✓			

	A	B	C	D
PUB			✓	
PUMPOUT STN	✓			
RESTAURANT	✓			
RV FACILITIES				
SHOPS / MALL			✓	
SHOWER	✓			
SWIM POOL			✓	
TAXI			✓	
TELEPHONE	✓			
TIDAL GRID				✓
TOILETS	✓			

UNOCAL 76

HOURS SUMMER		
8AM - 4PM DAILY	DIESEL	✓
HOURS WINTER	GASOLINE	✓
8AM - 4PM M - SAT	STOVE OIL	
	PROPANE	
TEL 388-0689	AVIATION	

MARINE

GIG HARBOR

LOCALE

ARABELLA'S LANDING MARINA
VHF: 68
TEL: 851-1793
FAX: 851-1793
Washington Area Codes 206, 360 & 509

CHART # 18445
N 47 19 W 122 34

3323 HARBORVIEW DRIVE
GIG HARBOR, WA.
98332

GENERAL

OFFICE HOURS

SUMMER:	9-8:30M-F10-8:30SS
WINTER:	9-5W/NIGHT STAFF

DAILY MOORAGE

SUMMER:	$.50/FT INC PWR.
WINTER:	SAME

MONTHLY MOORAGE

SUMMER:	$7.25 - $8.00 / FT
WINTER:	SAME

ON THE DOCK SERVICES

POWER	✓	LIGHTING	✓
30 AMP	✓	CABLE	
WATER	✓	PHONE	✓
GARBAGE	✓	DERRICK	
WASTE OIL		LIVE ABRD	✓

Note: All marina information is subject to; change without notice, misrepresentation and human error. In no way are the facilities mentioned in this book obligated to honor the rates and services listed. All information is given without guarantee. No part of this book is intended for navigation.

PUBLIC SERVICES

A: Located at Marina   B: Within Walking   C: Within 20 Miles   D: Not Available

	A	B	C	D		A	B	C	D		A	B	C	D
ACCOMMODATION	✓				GOLFING			✓		PUB		✓		
BAIT & TACKLE		✓			GROCERY		✓			PUMPOUT STN	✓			
BANK MACHINE		✓			HARDWARE		✓			RESTAURANT		✓		
BOAT CHARTER			✓		HOSPITAL			✓		RV FACILITIES		✓		
BOAT LAUNCH		✓			ICE		✓			SHOPS / MALL		✓		
BOAT RENTAL		✓			LAUNDRY	✓				SHOWER	✓			
CAMPING			✓		BOAT LIFT	✓				SWIM POOL			✓	
CAR RENTAL			✓		LIQUOR STORE			✓		TAXI	✓			
CHARTS		✓			24 HR PARKING	✓				TELEPHONE	✓			
DIVE SHOP			✓		POST OFFICE		✓			TIDAL GRID			✓	
FISH LICENSE		✓			PROPANE			✓		TOILETS	✓			

HOURS SUMMER	NO FUEL FLOAT	DIESEL	
		GASOLINE	
HOURS WINTER		STOVE OIL	
		PROPANE	
TEL		AVIATION	

GIG HARBOR'S DESTINATION MARINA. COMBINED USE PERMANENT & OVERNIGHT. 30,50,125,250 AMP. FREE SHOWERS AND COFFEE. 100% HANDICAP ACCESSIBLE. LOCATED IN THE MIDDLE OF TOWN. CAN ACCOMODATE 100 PLUS FT BOAT. DOCK HANDLERS. RESERVATIONS ENCOURAGED.

GIG HARBOR

GIG HARBOR MARINA & BOATYARD
VHF:
TEL: 858-3535   CHART # 18445
FAX: 851-4950   N 47 19 W 122 34
Washington Area Codes 206, 360 & 509

3117 HARBORVIEW DRIVE
PO BOX 387
GIG HARBOR, WA.
98335

GENERAL

OFFICE HOURS
SUMMER: | 8AM - 4:30 PM M - F
WINTER: | SAME

DAILY MOORAGE
SUMMER: | NO TRANSIENT
WINTER: | SAME

MONTHLY MOORAGE
SUMMER: | $145.00 - $305.00
WINTER: | SAME

VISA YES   MasterCard YES

ON THE DOCK SERVICES
POWER	✓	LIGHTING	✓
30 AMP	✓	CABLE	
WATER	✓	PHONE	✓
GARBAGE	✓	DERRICK	✓
WASTE OIL		LIVE ABRD	

WHARVES\FLOATS   25' TO 50' SLIPS

Note: All marina information is subject to; change without notice, misinterpretation, misrepresentation and human error. In no way are the facilities mentioned in this book obligated to honor the rates and services listed. All information is given without guarantee. No part of this book is intended for navigation.

PUBLIC SERVICES

A: Located at Marina   B: Within Walking   C: Within 20 Miles   D: Not Available

	A	B	C	D
ACCOMMODATION			✓	
BAIT & TACKLE	✓			
BANK MACHINE		✓		
BOAT CHARTER		✓		
BOAT LAUNCH		✓		
BOAT RENTAL		✓		
CAMPING			✓	
CAR RENTAL			✓	
CHARTS	✓			
DIVE SHOP			✓	
FISH LICENSE	✓			

	A	B	C	D
GOLFING			✓	
GROCERY		✓		
HARDWARE	✓			
HOSPITAL			✓	
ICE	✓			
LAUNDRY			✓	
BOAT LIFT	✓			
LIQUOR STORE			✓	
24 HR PARKING	✓			
POST OFFICE		✓		
PROPANE			✓	

	A	B	C	D
PUB		✓		
PUMPOUT STN		✓		
RESTAURANT		✓		
RV FACILITIES		✓		
SHOPS / MALL		✓		
SHOWER		✓		
SWIM POOL			✓	
TAXI		✓		
TELEPHONE	✓			
TIDAL GRID			✓	
TOILETS	✓			

HISTORICAL MARINA - ORIGINAL SITE OF SKANSIE'S SHIP BUILDING CO. LOCATED IN THE CENTER OF GIG HARBOR. PERMANENT MOORAGE AND YARD SERVICES WITH TRAVEL LIFT AND RAILWAY AVAILABLE.

SEE HAUL OUT SECTION OF THIS BOOK.

HOURS SUMMER
HOURS WINTER
TEL

NO FUEL FLOAT

DIESEL
GASOLINE
STOVE OIL
PROPANE
AVIATION

GIG HARBOR

LOCALE

GIG HARBOR PUBLIC DOCK
VHF:
TEL: CHART # 18445
FAX: N 47 19 W 122 34
Washington Area Codes 206, 360 & 509

N. 3300 HARBORVIEW DR.
GIG HARBOR, WA.

GENERAL

OFFICE HOURS

SUMMER:	UNATTENDED
WINTER:	

DAILY MOORAGE

SUMMER:	$.25 PER FT
WINTER:	SAME

MONTHLY MOORAGE

SUMMER:	N/A
WINTER:	N/A

VISA   MasterCard   DISCOVER

ON THE DOCK SERVICES

POWER		LIGHTING	
30 AMP		CABLE	
WATER		PHONE	
GARBAGE	✓	DERRICK	
WASTE OIL		LIVE ABRD	

Note: All marina information is subject to; change without notice, misinterpretation, misrepresentation and human error. In no way are the facilities mentioned in this book obligated to honor the rates and services listed. All information is given without guarantee. No part of this book is intended for navigation.

PUBLIC SERVICES

A: Located at Marina   B: Within Walking   C: Within 20 Miles   D: Not Available

	A	B	C	D		A	B	C	D		A	B	C	D
ACCOMMODATION		✓			GOLFING			✓		PUB		✓		
BAIT & TACKLE		✓			GROCERY		✓			PUMPOUT STN		✓		
BANK MACHINE		✓			HARDWARE		✓			RESTAURANT		✓		
BOAT CHARTER			✓		HOSPITAL			✓		RV FACILITIES		✓		
BOAT LAUNCH		✓			ICE		✓			SHOPS / MALL		✓		
BOAT RENTAL		✓			LAUNDRY		✓			SHOWER		✓		
CAMPING			✓		BOAT LIFT		✓			SWIM POOL			✓	
CAR RENTAL			✓		LIQUOR STORE			✓		TAXI	✓			
CHARTS		✓			24 HR PARKING		✓			TELEPHONE	✓			
DIVE SHOP			✓		POST OFFICE		✓			TIDAL GRID			✓	
FISH LICENSE		✓			PROPANE			✓		TOILETS	✓			

HOURS SUMMER	**NO FUEL FLOAT**	DIESEL	
		GASOLINE	
HOURS WINTER		STOVE OIL	
		PROPANE	
TEL		AVIATION	

24 HOUR MAXIMUM STAY.
PAY AT BOX.

LOCALE

HARBORVIEW MARINA
VHF:
TEL: 851-3948   CHART # 18445
FAX: N 47 19 W 122 34
Washington Area Codes 206, 360 & 509

3219 HARBORVIEW DRIVE
GIG HARBOR, WA.
98335

GENERAL

OFFICE HOURS
SUMMER:	NONE
WINTER:	NONE

DAILY MOORAGE
SUMMER:	PRIVATE CONDO
WINTER:	MARINA

MONTHLY MOORAGE
SUMMER:	CALL FOR INFO
WINTER:	

VISA   MasterCard

ON THE DOCK SERVICES
POWER	✓	LIGHTING	✓
30 AMP	✓	CABLE	✓
WATER	✓	PHONE	✓
GARBAGE	✓	DERRICK	
WASTE OIL	✓	LIVE ABRD	✓

Note: All marina information is subject to; change without notice, misinterpretation, misrepresentation and human error. In no way are the facilities mentioned in this book obligated to honor the rates and services listed. All information is given without guarantee. No part of this book is intended for navigation.

PUBLIC SERVICES

A: Located at Marina   B: Within Walking   C: Within 20 Miles   D: Not Available

	A	B	C	D
ACCOMMODATION		✓		
BAIT & TACKLE		✓		
BANK MACHINE		✓		
BOAT CHARTER			✓	
BOAT LAUNCH		✓		
BOAT RENTAL		✓		
CAMPING			✓	
CAR RENTAL			✓	
CHARTS		✓		
DIVE SHOP			✓	
FISH LICENSE		✓		

	A	B	C	D
GOLFING			✓	
GROCERY		✓		
HARDWARE		✓		
HOSPITAL			✓	
ICE		✓		
LAUNDRY			✓	
BOAT LIFT		✓		
LIQUOR STORE			✓	
24 HR PARKING	✓			
POST OFFICE		✓		
PROPANE			✓	

	A	B	C	D
PUB		✓		
PUMPOUT STN		✓		
RESTAURANT		✓		
RV FACILITIES		✓		
SHOPS / MALL		✓		
SHOWER		✓		
SWIM POOL				✓
TAXI	✓			
TELEPHONE	✓			
TIDAL GRID				
TOILETS	✓			

HOURS SUMMER			DIESEL	
HOURS WINTER	NO FUEL FLOAT		GASOLINE	
			STOVE OIL	
			PROPANE	
TEL			AVIATION	

GIG HARBOR

LOCALE

MILLVILLE MARINA
VHF:
TEL: 851-3872   CHART # 18445
FAX: 858-6939   N 47 19 W 122 34
Washington Area Codes 206, 360 & 509

3519 HARBORVIEW DR.
GIG HARBOR, WA.
98335

GENERAL

OFFICE HOURS
SUMMER:	9AM - 5PM DAILY
WINTER:	SAME

DAILY MOORAGE
SUMMER:	NONE
WINTER:	NONE

MONTHLY MOORAGE
SUMMER:	$5.50 PER FT
WINTER:	SAME

VISA ☐   MasterCard ☐
☐   DISCOVER ☐

ON THE DOCK SERVICES
POWER	✓	LIGHTING	✓
30 AMP	✓	CABLE	
WATER	✓	PHONE	✓
GARBAGE	✓	DERRICK	
WASTE OIL		LIVE ABRD	

Note: All marina information is subject to; change without notice, misinterpretation, misrepresentation and human error. In no way are the facilities mentioned in this book obligated to honor the rates and services listed. All information is given without guarantee. No part of this book is intended for navigation.

PUBLIC SERVICES

A: Located at Marina   B: Within Walking   C: Within 20 Miles   D: Not Available

	A	B	C	D		A	B	C	D		A	B	C	D
ACCOMMODATION		✓			GOLFING			✓		PUB		✓		
BAIT & TACKLE		✓			GROCERY		✓			PUMPOUT STN		✓		
BANK MACHINE		✓			HARDWARE		✓			RESTAURANT		✓		
BOAT CHARTER			✓		HOSPITAL			✓		RV FACILITIES		✓		
BOAT LAUNCH		✓			ICE		✓			SHOPS / MALL		✓		
BOAT RENTAL			✓		LAUNDRY		✓			SHOWER		✓		
CAMPING			✓		BOAT LIFT		✓			SWIM POOL			✓	
CAR RENTAL			✓		LIQUOR STORE			✓		TAXI		✓		
CHARTS		✓			24 HR PARKING	✓				TELEPHONE		✓		
DIVE SHOP			✓		POST OFFICE		✓			TIDAL GRID			✓	
FISH LICENSE		✓			PROPANE			✓		TOILETS		✓		

HOURS SUMMER	NO FUEL FLOAT	DIESEL	☐
		GASOLINE	☐
HOURS WINTER		STOVE OIL	☐
		PROPANE	☐
TEL		AVIATION	☐

33

GIG HARBOR

LOCALE

MURPHY'S LANDING MARINA
VHF:
TEL: 851-3093   CHART # 18445
FAX: N 47 19 W 122 34
Washington Area Codes 206, 360 & 509

3901 HARBORVIEW DRIVE
GIG HARBOR, WA.
98332

GENERAL

OFFICE HOURS
SUMMER:	M , W & F AM ONLY
WINTER:	SAME

DAILY MOORAGE
SUMMER:	$10-$12/NIGHT
WINTER:	MAX 40'

MONTHLY MOORAGE
SUMMER:	$5.75-$6.25/FT
WINTER:	SAME

VISA   MasterCard
●-◎-●   DISCOVER

ON THE DOCK SERVICES
POWER	✓	LIGHTING	✓
30 AMP	✓	CABLE	✓
WATER	✓	PHONE	✓
GARBAGE	✓	DERRICK	
WASTE OIL		LIVE ABRD	✓

Note: All marina information is subject to; change without notice, misinterpretation, misrepresentation and human error. In no way are the facilities mentioned in this book obligated to honor the rates and services listed. All information is given without guarantee. No part of this book is intended for navigation.

PUBLIC SERVICES

A: Located at Marina   B: Within Walking   C: Within 20 Miles   D: Not Available

	A	B	C	D
ACCOMMODATION		✓		
BAIT & TACKLE		✓		
BANK MACHINE		✓		
BOAT CHARTER		✓		
BOAT LAUNCH		✓		
BOAT RENTAL		✓		
CAMPING		✓		
CAR RENTAL			✓	
CHARTS		✓		
DIVE SHOP		✓		
FISH LICENSE		✓		

	A	B	C	D
GOLFING			✓	
GROCERY		✓		
HARDWARE		✓		
HOSPITAL			✓	
ICE		✓		
LAUNDRY	✓			
BOAT LIFT		✓		
LIQUOR STORE		✓		
24 HR PARKING	✓			
POST OFFICE		✓		
PROPANE			✓	

	A	B	C	D
PUB		✓		
PUMPOUT STN	✓			
RESTAURANT		✓		
RV FACILITIES		✓		
SHOPS / MALL		✓		
SHOWER	✓			
SWIM POOL			✓	
TAXI			✓	
TELEPHONE	✓			
TIDAL GRID			✓	
TOILETS	✓			

HOURS SUMMER		DIESEL	
	NO	GASOLINE	
HOURS WINTER	FUEL	STOVE OIL	
	FLOAT	PROPANE	
TEL		AVIATION	

34

GIG HARBOR

LOCALE

NEVILLE'S SHORELINE RESTAURANT
VHF:
TEL: 851-9822   CHART # 18445
FAX: 851-6356   N 47 19 W 122 34
Washington Area Codes 206, 360 & 509

8827 N. HARBORVIEW DRIVE
GIG HARBOR, WA.
98332

GENERAL

OFFICE HOURS

SUMMER:	RESTAURANT HRS
WINTER:	SAME

DAILY MOORAGE

SUMMER:	RESTAURANT
WINTER:	PATRONS ONLY

MONTHLY MOORAGE

SUMMER:	
WINTER:	

VISA	YES	MasterCard	YES
◉	YES	DISCOVER	

ON THE DOCK SERVICES

POWER		LIGHTING	✓
30 AMP		CABLE	
WATER		PHONE	
GARBAGE		DERRICK	
WASTE OIL		LIVE ABRD	

Note: All marina information is subject to; change without notice, misrepresentation, misrepresentation and human error. In no way are the facilities mentioned in this book obligated to honor the rates and services listed. All information is given without guarantee. No part of this book is intended for navigation.

PUBLIC SERVICES

A: Located at Marina   B: Within Walking   C: Within 20 Miles   D: Not Available

	A	B	C	D
ACCOMMODATION		✓		
BAIT & TACKLE		✓		
BANK MACHINE		✓		
BOAT CHARTER			✓	
BOAT LAUNCH		✓		
BOAT RENTAL	✓			
CAMPING			✓	
CAR RENTAL			✓	
CHARTS		✓		
DIVE SHOP			✓	
FISH LICENSE		✓		

	A	B	C	D
GOLFING			✓	
GROCERY		✓		
HARDWARE		✓		
HOSPITAL			✓	
ICE		✓		
LAUNDRY		✓		
BOAT LIFT		✓		
LIQUOR STORE			✓	
24 HR PARKING		✓		
POST OFFICE		✓		
PROPANE			✓	

	A	B	C	D
PUB	✓			
PUMPOUT STN		✓		
RESTAURANT	✓			
RV FACILITIES		✓		
SHOPS / MALL		✓		
SHOWER		✓		
SWIM POOL			✓	
TAXI		✓		
TELEPHONE	✓			
TIDAL GRID			✓	
TOILETS	✓			

HOURS SUMMER	**NO FUEL FLOAT**	DIESEL
		GASOLINE
HOURS WINTER		STOVE OIL
		PROPANE
TEL		AVIATION

GIG HARBOR

PENINSULA YACHT BASIN
VHF:
TEL: 858-2250   CHART # 18445
FAX: N 47 19 W 122 34
Washington Area Codes 206, 360 & 509

8913 N. HARBORVIEW DRIVE
GIG HARBOR, WA.
98332

GENERAL

OFFICE HOURS
SUMMER:	T - ST 8AM - 5PM
WINTER:	M - F 8AM - 5PM

DAILY MOORAGE
SUMMER:	$.40 PER FT
WINTER:	SAME

MONTHLY MOORAGE
SUMMER:	$5.50/FT OPEN
WINTER:	SAME

VISA   MasterCard
DISCOVER

ON THE DOCK SERVICES
POWER	✓	LIGHTING	✓
30 AMP	✓	CABLE	
WATER	✓	PHONE	
GARBAGE	✓	DERRICK	
WASTE OIL		LIVE ABRD	

WHARVES\FLOATS   MAX 80 FT

Note: All marina information is subject to; change without notice, misinterpretation, misrepresentation and human error. In no way are the facilities mentioned in this book obligated to honor the rates and services listed. All information is given without guarantee. No part of this book is intended for navigation.

PUBLIC SERVICES

A: Located at Marina   B: Within Walking   C: Within 20 Miles   D: Not Available

	A	B	C	D
ACCOMMODATION	✓			
BAIT & TACKLE		✓		
BANK MACHINE	✓			
BOAT CHARTER	✓			
BOAT LAUNCH	✓			
BOAT RENTAL	✓			
CAMPING			✓	
CAR RENTAL			✓	
CHARTS	✓			
DIVE SHOP	✓			
FISH LICENSE	✓			

	A	B	C	D
GOLFING			✓	
GROCERY		✓		
HARDWARE		✓		
HOSPITAL			✓	
ICE		✓		
LAUNDRY			✓	
BOAT LIFT			✓	
LIQUOR STORE			✓	
24 HR PARKING	✓			
POST OFFICE		✓		
PROPANE			✓	

	A	B	C	D
PUB		✓		
PUMPOUT STN		✓		
RESTAURANT		✓		
RV FACILITIES			✓	
SHOPS / MALL		✓		
SHOWER	✓			
SWIM POOL			✓	
TAXI			✓	
TELEPHONE	✓			
TIDAL GRID			✓	
TOILETS	✓			

CONDOMINIUM MOORAGE AVAILABLE.
RECIPROCAL YACHT CLUB ,TRANSIENT, AND
COVERED MOORAGE .

	NO FUEL FLOAT		
HOURS SUMMER		DIESEL	
		GASOLINE	
HOURS WINTER		STOVE OIL	
		PROPANE	
TEL		AVIATION	

GIG HARBOR

LOCALE

PLEASURECRAFT MARINA
VHF:
TEL: 858-2350   CHART # 18445
FAX: 858-2350   N 47 19 W 122 34
Washington Area Codes 206, 360 & 509

3215 HARBORVIEW DRIVE
GIG HARBOR, WA.
98335

GENERAL

OFFICE HOURS

SUMMER:	N/A
WINTER:	N/A

DAILY MOORAGE

SUMMER:	N/A
WINTER:	N/A

MONTHLY MOORAGE

SUMMER:	$6.75 / STALL FT
WINTER:	SAME

ON THE DOCK SERVICES

POWER	✓	LIGHTING	✓
30 AMP	✓	CABLE	✓
WATER	✓	PHONE	✓
GARBAGE	✓	DERRICK	
WASTE OIL		LIVE ABRD	

Note: All marina information is subject to; change without notice, misinterpretation, misrepresentation and human error. In no way are the facilities mentioned in this book obligated to honor the rates and services listed. All information is given without guarantee. No part of this book is intended for navigation.

PUBLIC SERVICES

A: Located at Marina   B: Within Walking   C: Within 20 Miles   D: Not Available

	A	B	C	D
ACCOMMODATION		✓		
BAIT & TACKLE		✓		
BANK MACHINE		✓		
BOAT CHARTER			✓	
BOAT LAUNCH		✓		
BOAT RENTAL		✓		
CAMPING			✓	
CAR RENTAL			✓	
CHARTS		✓		
DIVE SHOP			✓	
FISH LICENSE		✓		

	A	B	C	D
GOLFING			✓	
GROCERY		✓		
HARDWARE		✓		
HOSPITAL			✓	
ICE		✓		
LAUNDRY			✓	
BOAT LIFT		✓		
LIQUOR STORE			✓	
24 HR PARKING	✓			
POST OFFICE		✓		
PROPANE			✓	

	A	B	C	D
PUB		✓		
PUMPOUT STN		✓		
RESTAURANT		✓		
RV FACILITIES		✓		
SHOPS / MALL		✓		
SHOWER		✓		
SWIM POOL				✓
TAXI				✓
TELEPHONE		✓		
TIDAL GRID			✓	
TOILETS		✓		

PRIVATE PERMANENT MOORAGE ONLY.

HOURS SUMMER	NO FUEL FLOAT	DIESEL	
		GASOLINE	
HOURS WINTER		STOVE OIL	
		PROPANE	
TEL		AVIATION	

37

GIG HARBOR

LOCALE	**STANICH DOCK** VHF: TEL: 851-9504 CHART # 18445 FAX: 857-3444 N 47 20.04 W122 35.06 Washington Area Codes 206, 360 & 509	8218 DOROTICH 5720 144TH NW. GIG HARBOR, WA. 98332

GENERAL

OFFICE HOURS
SUMMER:	8AM - 5PM
WINTER:	SAME

DAILY MOORAGE
SUMMER:	
WINTER:	

MONTHLY MOORAGE
SUMMER:	$7.00 PER FT
WINTER:	SAME

VISA ☐   MasterCard ☐
☐   DISCOVER ☐

ON THE DOCK SERVICES
POWER	✓	LIGHTING	
30 AMP		CABLE	
WATER	✓	PHONE	
GARBAGE		DERRICK	✓
WASTE OIL		LIVE ABRD	

WHARVES\FLOATS   UP TO 190 FT

Note: All marina information is subject to; change without notice, misrepresentation and human error. In no way are the facilities mentioned in this book obligated to honor the rates and services listed. All information is given without guarantee. No part of this book is intended for navigation.

PUBLIC SERVICES

A: Located at Marina   B: Within Walking   C: Within 20 Miles   D: Not Available

	A	B	C	D		A	B	C	D		A	B	C	D
ACCOMMODATION		✓			GOLFING			✓		PUB		✓		
BAIT & TACKLE		✓			GROCERY		✓			PUMPOUT STN			✓	
BANK MACHINE		✓			HARDWARE		✓			RESTAURANT		✓		
BOAT CHARTER				✓	HOSPITAL			✓		RV FACILITIES			✓	
BOAT LAUNCH			✓		ICE		✓			SHOPS / MALL		✓		
BOAT RENTAL		✓			LAUNDRY				✓	SHOWER				✓
CAMPING				✓	BOAT LIFT				✓	SWIM POOL				✓
CAR RENTAL				✓	LIQUOR STORE			✓		TAXI	✓			
CHARTS				✓	24 HR PARKING				✓	TELEPHONE		✓		
DIVE SHOP		✓			POST OFFICE		✓			TIDAL GRID				✓
FISH LICENSE		✓			PROPANE			✓		TOILETS				✓

PRIVATE FACILITY. MOORAGE AVAILABLE IN SUMMER OR WITH PRIOR SCHEDULING.
MECHANICAL, ELECTRICAL , INSURANCE REPAIRS.
COMMERCIAL PIER LOAD / UNLOADING WITH APPOINTMENT.

HOURS SUMMER
HOURS WINTER
TEL

NO FUEL FLOAT

DIESEL	☐
GASOLINE	☐
STOVE OIL	☐
PROPANE	☐
AVIATION	☐

38

GIG HARBOR

LOCALE

TIDES TAVERN
VHF:
TEL: 858-3982   CHART # 18445
FAX: 858-3914   N 47 19 W 122 34
Washington Area Codes 206, 360 & 509

2925 HARBOR VIEW DR.
P.O. BOX 208
GIG HARBOR, WA.
98335

GENERAL

OFFICE HOURS

SUMMER:	TAVERN HOURS
WINTER:	SAME

DAILY MOORAGE

SUMMER:	RESTAURANT
WINTER:	PATRONS

MONTHLY MOORAGE

SUMMER:	N/A
WINTER:	N/A

VISA — YES   MasterCard — YES
(card) — YES   DISCOVER — [ ]

ON THE DOCK SERVICES

POWER		LIGHTING	
30 AMP		CABLE	
WATER		PHONE	
GARBAGE		DERRICK	
WASTE OIL		LIVE ABRD	

Note: All marina information is subject to; change without notice, misrepresentation, misrepresentation and human error. In no way are the facilities mentioned in this book obligated to honor the rates and services listed. All information is given without guarantee. No part of this book is intended for navigation.

PUBLIC SERVICES

A: Located at Marina   B: Within Walking   C: Within 20 Miles   D: Not Available

	A	B	C	D
ACCOMMODATION		✓		
BAIT & TACKLE		✓		
BANK MACHINE		✓		
BOAT CHARTER			✓	
BOAT LAUNCH		✓		
BOAT RENTAL			✓	
CAMPING			✓	
CAR RENTAL			✓	
CHARTS		✓		
DIVE SHOP		✓		
FISH LICENSE		✓		

	A	B	C	D
GOLFING			✓	
GROCERY		✓		
HARDWARE		✓		
HOSPITAL			✓	
ICE		✓		
LAUNDRY		✓		
BOAT LIFT		✓		
LIQUOR STORE	✓			
24 HR PARKING	✓			
POST OFFICE		✓		
PROPANE			✓	

	A	B	C	D
PUB	✓			
PUMPOUT STN		✓		
RESTAURANT	✓			
RV FACILITIES		✓		
SHOPS / MALL		✓		
SHOWER		✓		
SWIM POOL			✓	
TAXI		✓		
TELEPHONE	✓			
TIDAL GRID			✓	
TOILETS	✓			

SHELL

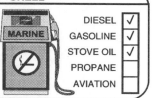

HOURS SUMMER
8-5:30M-F8:30-2:30S

HOURS WINTER
8:30 AM - 2:30 PM

TEL   858-9131

DIESEL	✓
GASOLINE	✓
STOVE OIL	✓
PROPANE	
AVIATION	

NOTE: FUEL FLOAT LOCATED NEXT DOOR TO TAVERN ON SEPARATE FLOAT.

GIG HARBOR

LOCALE

WESTSHORE MARINA
VHF:
TEL: 858-3953   CHART # 18445
FAX: N 47 19 W 122 34
Washington Area Codes 206, 360 & 509

3815 HARBORVIEW DRIVE
GIG HARBOR, WA.
98332

GENERAL

OFFICE HOURS
SUMMER:	VARIES
WINTER:	SAME

DAILY MOORAGE
SUMMER:	NO TRANSIENT
WINTER:	SAME

MONTHLY MOORAGE
SUMMER:	$5.00 PER FT
WINTER:	SAME

VISA   MasterCard   [ ]   [ ]

ON THE DOCK SERVICES
POWER	✓	LIGHTING	✓
30 AMP	✓	CABLE	✓
WATER	✓	PHONE	✓
GARBAGE	✓	DERRICK	
WASTE OIL	✓	LIVE ABRD	✓

Note: All marina information is subject to; change without notice, misinterpretation, misrepresentation and human error. In no way are the facilities mentioned in this book obligated to honor the rates and services listed. All information is given without guarantee. No part of this book is intended for navigation.

PUBLIC SERVICES

A: Located at Marina   B: Within Walking   C: Within 20 Miles   D: Not Available

	A	B	C	D
ACCOMMODATION		✓		
BAIT & TACKLE		✓		
BANK MACHINE		✓		
BOAT CHARTER			✓	
BOAT LAUNCH		✓		
BOAT RENTAL			✓	
CAMPING			✓	
CAR RENTAL			✓	
CHARTS		✓		
DIVE SHOP			✓	
FISH LICENSE		✓		

	A	B	C	D
GOLFING			✓	
GROCERY		✓		
HARDWARE		✓		
HOSPITAL			✓	
ICE		✓		
LAUNDRY		✓		
BOAT LIFT		✓		
LIQUOR STORE			✓	
24 HR PARKING	✓			
POST OFFICE		✓		
PROPANE			✓	

	A	B	C	D
PUB		✓		
PUMPOUT STN		✓		
RESTAURANT		✓		
RV FACILITIES		✓		
SHOPS / MALL		✓		
SHOWER		✓		
SWIM POOL			✓	
TAXI		✓		
TELEPHONE	✓			
TIDAL GRID			✓	
TOILETS		✓		

HOURS SUMMER		NO FUEL FLOAT	DIESEL	[ ]
HOURS WINTER			GASOLINE	[ ]
			STOVE OIL	[ ]
			PROPANE	[ ]
TEL			AVIATION	[ ]

HARTSTENE ISLAND

LOCALE

JARRELL'S COVE
VHF:
TEL: 426-8823   CHART # 18445
FAX: N 47 17 W 122 53
Washington Area Codes 206, 360 & 509

E. 220 WILSON RD.
SHELTON, WA.
98584

GENERAL

OFFICE HOURS

SUMMER:	8AM-8PM
WINTER:	8:30-4:30 W-SUN

DAILY MOORAGE

SUMMER:	$.50/FT PLS PWR
WINTER:	SAME

MONTHLY MOORAGE

SUMMER:	$3.95/FT PLUS PWR
WINTER:	SAME

VISA	YES	MasterCard	YES
	YES	DISCOVER	YES

ON THE DOCK SERVICES

POWER	✓	LIGHTING	✓
30 AMP	✓	CABLE	
WATER	✓	PHONE	✓
GARBAGE	✓	DERRICK	
WASTE OIL		LIVE ABRD	✓

WHARVES\FLOATS   100' GUEST

Note: All marina information is subject to; change without notice, misrepresentation and human error. In no way are the facilities mentioned in this book obligated to honor the rates and services listed. All information is given without guarantee. No part of this book is intended for navigation.

PUBLIC SERVICES

A: Located at Marina   B: Within Walking   C: Within 20 Miles   D: Not Available

	A	B	C	D
ACCOMMODATION				✓
BAIT & TACKLE	✓			
BANK MACHINE			✓	
BOAT CHARTER				✓
BOAT LAUNCH		✓		
BOAT RENTAL	✓			
CAMPING		✓		
CAR RENTAL				✓
CHARTS				✓
DIVE SHOP				✓
FISH LICENSE	✓			

	A	B	C	D
GOLFING			✓	
GROCERY	✓			
HARDWARE			✓	
HOSPITAL			✓	
ICE	✓			
LAUNDRY	✓			
BOAT LIFT			✓	
LIQUOR STORE			✓	
24 HR PARKING	✓			
POST OFFICE			✓	
PROPANE	✓			

	A	B	C	D
PUB			✓	
PUMPOUT STN	✓			
RESTAURANT			✓	
RV FACILITIES	✓			
SHOPS / MALL			✓	
SHOWER	✓			
SWIM POOL				✓
TAXI	✓			
TELEPHONE	✓			
TIDAL GRID				✓
TOILETS	✓			

CHEVRON

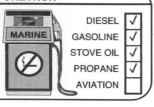

MARINE

HOURS SUMMER
8AM-8PM DAILY
HOURS WINTER
8:30-4:30 W-SUN
TEL

DIESEL	✓
GASOLINE	✓
STOVE OIL	✓
PROPANE	✓
AVIATION	

JARRELL COVE STATE PARK ACROSS THE HARBOR WITH CAMPING, MOORING BUOYS AND TWO DOCKS. GOOD ANCHORAGE.
PUBLIC BEACH ADJACENT TO MARINA WITH GOOD CLAMMING. FISHING IS GOOD OFF THE DOCK. EMERGENCY SERVICES AVAILABLE. OVERNIGHT MOORAGE ON A SPACE AVAILABLE BASIS. 1-800-362-8823

HOOD CANAL

LOCALE

HOOD CANAL MARINA
VHF: 16 CB 14
TEL: 898-2252   CHART # 18445
FAX: 898-8888   N 47 22 W 123 06
Washington Area Codes 206, 360 & 509

E. 5101 HWY 106
PO BOX 86
UNION, WA.
98592

GENERAL

OFFICE HOURS
SUMMER:	8AM-5PM DAILY
WINTER:	SAME

DAILY MOORAGE
SUMMER:	VARIES
WINTER:	SAME

MONTHLY MOORAGE
SUMMER:	VARIES
WINTER:	SAME

VISA YES   MasterCard YES
● YES   DISCOVER

ON THE DOCK SERVICES
POWER	✓	LIGHTING	✓
30 AMP	✓	CABLE	
WATER	✓	PHONE	
GARBAGE	✓	DERRICK	
WASTE OIL	✓	LIVE ABRD	

Note: All marina information is subject to; change without notice, misinterpretation, misrepresentation and human error. In no way are the facilities mentioned in this book obligated to honor the rates and services listed. All information is given without guarantee. No part of this book is intended for navigation.

PUBLIC SERVICES

A: Located at Marina   B: Within Walking   C: Within 20 Miles   D: Not Available

	A	B	C	D
ACCOMMODATION			✓	
BAIT & TACKLE	✓			
BANK MACHINE			✓	
BOAT CHARTER				✓
BOAT LAUNCH	✓			
BOAT RENTAL	✓			
CAMPING			✓	
CAR RENTAL			✓	
CHARTS	✓			
DIVE SHOP			✓	
FISH LICENSE		✓		

	A	B	C	D
GOLFING		✓		
GROCERY	✓			
HARDWARE	✓			
HOSPITAL			✓	
ICE	✓			
LAUNDRY		✓		
BOAT LIFT	✓			
LIQUOR STORE		✓		
24 HR PARKING	✓			
POST OFFICE		✓		
PROPANE		✓		

	A	B	C	D
PUB		✓		
PUMPOUT STN		✓		
RESTAURANT		✓		
RV FACILITIES	✓			
SHOPS / MALL				✓
SHOWER		✓		
SWIM POOL		✓		
TAXI			✓	
TELEPHONE	✓			
TIDAL GRID	✓			
TOILETS	✓			

CRABBING AND SHRIMPING GEAR AVAILABLE.
SHRIMP SEASON LATE MAY THROUGH EARLY JUNE.
LOCATED IN UNION NEAR TWANOH AND POTLATCH STATE PARKS.
BOATS AND JET SKIS FOR RENT.
UNOCAL CARD ACCEPTED AT FUEL FLOAT.

UNOCAL 76

HOURS SUMMER
8AM-5PM
HOURS WINTER

TEL 898-2252

DIESEL	✓
GASOLINE	✓
STOVE OIL	
PROPANE	
AVIATION	

HOOD CANAL

HOODSPORT MARINA & CAFE
VHF:
TEL: 877-9657   CHART # 18445
FAX: N 47 26 W 123 06
Washington Area Codes 206, 360 & 509

24080 N. HIGHWAY 101
HOODSPORT, WA.
98548

GENERAL

OFFICE HOURS

SUMMER:	11AM - 9PM
WINTER:	SAME

DAILY MOORAGE

SUMMER:	$10 PER DAY
WINTER:	SAME

MONTHLY MOORAGE

SUMMER:	$2.25 PER FT *
WINTER:	

VISA YES   MasterCard YES

ON THE DOCK SERVICES

POWER		LIGHTING	
30 AMP		CABLE	
WATER		PHONE	
GARBAGE		DERRICK	
WASTE OIL		LIVE ABRD	✓

Note: All marina information is subject to; change without notice, misinterpretation, misrepresentation and human error. In no way are the facilities mentioned in this book obligated to honor the rates and services listed. All information is given without guarantee. No part of this book is intended for navigation.

PUBLIC SERVICES

A: Located at Marina   B: Within Walking   C: Within 20 Miles   D: Not Available

	A	B	C	D
ACCOMMODATION		✓		
BAIT & TACKLE			✓	
BANK MACHINE		✓		
BOAT CHARTER				✓
BOAT LAUNCH			✓	
BOAT RENTAL				✓
CAMPING			✓	
CAR RENTAL			✓	
CHARTS			✓	
DIVE SHOP			✓	
FISH LICENSE		✓		

	A	B	C	D
GOLFING			✓	
GROCERY		✓		
HARDWARE			✓	
HOSPITAL			✓	
ICE	✓			
LAUNDRY			✓	
BOAT LIFT			✓	
LIQUOR STORE		✓		
24 HR PARKING	✓			
POST OFFICE		✓		
PROPANE		✓		

	A	B	C	D
PUB		✓		
PUMPOUT STN			✓	
RESTAURANT	✓			
RV FACILITIES			✓	
SHOPS / MALL		✓		
SHOWER		✓		
SWIM POOL				✓
TAXI				✓
TELEPHONE	✓			
TIDAL GRID				✓
TOILETS		✓		

HOURS SUMMER	NO FUEL FLOAT	DIESEL	
		GASOLINE	
HOURS WINTER		STOVE OIL	
		PROPANE	
TEL		AVIATION	

HOOD CANAL

<table>
<tr><td>LOCALE</td><td>

PLEASANT HARBOR MARINA
VHF: 9 &16
TEL: 796-4611   CHART # 18445
FAX: 796-4898   N 47 39.17 W 122 55.05
Washington Area Codes 206, 360 & 509

</td><td>

308913 HIGHWAY 101
BRINNON, WA.
98320

</td></tr>
</table>

GENERAL

OFFICE HOURS
SUMMER:	8AM - 7PM
WINTER:	SAME

DAILY MOORAGE
SUMMER:	$.50/FT TO $35
WINTER:	SAME

MONTHLY MOORAGE
SUMMER:	VARIES
WINTER:	

VISA	YES	MasterCard	YES
	YES	DISCOVER	YES

ON THE DOCK SERVICES
POWER	✓	LIGHTING	✓
30 AMP	✓	CABLE	
WATER	✓	PHONE	✓
GARBAGE	✓	DERRICK	
WASTE OIL	✓	LIVE ABRD	✓

WHARVES\FLOATS   ~ 9000'

Note: All marina information is subject to; change without notice, misinterpretation, misrepresentation and human error. In no way are the facilities mentioned in this book obligated to honor the rates and services listed. All information is given without guarantee. No part of this book is intended for navigation.

PUBLIC SERVICES

A: Located at Marina   B: Within Walking   C: Within 20 Miles   D: Not Available

	A	B	C	D
ACCOMMODATION	✓			
BAIT & TACKLE	✓			
BANK MACHINE			✓	
BOAT CHARTER				✓
BOAT LAUNCH			✓	
BOAT RENTAL				✓
CAMPING		✓		
CAR RENTAL				✓
CHARTS	✓			
DIVE SHOP			✓	
FISH LICENSE	✓			

	A	B	C	D
GOLFING				✓
GROCERY	✓			
HARDWARE	✓			
HOSPITAL				✓
ICE	✓			
LAUNDRY	✓			
BOAT LIFT				✓
LIQUOR STORE			✓	
24 HR PARKING	✓			
POST OFFICE			✓	
PROPANE	✓			

	A	B	C	D
PUB	✓			
PUMPOUT STN	✓			
RESTAURANT	✓			
RV FACILITIES		✓		
SHOPS / MALL			✓	
SHOWER	✓			
SWIM POOL	✓			
TAXI				✓
TELEPHONE	✓			
TIDAL GRID				✓
TOILETS	✓			

HOUSE BOAT RENTALS FOR COUPLES. EXPANSIONS EXPECTED THROUGH '96. NEW CONCRETE DOCKS AND CABLE TV TO FOLLOW.

CHEVRON

HOURS SUMMER	DIESEL	✓
8AM-7PM	GASOLINE	✓
HOURS WINTER	STOVE OIL	✓
8AM-7PM	PROPANE	✓
TEL 796-4611	AVIATION	

MARINE

44

HOOD CANAL

PLEASANT HARBOR OLD MARINA

VHF:
TEL: 796-4040   CHART # 18445
FAX: N 47 39 W 122 54
Washington Area Codes 206, 360 & 509

308717 HIGHWAY 101
PO BOX 310
BRINNON, WA.
98320

GENERAL

OFFICE HOURS

SUMMER:	N/A
WINTER:	N/A

DAILY MOORAGE

SUMMER:	NO TRANSIENT
WINTER:	SAME

MONTHLY MOORAGE

SUMMER:	$2.25 / FT ANNUAL
WINTER:	LEASE ONLY

VISA   MasterCard   DISCOVER

ON THE DOCK SERVICES

POWER	✓	LIGHTING	✓
30 AMP	✓	CABLE	
WATER	✓	PHONE	✓
GARBAGE	✓	DERRICK	
WASTE OIL	✓	LIVE ABRD	✓

WHARVES\FLOATS   100 SLIPS

Note: All marina information is subject to; change without notice, misinterpretation, misrepresentation and human error. In no way are the facilities mentioned in this book obligated to honor the rates and services listed. All information is given without guarantee. No part of this book is intended for navigation.

PUBLIC SERVICES

A: Located at Marina   B: Within Walking   C: Within 20 Miles   D: Not Available

	A	B	C	D		A	B	C	D		A	B	C	D
ACCOMMODATION					GOLFING					PUB				
BAIT & TACKLE					GROCERY					PUMPOUT STN		✓		
BANK MACHINE					HARDWARE					RESTAURANT				
BOAT CHARTER					HOSPITAL					RV FACILITIES				
BOAT LAUNCH					ICE		✓			SHOPS / MALL				
BOAT RENTAL					LAUNDRY	✓				SHOWER	✓			
CAMPING					BOAT LIFT					SWIM POOL				
CAR RENTAL					LIQUOR STORE					TAXI				
CHARTS					24 HR PARKING	✓				TELEPHONE	✓			
DIVE SHOP					POST OFFICE					TIDAL GRID				
FISH LICENSE					PROPANE					TOILETS	✓			

NO FUEL FLOAT

HOURS SUMMER		DIESEL	
		GASOLINE	
HOURS WINTER		STOVE OIL	
		PROPANE	
TEL		AVIATION	

THIS FACILITY IS FOR PERMANENT LONG-TERM
MOORAGE ONLY.
MINIMUM TWO YEAR WAITING LIST.

PORT OF HOODSPORT
VHF:
TEL: CHART # 18445
FAX: N 47 26 W 123 06
Washington Area Codes 206, 360 & 509

LOCALE

GENERAL

OFFICE HOURS

SUMMER:	NO OFFICE
WINTER:	

DAILY MOORAGE

SUMMER:	FREE
WINTER:	24 HR MAX

MONTHLY MOORAGE

SUMMER:	N/A
WINTER:	N/A

VISA   MasterCard

DISCOVER

ON THE DOCK SERVICES

POWER		LIGHTING	✓
30 AMP		CABLE	
WATER		PHONE	
GARBAGE		DERRICK	
WASTE OIL		LIVE ABRD	

WHARVES\FLOATS   UP TO 200 FT

Note: All marina information is subject to; change without notice, misinterpretation, misrepresentation and human error. In no way are the facilities mentioned in this book obligated to honor the rates and services listed. All information is given without guarantee. No part of this book is intended for navigation.

PUBLIC SERVICES

A: Located at Marina   B: Within Walking   C: Within 20 Miles   D: Not Available

	A	B	C	D
ACCOMMODATION		✓		
BAIT & TACKLE		✓		
BANK MACHINE		✓		
BOAT CHARTER				✓
BOAT LAUNCH			✓	
BOAT RENTAL				✓
CAMPING			✓	
CAR RENTAL			✓	
CHARTS				✓
DIVE SHOP	✓			
FISH LICENSE		✓		

	A	B	C	D
GOLFING			✓	
GROCERY		✓		
HARDWARE			✓	
HOSPITAL			✓	
ICE	✓			
LAUNDRY			✓	
BOAT LIFT			✓	
LIQUOR STORE	✓			
24 HR PARKING	✓			
POST OFFICE	✓			
PROPANE			✓	

	A	B	C	D
PUB		✓		
PUMPOUT STN			✓	
RESTAURANT		✓		
RV FACILITIES			✓	
SHOPS / MALL		✓		
SHOWER		✓		
SWIM POOL				✓
TAXI				✓
TELEPHONE		✓		
TIDAL GRID				✓
TOILETS		✓		

HOURS SUMMER		NO FUEL FLOAT		DIESEL	
				GASOLINE	
HOURS WINTER				STOVE OIL	
				PROPANE	
TEL				AVIATION	

HOOD CANAL

LOCALE

REST-A-WHILE MARINA
VHF:
TEL: 877-9122   CHART # 18445
FAX: N 47 27 W 123 06
Washington Area Codes 206, 360 & 509

N. 27001 HIGHWAY 101
HOODSPORT, WA.
98548

GENERAL

OFFICE HOURS

SUMMER:	8AM - 5PM DAILY
WINTER:	9AM - 4PM TH -MON

DAILY MOORAGE

SUMMER:	LIMITED $5/DAY
WINTER:	

MONTHLY MOORAGE

SUMMER:	DRY STORAGE
WINTER:	ONLY

VISA ☐   MasterCard ☐
☐   DISCOVER ☐

ON THE DOCK SERVICES

POWER	☐	LIGHTING	✓
30 AMP	☐	CABLE	☐
WATER	☐	PHONE	☐
GARBAGE	✓	DERRICK	☐
WASTE OIL	☐	LIVE ABRD	☐

Note: All marina information is subject to; change without notice, misrepresentation, misrepresentation and human error. In no way are the facilities mentioned in this book obligated to honor the rates and services listed. All information is given without guarantee. No part of this book is intended for navigation.

PUBLIC SERVICES

A: Located at Marina   B: Within Walking   C: Within 20 Miles   D: Not Available

	A	B	C	D
ACCOMMODATION		✓		
BAIT & TACKLE	✓			
BANK MACHINE			✓	
BOAT CHARTER				✓
BOAT LAUNCH	✓			
BOAT RENTAL	✓			
CAMPING	✓			
CAR RENTAL			✓	
CHARTS			✓	
DIVE SHOP			✓	
FISH LICENSE	✓			

	A	B	C	D
GOLFING			✓	
GROCERY	✓			
HARDWARE			✓	
HOSPITAL			✓	
ICE	✓			
LAUNDRY	✓			
BOAT LIFT				✓
LIQUOR STORE			✓	
24 HR PARKING	✓			
POST OFFICE	✓			
PROPANE	✓			

	A	B	C	D
PUB			✓	
PUMPOUT STN			✓	
RESTAURANT	✓			
RV FACILITIES	✓			
SHOPS / MALL			✓	
SHOWER	✓			
SWIM POOL				✓
TAXI				✓
TELEPHONE	✓			
TIDAL GRID				✓
TOILETS	✓			

HOURS SUMMER

HOURS WINTER

TEL

NO FUEL FLOAT

DIESEL	☐
GASOLINE	☐
STOVE OIL	☐
PROPANE	☐
AVIATION	☐

47

LOCALE

SEABECK MARINA & MOORAGE
VHF: 16 CB: 13
TEL: 830-5179
FAX:
Washington Area Codes 206, 360 & 509

CHART # 18445
N 47 39 W 122 50

15376 SEABECK HWY N.W.
PO BOX 177
SEABECK, WA.
98380

GENERAL

OFFICE HOURS
SUMMER:	8-5M-F, 8-6S&S
WINTER:	9-5 M - F

DAILY MOORAGE
SUMMER:	$6.00-$12.00
WINTER:	SAME

MONTHLY MOORAGE
SUMMER:	$4.50*
WINTER:	SAME

VISA YES   MasterCard YES
DISCOVER YES

ON THE DOCK SERVICES
POWER		LIGHTING	
30 AMP		CABLE	
WATER	✓	PHONE	
GARBAGE	✓	DERRICK	
WASTE OIL		LIVE ABRD	

Note: All marina information is subject to; change without notice, misinterpretation, misrepresentation and human error. In no way are the facilities mentioned in this book obligated to honor the rates and services listed. All information is given without guarantee. No part of this book is intended for navigation.

PUBLIC SERVICES

A: Located at Marina   B: Within Walking   C: Within 20 Miles   D: Not Available

	A	B	C	D		A	B	C	D		A	B	C	D
ACCOMMODATION			✓		GOLFING			✓		PUB			✓	
BAIT & TACKLE	✓				GROCERY	✓				PUMPOUT STN			✓	
BANK MACHINE	✓				HARDWARE			✓		RESTAURANT	✓			
BOAT CHARTER				✓	HOSPITAL			✓		RV FACILITIES			✓	
BOAT LAUNCH	✓				ICE	✓				SHOPS / MALL			✓	
BOAT RENTAL				✓	LAUNDRY			✓		SHOWER			✓	
CAMPING			✓		BOAT LIFT			✓		SWIM POOL				✓
CAR RENTAL			✓		LIQUOR STORE			✓		TAXI	✓			
CHARTS	✓				24 HR PARKING	✓				TELEPHONE	✓			
DIVE SHOP			✓		POST OFFICE	✓				TIDAL GRID				✓
FISH LICENSE		✓			PROPANE	✓				TOILETS	✓			

WATER AT TOP OF DOCK.
SCENIC BEACH STATE PARK NEARBY
EIGHT MILES FROM SILVERDALE.

TEXACO
MARINE

HOURS SUMMER		DIESEL	
AS ABOVE		GASOLINE	✓
HOURS WINTER		STOVE OIL	
AS ABOVE		PROPANE	
TEL 830-5129		AVIATION	

HOOD CANAL

LOCALE

SUNRISE MOTEL & RESORT
VHF:
TEL: 877-5301   CHART # 18445
FAX: N 47 26 W 123 06
Washington Area Codes 206, 360 & 509

N 24520 HWY 101
HOODSPORT, WA.
98548

GENERAL

OFFICE HOURS

SUMMER:	24 HRS
WINTER:	SAME

DAILY MOORAGE

SUMMER:	$6.00 PER DAY
WINTER:	MAX 24 FT

MONTHLY MOORAGE

SUMMER:	$4.00 PER FT
WINTER:	SAME

VISA   MasterCard   DISCOVER

ON THE DOCK SERVICES

POWER		LIGHTING	✓
30 AMP		CABLE	
WATER		PHONE	
GARBAGE	✓	DERRICK	
WASTE OIL		LIVE ABRD	✓

Note: All marina information is subject to; change without notice, misinterpretation, misrepresentation and human error. In no way are the facilities mentioned in this book obligated to honor the rates and services listed. All information is given without guarantee. No part of this book is intended for navigation.

PUBLIC SERVICES

A: Located at Marina   B: Within Walking   C: Within 20 Miles   D: Not Available

	A	B	C	D
ACCOMMODATION	✓			
BAIT & TACKLE		✓		
BANK MACHINE		✓		
BOAT CHARTER				✓
BOAT LAUNCH			✓	
BOAT RENTAL		✓		
CAMPING			✓	
CAR RENTAL			✓	
CHARTS		✓		
DIVE SHOP		✓		
FISH LICENSE		✓		

	A	B	C	D
GOLFING			✓	
GROCERY		✓		
HARDWARE				
HOSPITAL				
ICE		✓		
LAUNDRY			✓	
BOAT LIFT				
LIQUOR STORE				
24 HR PARKING	✓			
POST OFFICE				
PROPANE				

	A	B	C	D
PUB				
PUMPOUT STN				
RESTAURANT				
RV FACILITIES				
SHOPS / MALL				
SHOWER				✓
SWIM POOL				
TAXI				
TELEPHONE	✓			
TIDAL GRID				
TOILETS		✓		

HOURS SUMMER		DIESEL	
	NO	GASOLINE	
	FUEL	STOVE OIL	
HOURS WINTER	FLOAT	PROPANE	
TEL		AVIATION	

UNDERWATER PARK AT MARINA - ARTIFICIAL REEFS.
AIR AVAILABLE $3.50 / FILL ON SITE.

LOCALE

PORT OF KINGSTON
VHF: 16
TEL: 297-3545   CHART # 18445
FAX: 297-2945   N 47 47 W 122 29
Washington Area Codes 206, 360 & 509

25864 WASHINGTON BLVD.
PO BOX 559
KINGSTON, WA.
98346

GENERAL

OFFICE HOURS
SUMMER:	8-5 SUN-TH 8-8 F&S
WINTER:	SAME

DAILY MOORAGE
SUMMER:	$.35 PER FT
WINTER:	SAME

MONTHLY MOORAGE
SUMMER:	$3.00/FT OPEN
WINTER:	$4.50/FT CVD + TAX

VISA	YES	MasterCard	YES
[card]	YES	DISCOVER	YES

ON THE DOCK SERVICES
POWER	✓	LIGHTING	✓
30 AMP	✓	CABLE	
WATER	✓	PHONE	
GARBAGE	✓	DERRICK	
WASTE OIL		LIVE ABRD	✓

Note: All marina information is subject to; change without notice, misinterpretation, misrepresentation and human error. In no way are the facilities mentioned in this book obligated to honor the rates and services listed. All information is given without guarantee. No part of this book is intended for navigation.

PUBLIC SERVICES

A: Located at Marina   B: Within Walking   C: Within 20 Miles   D: Not Available

	A	B	C	D
ACCOMMODATION		✓		
BAIT & TACKLE		✓		
BANK MACHINE		✓		
BOAT CHARTER	✓			
BOAT LAUNCH	✓			
BOAT RENTAL				✓
CAMPING				✓
CAR RENTAL				✓
CHARTS		✓		
DIVE SHOP				✓
FISH LICENSE		✓		

	A	B	C	D
GOLFING			✓	
GROCERY		✓		
HARDWARE		✓		
HOSPITAL			✓	
ICE		✓		
LAUNDRY	✓			
BOAT LIFT			✓	
LIQUOR STORE		✓		
24 HR PARKING	✓			
POST OFFICE		✓		
PROPANE	✓			

	A	B	C	D
PUB	✓			
PUMPOUT STN	✓			
RESTAURANT	✓			
RV FACILITIES				✓
SHOPS / MALL		✓		
SHOWER	✓			
SWIM POOL				✓
TAXI	✓			
TELEPHONE	✓			
TIDAL GRID				✓
TOILETS	✓			

CREDIT CARDS ACCEPTED AT FUEL FLOAT ONLY.

CHANNEL ENTRANCE NARROW. ENTER THROUGH MIDDLE WITH CAUTION.

TRANSIENT USE DOCK BY BREAKWATER. PARK AREA WITH BBQ'S. NEW KINGSTON COVE YACHT CLUB FACILITIES AVAILABLE FOR RENT.

TEXACO

HOURS SUMMER	MARINE	DIESEL	✓
AS ABOVE		GASOLINE	✓
HOURS WINTER		STOVE OIL	
		PROPANE	✓
TEL 297-3545		AVIATION	

LA CONNER

LOCALE

LA CONNER CITY FLOATS
VHF:
TEL: 466-3125   CHART # 18423
FAX: 466-3901   N 48 24 W 122 30
Washington Area Codes 206, 360 & 509

CITY OF LA CONNER
LA CONNER, WA.
98257

GENERAL

OFFICE HOURS
SUMMER:	8AM - 5PM
WINTER:	SAME

DAILY MOORAGE
SUMMER:	VARIES
WINTER:	SAME

MONTHLY MOORAGE
SUMMER:	N/A
WINTER:	N/A

ON THE DOCK SERVICES
POWER		LIGHTING	
30 AMP		CABLE	
WATER		PHONE	
GARBAGE	✓	DERRICK	
WASTE OIL		LIVE ABRD	

Note: All marina information is subject to; change without notice, misinterpretation, misrepresentation and human error. In no way are the facilities mentioned in this book obligated to honor the rates and services listed. All information is given without guarantee. No part of this book is intended for navigation.

PUBLIC SERVICES

A: Located at Marina   B: Within Walking   C: Within 20 Miles   D: Not Available

	A	B	C	D
ACCOMMODATION		✓		
BAIT & TACKLE		✓		
BANK MACHINE		✓		
BOAT CHARTER		✓		
BOAT LAUNCH		✓		
BOAT RENTAL				✓
CAMPING			✓	
CAR RENTAL				✓
CHARTS			✓	
DIVE SHOP			✓	
FISH LICENSE				✓

	A	B	C	D
GOLFING			✓	
GROCERY		✓		
HARDWARE		✓		
HOSPITAL			✓	
ICE	✓			
LAUNDRY	✓			
BOAT LIFT	✓			
LIQUOR STORE	✓			
24 HR PARKING	✓			
POST OFFICE	✓			
PROPANE	✓			

	A	B	C	D
PUB		✓		
PUMPOUT STN				✓
RESTAURANT		✓		
RV FACILITIES		✓		
SHOPS / MALL		✓		
SHOWER		✓		
SWIM POOL				✓
TAXI				✓
TELEPHONE		✓		
TIDAL GRID				✓
TOILETS		✓		

HOURS SUMMER		DIESEL	
	NO FUEL FLOAT	GASOLINE	
HOURS WINTER		STOVE OIL	
		PROPANE	
TEL		AVIATION	

MOORAGE RATES VARY AND ARE DISPLAYED AT FLOAT.
PUBLIC FLOAT - FIRST COME FIRST SERVE.

LA CONNER

LA CONNER MARINA
VHF: 68
TEL: 466-3118   CHART # 18423
FAX: 466-3119   N 48 24 W 122 30
Washington Area Codes 206, 360 & 509

PORT OF SKAGIT COUNTY
P.O. BOX 456
LA CONNER, WA.
98257

OFFICE HOURS

SUMMER:	8 AM - 5 PM
WINTER:	8 AM - 5 PM

DAILY MOORAGE

SUMMER:	$.40 PER FT
WINTER:	$.30 PER FT

MONTHLY MOORAGE

SUMMER:	$99.00 - $291.00
WINTER:	$99.00 - $291.00

ON THE DOCK SERVICES

POWER	✓	LIGHTING	✓
30 AMP	✓	CABLE	
WATER	✓	PHONE	
GARBAGE	✓	DERRICK	
WASTE OIL	✓	LIVE ABRD	✓

WHARVES\FLOATS   2400 FT

Note: All marina information is subject to; change without notice, misinterpretation, misrepresentation and human error. In no way are the facilities mentioned in this book obligated to honor the rates and services listed. All information is given without guarantee. No part of this book is intended for navigation.

A: Located at Marina   B: Within Walking   C: Within 20 Miles   D: Not Available

	A	B	C	D
ACCOMMODATION		✓		
BAIT & TACKLE	✓			
BANK MACHINE		✓		
BOAT CHARTER			✓	
BOAT LAUNCH	✓			
BOAT RENTAL	✓			
CAMPING			✓	
CAR RENTAL			✓	
CHARTS	✓			
DIVE SHOP			✓	
FISH LICENSE	✓			

	A	B	C	D
GOLFING			✓	
GROCERY		✓		
HARDWARE			✓	
HOSPITAL			✓	
ICE	✓			
LAUNDRY	✓			
BOAT LIFT	✓			
LIQUOR STORE		✓		
24 HR PARKING	✓			
POST OFFICE		✓		
PROPANE	✓			

	A	B	C	D
PUB	✓			
PUMPOUT STN	✓			
RESTAURANT	✓			
RV FACILITIES			✓	
SHOPS / MALL		✓		
SHOWER	✓			
SWIM POOL			✓	
TAXI			✓	
TELEPHONE	✓			
TIDAL GRID				✓
TOILETS	✓			

CHEVRON

HOURS SUMMER		
8 AM - 6 PM		
HOURS WINTER		
8 AM - 4 PM		
TEL 466-4478		

MARINE

DIESEL	✓
GASOLINE	✓
STOVE OIL	
PROPANE	
AVIATION	

LAKE WASHINGTON

LOCALE

BELLEVUE YACHT BASIN
VHF:
TEL: 747-6464
FAX:
Washington Area Codes 206, 360 & 509

CHART # 18447
N 47 36.50 W 122 13.10

P.O. BOX 884
BELLEVUE, WA.
98009

GENERAL

OFFICE HOURS
SUMMER:	VARIES 8 - 5
WINTER:	SAME

DAILY MOORAGE
SUMMER:	N/A
WINTER:	N/A

MONTHLY MOORAGE
SUMMER:	$7 OPEN $8 CVRD
WINTER:	SAME

VISA · MasterCard · DISCOVER

ON THE DOCK SERVICES
POWER	✓	LIGHTING	✓
30 AMP	✓	CABLE	
WATER	✓	PHONE	✓
GARBAGE	✓	DERRICK	
WASTE OIL		LIVE ABRD	

Note: All marina information is subject to; change without notice, misinterpretation, misrepresentation and human error. In no way are the facilities mentioned in this book obligated to honor the rates and services listed. All information is given without guarantee. No part of this book is intended for navigation.

PUBLIC SERVICES

A: Located at Marina   B: Within Walking   C: Within 20 Miles   D: Not Available

	A	B	C	D
ACCOMMODATION		✓		
BAIT & TACKLE		✓		
BANK MACHINE		✓		
BOAT CHARTER			✓	
BOAT LAUNCH			✓	
BOAT RENTAL				✓
CAMPING				✓
CAR RENTAL		✓		
CHARTS		✓		
DIVE SHOP		✓		
FISH LICENSE		✓		

	A	B	C	D
GOLFING				✓
GROCERY		✓		
HARDWARE		✓		
HOSPITAL		✓		
ICE		✓		
LAUNDRY				✓
BOAT LIFT			✓	
LIQUOR STORE		✓		
24 HR PARKING	✓			
POST OFFICE		✓		
PROPANE			✓	

	A	B	C	D
PUB		✓		
PUMPOUT STN		✓		
RESTAURANT		✓		
RV FACILITIES				✓
SHOPS / MALL		✓		
SHOWER				✓
SWIM POOL				✓
TAXI	✓			
TELEPHONE	✓			
TIDAL GRID				✓
TOILETS	✓			

NO FUEL FLOAT
HOURS SUMMER	DIESEL
	GASOLINE
HOURS WINTER	STOVE OIL
	PROPANE
TEL	AVIATION

53

LOCALE

CARILLON POINT
VHF:
TEL: 822-1700
FAX: 828-3094
Washington Area Codes 206, 360 & 509

CHART # 18477
N 47 39.20 W 122 12.50

3240 CARILLON POINT
KIRKLAND, WA.
98033-7354

GENERAL

OFFICE HOURS

SUMMER:	8 AM - 5 PM M - F
WINTER:	8 AM - 5 PM M - F

DAILY MOORAGE

SUMMER:	INQUIRE*
WINTER:	

MONTHLY MOORAGE

SUMMER:	VARIES*
WINTER:	

VISA [ ]   MasterCard [ ] YES
[ ] [ ]   DISCOVER [ ]

ON THE DOCK SERVICES

POWER	✓	LIGHTING	✓
30 AMP	✓	CABLE	✓
WATER	✓	PHONE	✓
GARBAGE	✓	DERRICK	
WASTE OIL	✓	LIVE ABRD	

WHARVES\FLOATS   UP TO 60 FT

Note: All marina information is subject to; change without notice, misinterpretation, misrepresentation and human error. In no way are the facilities mentioned in this book obligated to honor the rates and services listed. All information is given without guarantee. No part of this book is intended for navigation.

PUBLIC SERVICES

A: Located at Marina   B: Within Walking   C: Within 20 Miles   D: Not Available

	A	B	C	D
ACCOMMODATION	✓			
BAIT & TACKLE				
BANK MACHINE	✓			
BOAT CHARTER				
BOAT LAUNCH			✓	
BOAT RENTAL		✓		
CAMPING				✓
CAR RENTAL			✓	
CHARTS		✓		
DIVE SHOP			✓	
FISH LICENSE				✓

	A	B	C	D
GOLFING				✓
GROCERY		✓		
HARDWARE		✓		
HOSPITAL			✓	
ICE		✓		
LAUNDRY				✓
BOAT LIFT				
LIQUOR STORE		✓		
24 HR PARKING	✓			
POST OFFICE	✓			
PROPANE				

	A	B	C	D
PUB			✓	
PUMPOUT STN	✓			
RESTAURANT	✓			
RV FACILITIES				✓
SHOPS / MALL	✓			
SHOWER	✓			
SWIM POOL			✓	
TAXI	✓			
TELEPHONE	✓			
TIDAL GRID				✓
TOILETS	✓			

50 AMP AVAILABLE

HOURS SUMMER

HOURS WINTER

TEL.

NO FUEL FLOAT

DIESEL [ ]
GASOLINE [ ]
STOVE OIL [ ]
PROPANE [ ]
AVIATION [ ]

LAKE WASHINGTON

LOCALE

DAVIDSON'S MARINA INC.
VHF:
TEL: 486-7141   CHART # 18447
FAX: 486-3695   N 47 45.20 W 122 15.8
Washington Area Codes 206, 360 & 509

6201 N.E. 175TH ST.
SEATTLE, WA.
98155

GENERAL

OFFICE HOURS

SUMMER:	9 AM - 5 PM DAILY
WINTER:	9 AM - 5 PM DAILY

DAILY MOORAGE

SUMMER:	N/A*
WINTER:	N/A*

MONTHLY MOORAGE

SUMMER:	$1.25 - $2.50 / FT*
WINTER:	$1.25 - $2.50 / FT

 YES   MasterCard YES
-C- YES   DISCOVER YES

ON THE DOCK SERVICES

POWER	✓	LIGHTING	✓
30 AMP	✓	CABLE	
WATER	✓	PHONE	
GARBAGE		DERRICK	✓
WASTE OIL	✓	LIVE ABRD	

WHARVES\FLOATS   UP TO 125 FT

Note: All marina information is subject to; change without notice, misinterpretation, misrepresentation and human error. In no way are the facilities mentioned in this book obligated to honor the rates and services listed. All information is given without guarantee. No part of this book is intended for navigation.

PUBLIC SERVICES

A: Located at Marina   B: Within Walking   C: Within 20 Miles   D: Not Available

	A	B	C	D
ACCOMMODATION			✓	
BAIT & TACKLE				✓
BANK MACHINE		✓		
BOAT CHARTER				✓
BOAT LAUNCH			✓	
BOAT RENTAL				✓
CAMPING				✓
CAR RENTAL				✓
CHARTS	✓			
DIVE SHOP				✓
FISH LICENSE				✓

	A	B	C	D
GOLFING			✓	
GROCERY		✓		
HARDWARE	✓			
HOSPITAL				✓
ICE	✓			
LAUNDRY		✓		
BOAT LIFT	✓			
LIQUOR STORE		✓		
24 HR PARKING	✓			
POST OFFICE		✓		
PROPANE		✓		

	A	B	C	D
PUB		✓		
PUMPOUT STN		✓		
RESTAURANT		✓		
RV FACILITIES				✓
SHOPS / MALL		✓		
SHOWER				✓
SWIM POOL				✓
TAXI	✓			
TELEPHONE	✓			
TIDAL GRID				✓
TOILETS	✓			

CHEVRON

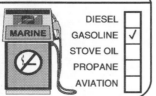

HOURS SUMMER
9 AM - 5 PM
HOURS WINTER

TEL

DIESEL	
GASOLINE	✓
STOVE OIL	
PROPANE	
AVIATION	

CALL IN ADVANCE IF TRANSIENT MOORAGE IS REQUIRED.

CHEVRON GAS DOCK LOCATED NEXT DOOR.

LAKE WASHINGTON

LOCALE

HARBOR VILLAGE MARINA
VHF: 16
TEL: 485-7557
FAX:
CHART # 18447
N 47 45.20 W 122 15.80
Washington Area Codes 206, 360 & 509

6155 N.E. 175TH ST.
SEATTLE, WA.
98155

GENERAL

OFFICE HOURS
SUMMER:	8 AM - 4 PM M - F
WINTER:	8 AM - 4 PM M - F

DAILY MOORAGE
SUMMER:	INQUIRE*
WINTER:	$10.00 PER NIGHT

MONTHLY MOORAGE
SUMMER:	INQUIRE*
WINTER:	

VISA   MasterCard   DISCOVER

ON THE DOCK SERVICES
POWER	✓	LIGHTING	✓
30 AMP	✓	CABLE	
WATER	✓	PHONE	✓
GARBAGE	✓	DERRICK	
WASTE OIL	✓	LIVE ABRD	

Note: All marina information is subject to; change without notice, misinterpretation, misrepresentation and human error. In no way are the facilities mentioned in this book obligated to honor the rates and services listed. All information is given without guarantee. No part of this book is intended for navigation.

PUBLIC SERVICES

A: Located at Marina   B: Within Walking   C: Within 20 Miles   D: Not Available

	A	B	C	D
ACCOMMODATION			✓	
BAIT & TACKLE				✓
BANK MACHINE		✓		
BOAT CHARTER				✓
BOAT LAUNCH			✓	
BOAT RENTAL				✓
CAMPING				✓
CAR RENTAL				✓
CHARTS		✓		
DIVE SHOP				✓
FISH LICENSE				✓

	A	B	C	D
GOLFING			✓	
GROCERY		✓		
HARDWARE		✓		
HOSPITAL				✓
ICE		✓		
LAUNDRY	✓			
BOAT LIFT	✓			
LIQUOR STORE		✓		
24 HR PARKING		✓		
POST OFFICE		✓		
PROPANE		✓		

	A	B	C	D
PUB	✓			
PUMPOUT STN	✓			
RESTAURANT	✓			
RV FACILITIES				✓
SHOPS / MALL		✓		
SHOWER	✓			
SWIM POOL			✓	
TAXI	✓			
TELEPHONE	✓			
TIDAL GRID				✓
TOILETS	✓			

50 AMP AVAILABLE

HOURS SUMMER		NO	DIESEL	
HOURS WINTER		FUEL	GASOLINE	
		FLOAT	STOVE OIL	
TEL			PROPANE	
			AVIATION	

LAKE WASHINGTON

KENMORE AIR HARBOR INC.
VHF:
TEL: 486-1257   CHART # 18447
FAX: 486-5471   N 47 45.20 W 122 15.80
Washington Area Codes 206, 360 & 509

6321 NE 175TH ST.
KENMORE, WA.
98028-0064

LOCALE

GENERAL

OFFICE HOURS

SUMMER:	8:30 AM - 5 PM M - F
WINTER:	8:30 AM - 5 PM M - F

DAILY MOORAGE

SUMMER:	N/A
WINTER:	N/A

MONTHLY MOORAGE

SUMMER:	$90.00 / MONTH
WINTER:	$90.00 / MONTH

VISA   MasterCard   DISCOVER

ON THE DOCK SERVICES

POWER		LIGHTING	
30 AMP		CABLE	
WATER		PHONE	
GARBAGE		DERRICK	
WASTE OIL		LIVE ABRD	

WHARVES\FLOATS   UP TO 24 FT

Note: All marina information is subject to; change without notice, misinterpretation, misrepresentation and human error. In no way are the facilities mentioned in this book obligated to honor the rates and services listed. All information is given without guarantee. No part of this book is intended for navigation.

PUBLIC SERVICES

A: Located at Marina   B: Within Walking   C: Within 20 Miles   D: Not Available

	A	B	C	D
ACCOMMODATION			✓	
BAIT & TACKLE				✓
BANK MACHINE		✓		
BOAT CHARTER				✓
BOAT LAUNCH		✓		
BOAT RENTAL				✓
CAMPING				✓
CAR RENTAL			✓	
CHARTS			✓	
DIVE SHOP			✓	
FISH LICENSE				✓

	A	B	C	D
GOLFING		✓		
GROCERY		✓		
HARDWARE			✓	
HOSPITAL				✓
ICE		✓		
LAUNDRY			✓	
BOAT LIFT		✓		
LIQUOR STORE		✓		
24 HR PARKING	✓			
POST OFFICE		✓		
PROPANE	✓			

	A	B	C	D
PUB		✓		
PUMPOUT STN			✓	
RESTAURANT		✓		
RV FACILITIES				✓
SHOPS / MALL		✓		
SHOWER			✓	
SWIM POOL				✓
TAXI	✓			
TELEPHONE	✓			
TIDAL GRID				✓
TOILETS	✓			

TEXACO

LOCATED AT KENMORE AIR HARBOR

HOURS SUMMER
7 AM - 9 PM
HOURS WINTER
8 AM - 5 PM
TEL   486-1257

MARINE

DIESEL	
GASOLINE	
STOVE OIL	
PROPANE	✓
AVIATION	✓

LAKE WASHINGTON

LOCALE

KIRKLAND YACHT CLUB MARINA

VHF:
TEL: 889-1940
FAX: 822-8723
Washington Area Codes 206, 360 & 509

CHART # 18447
N 47 40.50 W 122 12.50

135 LAKE STREET S.
SUITE 115
KIRKLAND, WA.
98033

GENERAL

OFFICE HOURS

SUMMER:	8 AM - 5 PM
WINTER:	8 AM - 5 PM

DAILY MOORAGE

SUMMER:	LIMITED
WINTER:	PUBLIC ACCESS

MONTHLY MOORAGE

SUMMER:	$7.75 PER FT*
WINTER:	$7.75 PER FT*

VISA, MasterCard, DISCOVER

ON THE DOCK SERVICES

POWER	✓	LIGHTING	✓
30 AMP	✓	CABLE	
WATER	✓	PHONE	
GARBAGE	✓	DERRICK	
WASTE OIL		LIVE ABRD	

WHARVES\FLOATS   UP TO 220 FT

Note: All marina information is subject to; change without notice, misinterpretation, misrepresentation and human error. In no way are the facilities mentioned in this book obligated to honor the rates and services listed. All information is given without guarantee. No part of this book is intended for navigation.

PUBLIC SERVICES

A: Located at Marina   B: Within Walking   C: Within 20 Miles   D: Not Available

	A	B	C	D
ACCOMMODATION			✓	
BAIT & TACKLE			✓	
BANK MACHINE		✓		
BOAT CHARTER			✓	
BOAT LAUNCH			✓	
BOAT RENTAL			✓	
CAMPING				✓
CAR RENTAL			✓	
CHARTS			✓	
DIVE SHOP			✓	
FISH LICENSE			✓	

	A	B	C	D
GOLFING			✓	
GROCERY		✓		
HARDWARE		✓		
HOSPITAL			✓	
ICE		✓		
LAUNDRY			✓	
BOAT LIFT			✓	
LIQUOR STORE		✓		
24 HR PARKING	✓			
POST OFFICE		✓		
PROPANE			✓	

	A	B	C	D
PUB	✓			
PUMPOUT STN			✓	
RESTAURANT	✓			
RV FACILITIES			✓	
SHOPS / MALL		✓		
SHOWER	✓			
SWIM POOL			✓	
TAXI	✓			
TELEPHONE	✓			
TIDAL GRID				✓
TOILETS	✓			

HOURS SUMMER		DIESEL
	NO FUEL FLOAT	GASOLINE
HOURS WINTER		STOVE OIL
		PROPANE
TEL		AVIATION

LAKE WASHINGTON

LOCALE

LAKEWOOD MOORAGE

VHF:
TEL: 722-3887
FAX: 722-3887
Washington Area Codes 206, 360 & 509

CHART # 18447
N 47 33.50 W 122 15.60

4500 LAKE WASHINGTON BLVD. S.
SEATTLE, WA.
98118

GENERAL

OFFICE HOURS

SUMMER:	10 AM - 7 PM T-SU
WINTER:	11 AM - 5 PM T-SU

DAILY MOORAGE

SUMMER:	$.50 PER FT*
WINTER:	MIN $10.00*

MONTHLY MOORAGE

SUMMER:	$5.25 PER FT*
WINTER:	

VISA   MasterCard   DISCOVER

ON THE DOCK SERVICES

POWER	✓	LIGHTING	
30 AMP	✓	CABLE	
WATER	✓	PHONE	
GARBAGE	✓	DERRICK	
WASTE OIL		LIVE ABRD	✓

WHARVES\FLOATS   UP TO 60 FT

Note: All marina information is subject to; change without notice, misinterpretation, misrepresentation and human error. In no way are the facilities mentioned in this book obligated to honor the rates and services listed. All information is given without guarantee. No part of this book is intended for navigation.

PUBLIC SERVICES

A: Located at Marina   B: Within Walking   C: Within 20 Miles   D: Not Available

	A	B	C	D
ACCOMMODATION			✓	
BAIT & TACKLE			✓	
BANK MACHINE			✓	
BOAT CHARTER			✓	
BOAT LAUNCH			✓	
BOAT RENTAL			✓	
CAMPING				✓
CAR RENTAL			✓	
CHARTS	✓			
DIVE SHOP			✓	
FISH LICENSE		✓		

	A	B	C	D
GOLFING				✓
GROCERY		✓		
HARDWARE	✓			
HOSPITAL			✓	
ICE	✓			
LAUNDRY	✓			
BOAT LIFT				✓
LIQUOR STORE			✓	
24 HR PARKING	✓			
POST OFFICE		✓		
PROPANE			✓	

	A	B	C	D
PUB			✓	
PUMPOUT STN			✓	
RESTAURANT		✓		
RV FACILITIES				✓
SHOPS / MALL			✓	
SHOWER			✓	
SWIM POOL				✓
TAXI	✓			
TELEPHONE	✓			
TIDAL GRID				✓
TOILETS	✓			

HOURS SUMMER	NO FUEL FLOAT	DIESEL	
HOURS WINTER		GASOLINE	
		STOVE OIL	
		PROPANE	
TEL		AVIATION	

LESCHI SAILBOAT MOORAGE

LOCALE

VHF:
TEL: 325-3730   CHART # 18447
FAX: N 47 36.10 W 122 16.80
Washington Area Codes 206, 360 & 509

320 LAKE WASHINGTON BLVD. S.
PO BOX 28548 COLUMBIA ST.
SEATTLE, WA.
98118

GENERAL

OFFICE HOURS
SUMMER:	10AM - 5PM TU-SAT
WINTER:	SAME

DAILY MOORAGE
SUMMER:	N/A
WINTER:	N/A

MONTHLY MOORAGE
SUMMER:	$5.25 PER FT
WINTER:	SAME

VISA ☐   MasterCard ☐
☐   DISCOVER ☐

ON THE DOCK SERVICES
POWER	✓	LIGHTING	✓
30 AMP		CABLE	
WATER	✓	PHONE	
GARBAGE	✓	DERRICK	
WASTE OIL		LIVE ABRD	

Note: All marina information is subject to; change without notice, misinterpretation, misrepresentation and human error. In no way are the facilities mentioned in this book obligated to honor the rates and services listed. All information is given without guarantee. No part of this book is intended for navigation.

PUBLIC SERVICES

A: Located at Marina   B: Within Walking   C: Within 20 Miles   D: Not Available

	A	B	C	D		A	B	C	D		A	B	C	D
ACCOMMODATION			✓		GOLFING				✓	PUB		✓		
BAIT & TACKLE			✓		GROCERY	✓				PUMPOUT STN			✓	
BANK MACHINE		✓			HARDWARE			✓		RESTAURANT	✓			
BOAT CHARTER				✓	HOSPITAL			✓		RV FACILITIES				✓
BOAT LAUNCH	✓				ICE	✓				SHOPS / MALL	✓			
BOAT RENTAL				✓	LAUNDRY			✓		SHOWER				✓
CAMPING				✓	BOAT LIFT			✓		SWIM POOL				✓
CAR RENTAL			✓		LIQUOR STORE		✓			TAXI	✓			
CHARTS					24 HR PARKING		✓			TELEPHONE	✓			
DIVE SHOP			✓		POST OFFICE		✓			TIDAL GRID				✓
FISH LICENSE				✓	PROPANE		✓			TOILETS	✓			

DEDICATED FOR DAY SAILOR UP TO 16 FT.

NO FUEL FLOAT

HOURS SUMMER	DIESEL ☐
	GASOLINE ☐
HOURS WINTER	STOVE OIL ☐
	PROPANE ☐
TEL	AVIATION ☐

LAKE WASHINGTON

LESCHI YACHT BASIN
VHF:
TEL: 328-4456   CHART # 18447
FAX: 323-6036   N 47 36.10 W 122 16.80
Washington Area Codes 206, 360 & 509

120 LAKESIDE
SEATTLE, WA.
98122

OFFICE HOURS

SUMMER:	8 AM - 5 PM
WINTER:	SAME

DAILY MOORAGE

SUMMER:	INQUIRE*
WINTER:	

MONTHLY MOORAGE

SUMMER:	$6.50 PER FT
WINTER:	SAME

ON THE DOCK SERVICES

POWER	✓	LIGHTING	✓
30 AMP	✓	CABLE	
WATER	✓	PHONE	
GARBAGE	✓	DERRICK	
WASTE OIL		LIVE ABRD	

WHARVES\FLOATS   UP TO 40 FT

Note: All marina information is subject to; change without notice, misinterpretation, misrepresentation and human error. In no way are the facilities mentioned in this book obligated to honor the rates and services listed. All information is given without guarantee. No part of this book is intended for navigation.

PUBLIC SERVICES

A: Located at Marina   B: Within Walking   C: Within 20 Miles   D: Not Available

	A	B	C	D
ACCOMMODATION			✓	
BAIT & TACKLE			✓	
BANK MACHINE		✓		
BOAT CHARTER				✓
BOAT LAUNCH		✓		
BOAT RENTAL				✓
CAMPING				✓
CAR RENTAL			✓	
CHARTS				
DIVE SHOP			✓	
FISH LICENSE				✓

	A	B	C	D
GOLFING				✓
GROCERY	✓			
HARDWARE			✓	
HOSPITAL			✓	
ICE	✓			
LAUNDRY				
BOAT LIFT			✓	
LIQUOR STORE		✓		
24 HR PARKING		✓		
POST OFFICE		✓		
PROPANE		✓		

	A	B	C	D
PUB		✓		
PUMPOUT STN			✓	
RESTAURANT	✓			
RV FACILITIES				✓
SHOPS / MALL	✓			
SHOWER				✓
SWIM POOL				✓
TAXI	✓			
TELEPHONE	✓			
TIDAL GRID				✓
TOILETS	✓			

CHEVRON

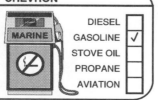

HOURS SUMMER
8 AM - 8 PM
HOURS WINTER
CLOSED
TEL   324-4100

DIESEL	
GASOLINE	✓
STOVE OIL	
PROPANE	
AVIATION	

PARKING AVAILABLE ON WEEKENDS
OTHERWISE 2 HRS MAX.
SEVERAL RESTAURANTS, SHOPS & PARKS
NEARBY.
DRY STORAGE AVAILABLE.

LAKE WASHINGTON

MARINA PARK
VHF:
TEL: 828-1218
FAX:
Washington Area Codes 206, 360 & 509

CHART # 18447
N 47 40.50 W 122 12.50

25 LAKE SHORE PLAZA
KIRKLAND, WA.
98033

GENERAL

OFFICE HOURS
SUMMER:	HONOR SYSTEM
WINTER:	

DAILY MOORAGE
SUMMER:	$4.00 - $15.00
WINTER:	SAME

MONTHLY MOORAGE
SUMMER:	N/A
WINTER:	N/A

VISA MasterCard DISCOVER

ON THE DOCK SERVICES
POWER		LIGHTING
30 AMP		CABLE
WATER		PHONE
GARBAGE		DERRICK
WASTE OIL		LIVE ABRD

Note: All marina information is subject to; change without notice, misinterpretation, misrepresentation and human error. In no way are the facilities mentioned in this book obligated to honor the rates and services listed. All information is given without guarantee. No part of this book is intended for navigation.

PUBLIC SERVICES

A: Located at Marina   B: Within Walking   C: Within 20 Miles   D: Not Available

	A	B	C	D
ACCOMMODATION			✓	
BAIT & TACKLE			✓	
BANK MACHINE		✓		
BOAT CHARTER			✓	
BOAT LAUNCH			✓	
BOAT RENTAL			✓	
CAMPING				✓
CAR RENTAL			✓	
CHARTS			✓	
DIVE SHOP			✓	
FISH LICENSE			✓	

	A	B	C	D
GOLFING			✓	
GROCERY		✓		
HARDWARE		✓		
HOSPITAL			✓	
ICE		✓		
LAUNDRY			✓	
BOAT LIFT			✓	
LIQUOR STORE		✓		
24 HR PARKING		✓		
POST OFFICE		✓		
PROPANE			✓	

	A	B	C	D
PUB		✓		
PUMPOUT STN			✓	
RESTAURANT		✓		
RV FACILITIES			✓	
SHOPS / MALL		✓		
SHOWER	✓			
SWIM POOL			✓	
TAXI	✓			
TELEPHONE	✓			
TIDAL GRID				✓
TOILETS	✓			

THE PORT OF SEATTLE AND CITY OF KIRKLAND ENTERED INTO AN AGREEMENT ESTABLISHING A JOINT ECONOMIC PARTNERSHIP FOR THE CREATION OF THE KIRKLAND COMMUNITY DOCK. THIS FACILITY IS THE FIRST AND ONLY DOCK OF ITS KIND DEVOTED EXCLUSIVELY TO COMMERCIAL BOATS AND TOURISM ON LAKE WASHINGTON.

HOURS SUMMER
HOURS WINTER
TEL

NO FUEL FLOAT

DIESEL	
GASOLINE	
STOVE OIL	
PROPANE	
AVIATION	

LAKE WASHINGTON

LOCALE

MEYDENBAUER BAY YACHT CLUB
VHF:
TEL: 454-8880   CHART # 18447
FAX: 454-1525   N 47 36.50 W 122 13.10
Washington Area Codes 206, 360 & 509

9927 MEYDENBAUER WAY SE.
P.O. BOX 863
BELLEVUE, WA.
98004

GENERAL

OFFICE HOURS

SUMMER:	9AM - 6PM
WINTER:	SAME

DAILY MOORAGE

SUMMER:	RECIPROCAL
WINTER:	ONLY

MONTHLY MOORAGE

SUMMER:	RECIPRICAL
WINTER:	ONLY

VISA   MasterCard   DISCOVER

ON THE DOCK SERVICES

POWER	✓	LIGHTING	✓
30 AMP		CABLE	
WATER	✓	PHONE	
GARBAGE	✓	DERRICK	
WASTE OIL		LIVE ABRD	

WHARVES\FLOATS   UP TO 50 FT

Note: All marina information is subject to; change without notice, misinterpretation, misrepresentation and human error. In no way are the facilities mentioned in this book obligated to honor the rates and services listed. All information is given without guarantee. No part of this book is intended for navigation.

PUBLIC SERVICES

A: Located at Marina   B: Within Walking   C: Within 20 Miles   D: Not Available

	A	B	C	D
ACCOMMODATION	✓			
BAIT & TACKLE		✓		
BANK MACHINE		✓		
BOAT CHARTER			✓	
BOAT LAUNCH		✓		
BOAT RENTAL				✓
CAMPING				✓
CAR RENTAL		✓		
CHARTS		✓		
DIVE SHOP		✓		
FISH LICENSE		✓		

	A	B	C	D
GOLFING				✓
GROCERY		✓		
HARDWARE		✓		
HOSPITAL		✓		
ICE	✓			
LAUNDRY				✓
BOAT LIFT			✓	
LIQUOR STORE		✓		
24 HR PARKING			✓	
POST OFFICE		✓		
PROPANE			✓	

	A	B	C	D
PUB		✓		
PUMPOUT STN	✓			
RESTAURANT		✓		
RV FACILITIES				✓
SHOPS / MALL		✓		
SHOWER				✓
SWIM POOL				✓
TAXI	✓			
TELEPHONE	✓			
TIDAL GRID				✓
TOILETS	✓			

20 AMP POWER ONLY.

HOURS SUMMER	NO FUEL FLOAT	DIESEL
		GASOLINE
HOURS WINTER		STOVE OIL
		PROPANE
TEL		AVIATION

LAKE WASHINGTON

LOCALE

PARKSHORE MARINA
VHF:
TEL: 725-3330   CHART # 18447
FAX: N 47 31.40 W 122 15.60
Washington Area Codes 206, 360 & 509

9050 SEWARD AVE. S.
SEATTLE, WA.
98118

GENERAL

OFFICE HOURS

SUMMER:	VARIES
WINTER:	SAME

DAILY MOORAGE

SUMMER:	$5.00 PER FT.
WINTER:	SAME

MONTHLY MOORAGE

SUMMER:	PRIVATE
WINTER:	SAME

VISA ☐   MasterCard ☐
☐   DISCOVER ☐

ON THE DOCK SERVICES

POWER	✓	LIGHTING	✓
30 AMP	✓	CABLE	✓
WATER	✓	PHONE	✓
GARBAGE	✓	DERRICK	
WASTE OIL		LIVE ABRD	✓

WHARVES\FLOATS   UP TO 50 FT

Note: All marina information is subject to; change without notice, misinterpretation, misrepresentation and human error. In no way are the facilities mentioned in this book obligated to honor the rates and services listed. All information is given without guarantee. No part of this book is intended for navigation.

PUBLIC SERVICES

A: Located at Marina   B: Within Walking   C: Within 20 Miles   D: Not Available

	A	B	C	D
ACCOMMODATION				
BAIT & TACKLE				
BANK MACHINE				
BOAT CHARTER				
BOAT LAUNCH				
BOAT RENTAL		✓		
CAMPING				
CAR RENTAL				
CHARTS				
DIVE SHOP				
FISH LICENSE				

	A	B	C	D
GOLFING			✓	
GROCERY		✓		
HARDWARE				
HOSPITAL				
ICE				
LAUNDRY				
BOAT LIFT				
LIQUOR STORE				
24 HR PARKING				
POST OFFICE				
PROPANE				

	A	B	C	D
PUB		✓		
PUMPOUT STN		✓		
RESTAURANT				
RV FACILITIES				
SHOPS / MALL				
SHOWER	✓			
SWIM POOL				
TAXI	✓			
TELEPHONE		✓		
TIDAL GRID				✓
TOILETS	✓			

HOURS SUMMER	NO FUEL FLOAT	DIESEL	
HOURS WINTER		GASOLINE	
		STOVE OIL	
		PROPANE	
TEL		AVIATION	

64

LAKE WASHINGTON

LOCALE

YARROW BAY MARINA
VHF:
TEL: 822-8081
FAX: 822-7405
Washington Area Codes 206, 360 & 509

CHART # 18447
N 47 39.20 W 122 12.50

5207 LAKE WASH, BLVD N.E.
KIRKLAND, WA.
98033

GENERAL

OFFICE HOURS

SUMMER:	9 AM - 7 PM
WINTER:	9 AM - 6 PM

DAILY MOORAGE

SUMMER:	NO TRANSIENT
WINTER:	NO TRANSIENT

MONTHLY MOORAGE

SUMMER:	INQURE*
WINTER:	

 YES   YES

YES   YES

ON THE DOCK SERVICES

POWER	✓	LIGHTING	✓
30 AMP	✓	CABLE	
WATER	✓	PHONE	
GARBAGE	✓	DERRICK	✓
WASTE OIL		LIVE ABRD	

WHARVES\FLOATS   UP TO 50 FT

Note: All marina information is subject to; change without notice, misinterpretation, misrepresentation and human error. In no way are the facilities mentioned in this book obligated to honor the rates and services listed. All information is given without guarantee. No part of this book is intended for navigation.

PUBLIC SERVICES

A: Located at Marina   B: Within Walking   C: Within 20 Miles   D: Not Available

	A	B	C	D
ACCOMMODATION	✓			
BAIT & TACKLE				✓
BANK MACHINE		✓		
BOAT CHARTER	✓			
BOAT LAUNCH			✓	
BOAT RENTAL	✓			
CAMPING				✓
CAR RENTAL			✓	
CHARTS	✓			
DIVE SHOP			✓	
FISH LICENSE			✓	

	A	B	C	D
GOLFING				✓
GROCERY			✓	
HARDWARE	✓			
HOSPITAL			✓	
ICE	✓			
LAUNDRY				
BOAT LIFT	✓			
LIQUOR STORE			✓	
24 HR PARKING	✓			
POST OFFICE			✓	
PROPANE			✓	

	A	B	C	D
PUB			✓	
PUMPOUT STN	✓			
RESTAURANT		✓		
RV FACILITIES				✓
SHOPS / MALL		✓		
SHOWER				✓
SWIM POOL			✓	
TAXI	✓			
TELEPHONE	✓			
TIDAL GRID				✓
TOILETS	✓			

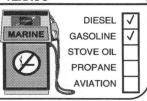

TEXACO

HOURS SUMMER		
9 AM - 7 PM	DIESEL	✓
HOURS WINTER	GASOLINE	✓
9 AM - 6 PM	STOVE OIL	
	PROPANE	
TEL 822-8081	AVIATION	

YEARLY MOORAGE RATES AVAILABLE.
BOTH COVERED & UNCOVERED MOORAGE.

LONGBRANCH

LOCALE

LAKEBAY MARINA IN MAYO COVE

VHF:
TEL: 884-3350
FAX: 884-3350
Washington Area Codes 206, 360 & 509

CHART # 18445
N 47 16 W 122 45

15 LORENZ RD. KPS
LAKEBAY, WA.
98349-9502

GENERAL

OFFICE HOURS

SUMMER:	8-6M-TH 8-7F&S
WINTER:	BY APPOINT ONLY

DAILY MOORAGE

SUMMER:	$.30/FT INC. PWR
WINTER:	

MONTHLY MOORAGE

SUMMER:	$3.00/FT PLUS PWR
WINTER:	SAME

VISA YES   MasterCard YES
☐   DISCOVER YES

ON THE DOCK SERVICES

POWER	✓	LIGHTING	✓
30 AMP	✓	CABLE	
WATER	✓	PHONE	
GARBAGE	✓	DERRICK	
WASTE OIL		LIVE ABRD	

WHARVES\FLOATS   1100 FT

Note: All marina information is subject to; change without notice, misinterpretation, misrepresentation and human error. In no way are the facilities mentioned in this book obligated to honor the rates and services listed. All information is given without guarantee. No part of this book is intended for navigation.

PUBLIC SERVICES

A: Located at Marina   B: Within Walking   C: Within 20 Miles   D: Not Available

	A	B	C	D
ACCOMMODATION			✓	
BAIT & TACKLE	✓			
BANK MACHINE			✓	
BOAT CHARTER				✓
BOAT LAUNCH	✓			
BOAT RENTAL				✓
CAMPING	✓			
CAR RENTAL				✓
CHARTS	✓			
DIVE SHOP				✓
FISH LICENSE			✓	

	A	B	C	D
GOLFING			✓	
GROCERY	✓			
HARDWARE	✓			
HOSPITAL				✓
ICE	✓			
LAUNDRY		✓		
BOAT LIFT				✓
LIQUOR STORE			✓	
24 HR PARKING	✓			
POST OFFICE			✓	
PROPANE	✓			

	A	B	C	D
PUB		✓		
PUMPOUT STN		✓		
RESTAURANT		✓		
RV FACILITIES	✓			
SHOPS / MALL			✓	
SHOWER	✓			
SWIM POOL				✓
TAXI				✓
TELEPHONE	✓			
TIDAL GRID				✓
TOILETS	✓			

PENROSE PARK WITHIN 500'. HIKING TRAILS IN PARK.

APPROACH CAN BE UNDER 10', CALL FOR INSTRUCTIONS IF WORRIED.

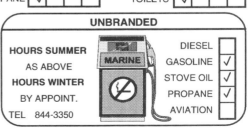

UNBRANDED

HOURS SUMMER
AS ABOVE
HOURS WINTER
BY APPOINT.
TEL   844-3350

DIESEL	
GASOLINE	✓
STOVE OIL	✓
PROPANE	✓
AVIATION	

LONGBRANCH

LONGBRANCH MARINA
VHF: 16
TEL: 884-5137   CHART # 18445
FAX: N 47 07 W 122 45
Washington Area Codes 206, 360 & 509

5215 KEY PENINSULA HWY S.
PO BOX 111
LAKEBAY, WA.
98349

GENERAL

OFFICE HOURS
SUMMER:	VARIES
WINTER:	SAME

DAILY MOORAGE
SUMMER:	$.35 / FT PLUS PWR
WINTER:	

MONTHLY MOORAGE
SUMMER:	LOCALS ONLY
WINTER:	

VISA   MasterCard   DISCOVER

ON THE DOCK SERVICES
POWER	✓	LIGHTING	✓
30 AMP	✓	CABLE	
WATER	✓	PHONE	
GARBAGE	✓	DERRICK	
WASTE OIL		LIVE ABRD	

WHARVES\FLOATS   800' GUEST MRG.

Note: All marina information is subject to; change without notice, misinterpretation, misrepresentation and human error. In no way are the facilities mentioned in this book obligated to honor the rates and services listed. All information is given without guarantee. No part of this book is intended for navigation.

PUBLIC SERVICES

A: Located at Marina   B: Within Walking   C: Within 20 Miles   D: Not Available

	A	B	C	D
ACCOMMODATION				✓
BAIT & TACKLE	✓			
BANK MACHINE				✓
BOAT CHARTER				✓
BOAT LAUNCH		✓		
BOAT RENTAL				✓
CAMPING			✓	
CAR RENTAL				✓
CHARTS				✓
DIVE SHOP		✓		
FISH LICENSE	✓			

	A	B	C	D
GOLFING				✓
GROCERY	✓			
HARDWARE				✓
HOSPITAL				✓
ICE	✓			
LAUNDRY			✓	
BOAT LIFT				✓
LIQUOR STORE			✓	
24 HR PARKING	✓			
POST OFFICE	✓			
PROPANE			✓	

	A	B	C	D
PUB				✓
PUMPOUT STN				✓
RESTAURANT		✓		
RV FACILITIES			✓	
SHOPS / MALL		✓		
SHOWER				✓
SWIM POOL				✓
TAXI				✓
TELEPHONE	✓			
TIDAL GRID				✓
TOILETS	✓			

COMPUSERVE, AMERICA ONLINE, PRODIGY.
STORE & CHOWDER HOUSE, BOOK EXCHANGE.

HOURS SUMMER	NO FUEL FLOAT	DIESEL
		GASOLINE
HOURS WINTER		STOVE OIL
		PROPANE
TEL		AVIATION

LOCALE

ISLANDS MARINE CENTRE

VHF: 69 & 16

TEL: 468-3377

FAX: 468-2283

CHART # 18423

N 48 31.5 W 122 55.2

Washington Area Codes 206, 360 & 509

FISHERMAN BAY ROAD

P.O. BOX 88

LOPEZ ISLAND, WA.

98261

GENERAL

OFFICE HOURS

SUMMER:	8:30-6 M-F 10-5 SAT
WINTER:	SAME

DAILY MOORAGE

SUMMER:	$.55 PER FT
WINTER:	$10 < 26 $15 >

MONTHLY MOORAGE

SUMMER:	$4.25 ON LEASE
WINTER:	VARIES BY SLIP*

VISA	YES	MasterCard	YES
(card)	YES	DISCOVER	YES

ON THE DOCK SERVICES

POWER 30 AMP	✓	LIGHTING	✓
WATER	✓	CABLE	
GARBAGE	✓	PHONE	✓
WASTE OIL		DERRICK	
		LIVE ABRD	✓

Note: All marina information is subject to; change without notice, misinterpretation, misrepresentation and human error. In no way are the facilities mentioned in this book obligated to honor the rates and services listed. All information is given without guarantee. No part of this book is intended for navigation.

PUBLIC SERVICES

A: Located at Marina   B: Within Walking   C: Within 20 Miles   D: Not Available

	A	B	C	D
ACCOMMODATION	✓			
BAIT & TACKLE	✓			
BANK MACHINE			✓	
BOAT CHARTER			✓	
BOAT LAUNCH	✓			
BOAT RENTAL			✓	
CAMPING			✓	
CAR RENTAL		✓		
CHARTS	✓			
DIVE SHOP				✓
FISH LICENSE	✓			

	A	B	C	D
GOLFING			✓	
GROCERY		✓		
HARDWARE	✓			
HOSPITAL			✓	
ICE	✓			
LAUNDRY		✓		
BOAT LIFT	✓			
LIQUOR STORE			✓	
24 HR PARKING	✓			
POST OFFICE		✓		
PROPANE			✓	

	A	B	C	D
PUB	✓			
PUMPOUT STN	✓			
RESTAURANT		✓		
RV FACILITIES			✓	
SHOPS / MALL	✓			
SHOWER	✓			
SWIM POOL		✓		
TAXI	✓			
TELEPHONE	✓			
TIDAL GRID				✓
TOILETS	✓			

CHECK OUT TIME IS 11 AM.
RECYCLE YOUR GARBAGE AS EVERYTHING IS PACKED OFF THE ISLAND.
RENTAL APPARTMENT IS AVAILABLE. CALL FOR RESERVATIONS.
EMERGENCY REPAIRS AVAILABLE.

HOURS SUMMER

HOURS WINTER

TEL

NO FUEL FLOAT

DIESEL	
GASOLINE	
STOVE OIL	
PROPANE	
AVIATION	

LOPEZ ISLAND

THE ISLANDER LOPEZ MARINA RESORT

LOCALE

VHF: 78
TEL: 468-2233   CHART # 18423
FAX: 468-3382   N 48 31.5 W 122 55.2
Washington Area Codes 206, 360 & 509

FISHERMAN BAY ROAD
BOX 459
LOPEZ ISLAND, WA.
98261

GENERAL

OFFICE HOURS

SUMMER:	8AM - 8PM
WINTER:	9AM - 5PM

DAILY MOORAGE

SUMMER:	$24-$32 PER DAY
WINTER:	$15 PER DAY

MONTHLY MOORAGE

SUMMER:	N/A
WINTER:	$120-$160

VISA	YES	MasterCard	YES
	YES	DISCOVER	YES

ON THE DOCK SERVICES

POWER	✓	LIGHTING	✓
30 AMP	✓	CABLE	
WATER	✓	PHONE	
GARBAGE	✓	DERRICK	
WASTE OIL		LIVE ABRD	✓

WHARVES\FLOATS   UP TO 80 FT

Note: All marina information is subject to; change without notice, misrepresentation, misrepresentation and human error. In no way are the facilities mentioned in this book obligated to honor the rates and services listed. All information is given without guarantee. No part of this book is intended for navigation.

PUBLIC SERVICES

A: Located at Marina   B: Within Walking   C: Within 20 Miles   D: Not Available

	A	B	C	D
ACCOMMODATION	✓			
BAIT & TACKLE	✓			
BANK MACHINE		✓		
BOAT CHARTER			✓	
BOAT LAUNCH		✓		
BOAT RENTAL			✓	
CAMPING			✓	
CAR RENTAL		✓		
CHARTS	✓			
DIVE SHOP			✓	
FISH LICENSE		✓		

	A	B	C	D
GOLFING			✓	
GROCERY		✓		
HARDWARE		✓		
HOSPITAL				✓
ICE	✓			
LAUNDRY	✓			
BOAT LIFT		✓		
LIQUOR STORE		✓		
24 HR PARKING	✓			
POST OFFICE		✓		
PROPANE			✓	

	A	B	C	D
PUB	✓			
PUMPOUT STN		✓		
RESTAURANT	✓			
RV FACILITIES			✓	
SHOPS / MALL	✓			
SHOWER	✓			
SWIM POOL	✓			
TAXI	✓			
TELEPHONE	✓			
TIDAL GRID				✓
TOILETS	✓			

CHEVRON

HOURS SUMMER
8AM-8PM

HOURS WINTER
9AM-5PM

TEL   468-3383

DIESEL	✓
GASOLINE	✓
STOVE OIL	
PROPANE	
AVIATION	

MOORING BUOYS AND EXPRESSO CART.

OLYMPIA

LOCALE

BOSTON HARBOR MARINA
VHF:
TEL: 357-5670   CHART # 18445
FAX: N 47 08 W 122 54
Washington Area Codes 206, 360 & 509

312 73RD AVE. N.E.
OLYMPIA, WA.
98506

GENERAL

OFFICE HOURS
SUMMER:	8AM-7PM DAILY
WINTER:	8:30AM-5PM DAILY

DAILY MOORAGE
SUMMER:	$.30/FT $6 MIN.
WINTER:	SAME

MONTHLY MOORAGE
SUMMER:	$85-$110 BY SLIP
WINTER:	SAME

VISA YES   MasterCard YES
DISCOVER YES

ON THE DOCK SERVICES
POWER	✓	LIGHTING	✓
30 AMP		CABLE	
WATER	✓	PHONE	
GARBAGE	✓	DERRICK	
WASTE OIL		LIVE ABRD	

WHARVES\FLOATS   110 SLIPS

Note: All marina information is subject to; change without notice, misinterpretation, misrepresentation and human error. In no way are the facilities mentioned in this book obligated to honor the rates and services listed. All information is given without guarantee. No part of this book is intended for navigation.

PUBLIC SERVICES

A: Located at Marina   B: Within Walking   C: Within 20 Miles   D: Not Available

	A	B	C	D
ACCOMMODATION			✓	
BAIT & TACKLE	✓			
BANK MACHINE			✓	
BOAT CHARTER			✓	
BOAT LAUNCH	✓			
BOAT RENTAL			✓	
CAMPING			✓	
CAR RENTAL			✓	
CHARTS	✓			
DIVE SHOP			✓	
FISH LICENSE	✓			

	A	B	C	D
GOLFING			✓	
GROCERY	✓			
HARDWARE	✓			
HOSPITAL			✓	
ICE	✓			
LAUNDRY			✓	
BOAT LIFT			✓	
LIQUOR STORE			✓	
24 HR PARKING	✓			
POST OFFICE			✓	
PROPANE			✓	

	A	B	C	D
PUB			✓	
PUMPOUT STN			✓	
RESTAURANT			✓	
RV FACILITIES			✓	
SHOPS / MALL			✓	
SHOWER			✓	
SWIM POOL			✓	
TAXI	✓			
TELEPHONE	✓			
TIDAL GRID				✓
TOILETS	✓			

FRESH CLAMS AND OYSTERS IN STOCK YEAR ROUND, FRESH SALMON WHEN IN SEASON. 24 HOUR CARD LOCK FUEL SYSTEM. ONLY CNG SOUTH OF SEATTLE. UNDER NEW OWNERSHIP.

CHEVRON

HOURS SUMMER
8AM-7PM
HOURS WINTER
8:30AM-5PM
TEL   357-5670

MARINE

DIESEL	
GASOLINE	✓
STOVE OIL	
PROPANE	
AVIATION	

OLYMPIA

EAST BAY MARINA PORT OF OLYMPIA
VHF: 65
TEL: 586-6802   CHART # 18445
FAX: 956-0780   N 47 03 W 122 53
Washington Area Codes 206, 360 & 509

1022 MARINE DRIVE N.E.
OLYMPIA, WA.
98501-6961

LOCALE

GENERAL

OFFICE HOURS
SUMMER:	8-6TU-F,8-5M&ST
WINTER:	8-5 M-F

DAILY MOORAGE
SUMMER:	$7 + $.30/FT >20'
WINTER:	SAME

MONTHLY MOORAGE
SUMMER:	$4.20-$4.50/FT
WINTER:	SAME

VISA   MasterCard   DISCOVER

ON THE DOCK SERVICES
POWER	✓	LIGHTING	✓
30 AMP	✓	CABLE	✓
WATER	✓	PHONE	✓
GARBAGE	✓	DERRICK	
WASTE OIL	✓	LIVE ABRD	✓

Note: All marina information is subject to; change without notice, misinterpretation, misrepresentation and human error. In no way are the facilities mentioned in this book obligated to honor the rates and services listed. All information is given without guarantee. No part of this book is intended for navigation.

PUBLIC SERVICES

A: Located at Marina   B: Within Walking   C: Within 20 Miles   D: Not Available

	A	B	C	D
ACCOMMODATION			✓	
BAIT & TACKLE		✓		
BANK MACHINE		✓		
BOAT CHARTER			✓	
BOAT LAUNCH	✓			
BOAT RENTAL				
CAMPING			✓	
CAR RENTAL		✓		
CHARTS		✓		
DIVE SHOP			✓	
FISH LICENSE		✓		

	A	B	C	D
GOLFING			✓	
GROCERY		✓		
HARDWARE		✓		
HOSPITAL			✓	
ICE		✓		
LAUNDRY	✓			
BOAT LIFT			✓	
LIQUOR STORE		✓		
24 HR PARKING	✓			
POST OFFICE		✓		
PROPANE			✓	

	A	B	C	D
PUB		✓		
PUMPOUT STN	✓			
RESTAURANT		✓		
RV FACILITIES			✓	
SHOPS / MALL		✓		
SHOWER	✓			
SWIM POOL			✓	
TAXI	✓			
TELEPHONE	✓			
TIDAL GRID				✓
TOILETS	✓			

HOURS SUMMER

HOURS WINTER

TEL

NO FUEL FLOAT

DIESEL
GASOLINE
STOVE OIL
PROPANE
AVIATION

71

LOCALE

FIDDLEHEAD MARINA
VHF:
TEL: 352-0528   CHART # 18445
FAX: N 47 03 W 122 54
Washington Area Codes 206, 360 & 509

'0'- 611 COLUMBIA STREET
OLYMPIA, WA.
98503

GENERAL

OFFICE HOURS
SUMMER:	NO REG HOURS
WINTER:	SAME

DAILY MOORAGE
SUMMER:	NO TRANSIENT
WINTER:	SAME

MONTHLY MOORAGE
SUMMER:	$4.50-$6.50/FT
WINTER:	SAME

VISA   MasterCard
[ ]   DISCOVER

ON THE DOCK SERVICES
POWER	✓	LIGHTING	✓
30 AMP	✓	CABLE	✓
WATER	✓	PHONE	✓
GARBAGE	✓	DERRICK	
WASTE OIL		LIVE ABRD	✓

Note: All marina information is subject to; change without notice, misinterpretation, misrepresentation and human error. In no way are the facilities mentioned in this book obligated to honor the rates and services listed. All information is given without guarantee. No part of this book is intended for navigation.

PUBLIC SERVICES

A: Located at Marina   B: Within Walking   C: Within 20 Miles   D: Not Available

	A	B	C	D
ACCOMMODATION		✓		
BAIT & TACKLE				
BANK MACHINE		✓		
BOAT CHARTER		✓		
BOAT LAUNCH			✓	
BOAT RENTAL				
CAMPING			✓	
CAR RENTAL		✓		
CHARTS		✓		
DIVE SHOP				
FISH LICENSE				

	A	B	C	D
GOLFING			✓	
GROCERY		✓		
HARDWARE		✓		
HOSPITAL			✓	
ICE		✓		
LAUNDRY			✓	
BOAT LIFT			✓	
LIQUOR STORE		✓		
24 HR PARKING	✓			
POST OFFICE	✓			
PROPANE			✓	

	A	B	C	D
PUB	✓			
PUMPOUT STN		✓		
RESTAURANT	✓			
RV FACILITIES			✓	
SHOPS / MALL	✓			
SHOWER	✓			
SWIM POOL				✓
TAXI	✓			
TELEPHONE	✓			
TIDAL GRID				✓
TOILETS	✓			

FREE VEGGIES FOR MOORAGE CUSTOMERS
FROM JOAN'S GARDEN.
OLYMPIA'S FIRST DOWNTOWN MARINA
EST. 1911.

HOURS SUMMER		DIESEL [ ]
	NO	GASOLINE [ ]
	FUEL	STOVE OIL [ ]
HOURS WINTER	FLOAT	PROPANE [ ]
TEL		AVIATION [ ]

OLYMPIA

LOCALE

ONE TREE ISLAND MARINA
VHF:
TEL: NO PHONE   CHART # 18445
FAX: N 47 03 W 122 54
Washington Area Codes 206, 360 & 509

N. COLUMBIA
OLYMPIA, WA.
98503

GENERAL

OFFICE HOURS
SUMMER:	NO OFFICE
WINTER:	SAME

DAILY MOORAGE
SUMMER:	NO TRANSIENT
WINTER:	SAME

MONTHLY MOORAGE
SUMMER:	
WINTER:	

VISA   MasterCard
DISCOVER

ON THE DOCK SERVICES
POWER	✓	LIGHTING	✓
30 AMP	✓	CABLE	✓
WATER	✓	PHONE	✓
GARBAGE	✓	DERRICK	
WASTE OIL		LIVE ABRD	✓

Note: All marina information is subject to; change without notice, misinterpretation, misrepresentation and human error. In no way are the facilities mentioned in this book obligated to honor the rates and services listed. All information is given without guarantee. No part of this book is intended for navigation.

PUBLIC SERVICES

A: Located at Marina   B: Within Walking   C: Within 20 Miles   D: Not Available

	A	B	C	D
ACCOMMODATION		✓		
BAIT & TACKLE		✓		
BANK MACHINE		✓		
BOAT CHARTER		✓		
BOAT LAUNCH			✓	
BOAT RENTAL			✓	
CAMPING			✓	
CAR RENTAL		✓		
CHARTS		✓		
DIVE SHOP	✓			
FISH LICENSE		✓		

	A	B	C	D
GOLFING			✓	
GROCERY		✓		
HARDWARE		✓		
HOSPITAL			✓	
ICE		✓		
LAUNDRY	✓			
BOAT LIFT			✓	
LIQUOR STORE		✓		
24 HR PARKING	✓			
POST OFFICE		✓		
PROPANE			✓	

	A	B	C	D
PUB	✓			
PUMPOUT STN		✓		
RESTAURANT	✓			
RV FACILITIES			✓	
SHOPS / MALL		✓		
SHOWER	✓			
SWIM POOL				✓
TAXI	✓			
TELEPHONE	✓			
TIDAL GRID				✓
TOILETS	✓			

HOURS SUMMER	
	NO FUEL FLOAT
HOURS WINTER	
TEL	

DIESEL	
GASOLINE	
STOVE OIL	
PROPANE	
AVIATION	

OLYMPIA

PERCIVAL LANDING

VHF:
TEL: 753-8382   CHART # 18445
FAX: N 47 03 W 122 54

Washington Area Codes 206, 360 & 509

222 N. COLUMBIA
OLYMPIA, WA.
98501

GENERAL

OFFICE HOURS

SUMMER:	NONE
WINTER:	

DAILY MOORAGE

SUMMER:	$6 - $9 NO PWR
WINTER:	$9 - $12 W/ PWR

MONTHLY MOORAGE

SUMMER:	MAX 7 DAYS IN 30
WINTER:	

VISA ☐ MasterCard ☐
☐ DISCOVER ☐

ON THE DOCK SERVICES

POWER	✓	LIGHTING	✓
30 AMP		CABLE	
WATER	✓	PHONE	
GARBAGE	✓	DERRICK	
WASTE OIL		LIVE ABRD	

Note: All marina information is subject to; change without notice, misinterpretation, misrepresentation and human error. In no way are the facilities mentioned in this book obligated to honor the rates and services listed. All information is given without guarantee. No part of this book is intended for navigation.

PUBLIC SERVICES

A: Located at Marina   B: Within Walking   C: Within 20 Miles   D: Not Available

	A	B	C	D
ACCOMMODATION		✓		
BAIT & TACKLE		✓		
BANK MACHINE		✓		
BOAT CHARTER		✓		
BOAT LAUNCH			✓	
BOAT RENTAL			✓	
CAMPING			✓	
CAR RENTAL		✓		
CHARTS		✓		
DIVE SHOP		✓		
FISH LICENSE		✓		

	A	B	C	D
GOLFING			✓	
GROCERY		✓		
HARDWARE		✓		
HOSPITAL			✓	
ICE		✓		
LAUNDRY			✓	
BOAT LIFT			✓	
LIQUOR STORE		✓		
24 HR PARKING	✓			
POST OFFICE		✓		
PROPANE			✓	

	A	B	C	D
PUB	✓			
PUMPOUT STN	✓			
RESTAURANT	✓			
RV FACILITIES				✓
SHOPS / MALL		✓		
SHOWER	✓			
SWIM POOL				✓
TAXI	✓			
TELEPHONE	✓			
TIDAL GRID				✓
TOILETS	✓			

LOCATED NEXT TO OLYMPIA YACHT CLUB.

HOURS SUMMER	NO FUEL FLOAT	DIESEL ☐
HOURS WINTER		GASOLINE ☐
		STOVE OIL ☐
		PROPANE ☐
TEL		AVIATION ☐

OLYMPIA

LOCALE

PUGET MARINA
VHF:
TEL: 491-7388   CHART # 18445
FAX: 923-9776   N 47 10 W 122 47
Washington Area Codes 206, 360 & 509

8141 WALNUT RD. NE
OLYMPIA, WA.
98516

GENERAL

OFFICE HOURS

SUMMER:	9AM-5PM M-SAT
WINTER:	SAME

DAILY MOORAGE

SUMMER:	$5 PER NIGHT
WINTER:	SAME

MONTHLY MOORAGE

SUMMER:	DRY STORAGE
WINTER:	SAME

VISA YES MasterCard
     DISCOVER

ON THE DOCK SERVICES

POWER		LIGHTING	
30 AMP		CABLE	
WATER		PHONE	
GARBAGE		DERRICK	
WASTE OIL		LIVE ABRD	

WHARVES\FLOATS   APROX 150 FT

Note: All marina information is subject to; change without notice, misinterpretation, misrepresentation and human error. In no way are the facilities mentioned in this book obligated to honor the rates and services listed. All information is given without guarantee. No part of this book is intended for navigation.

PUBLIC SERVICES

A: Located at Marina **B: Within Walking** **C: Within 20 Miles** **D: Not Available**

	A	B	C	D		A	B	C	D		A	B	C	D
ACCOMMODATION			✓		GOLFING			✓		PUB			✓	
BAIT & TACKLE	✓				GROCERY			✓		PUMPOUT STN			✓	
BANK MACHINE			✓		HARDWARE			✓		RESTAURANT			✓	
BOAT CHARTER			✓		HOSPITAL			✓		RV FACILITIES			✓	
BOAT LAUNCH	✓				ICE			✓		SHOPS / MALL			✓	
BOAT RENTAL			✓		LAUNDRY			✓		SHOWER			✓	
CAMPING			✓		BOAT LIFT				✓	SWIM POOL			✓	
CAR RENTAL			✓		LIQUOR STORE			✓		TAXI			✓	
CHARTS			✓		24 HR PARKING	✓				TELEPHONE			✓	
DIVE SHOP			✓		POST OFFICE			✓		TIDAL GRID			✓	
FISH LICENSE			✓		PROPANE			✓		TOILETS	✓			

GAS ENGINE REPAIRS, DRY STORAGE MAX 25' BOAT.

HOURS SUMMER	NO FUEL FLOAT	DIESEL	
		GASOLINE	
HOURS WINTER		STOVE OIL	
		PROPANE	
TEL		AVIATION	

WEST BAY MARINA
VHF:
TEL: 943-2080
FAX: 943-2022
Washington Area Codes 206, 360 & 509

CHART # 18445
N 47 04 W 122 54

2100 WEST BAY DRIVE
OLYMPIA, WA.
98502

GENERAL

OFFICE HOURS

SUMMER:	9AM - 5PM DAILY
WINTER:	SAME

DAILY MOORAGE

SUMMER:	LIMITED TRANS.
WINTER:	SAME

MONTHLY MOORAGE

SUMMER:	$4.75 - $7.25/FT
WINTER:	SAME

VISA	YES	MasterCard	YES
		DISCOVER	

ON THE DOCK SERVICES

POWER	✓	LIGHTING	✓
30 AMP	✓	CABLE	✓
WATER	✓	PHONE	✓
GARBAGE	✓	DERRICK	
WASTE OIL		LIVE ABRD	✓

Note: All marina information is subject to; change without notice, misinterpretation, misrepresentation and human error. In no way are the facilities mentioned in this book obligated to honor the rates and services listed. All information is given without guarantee. No part of this book is intended for navigation.

PUBLIC SERVICES

A: Located at Marina   B: Within Walking   C: Within 20 Miles   D: Not Available

	A	B	C	D		A	B	C	D		A	B	C	D
ACCOMMODATION			✓		GOLFING			✓		PUB	✓			
BAIT & TACKLE			✓		GROCERY	✓				PUMPOUT STN	✓			
BANK MACHINE			✓		HARDWARE	✓				RESTAURANT	✓			
BOAT CHARTER			✓		HOSPITAL			✓		RV FACILITIES			✓	
BOAT LAUNCH	✓				ICE	✓				SHOPS / MALL			✓	
BOAT RENTAL			✓		LAUNDRY	✓				SHOWER	✓			
CAMPING			✓		BOAT LIFT	✓				SWIM POOL			✓	
CAR RENTAL			✓		LIQUOR STORE			✓		TAXI	✓			
CHARTS	✓				24 HR PARKING	✓				TELEPHONE	✓			
DIVE SHOP			✓		POST OFFICE	✓				TIDAL GRID				✓
FISH LICENSE		✓			PROPANE	✓				TOILETS	✓			

SEE HAUL OUT SECTION OF THIS BOOK.

WEST BAY MARINA

HOURS SUMMER		DIESEL	✓
9AM-5PM	MARINE	GASOLINE	✓
HOURS WINTER		STOVE OIL	✓
SAME		PROPANE	✓
TEL 943-2080		AVIATION	

OLYMPIA

LOCALE

ZITTEL'S MARINA
VHF:
TEL: 459-1950
FAX: 459-8984
Washington Area Codes 206, 360 & 509

CHART # 18445
N 47 10 W 122 48

9144 GALLEA ST. N.E.
OLYMPIA, WA.
98506

GENERAL

OFFICE HOURS
SUMMER:	7:30-6 M-F 7-7 S&S
WINTER:	SAME

DAILY MOORAGE
SUMMER:	VARIES
WINTER:	SAME

MONTHLY MOORAGE
SUMMER:	VARIES
WINTER:	SAME

 YES   YES

ON THE DOCK SERVICES
POWER	✓	LIGHTING	✓
30 AMP	✓	CABLE	
WATER	✓	PHONE	
GARBAGE	✓	DERRICK	
WASTE OIL		LIVE ABRD	

Note: All marina information is subject to; change without notice, misinterpretation, misrepresentation and human error. In no way are the facilities mentioned in this book obligated to honor the rates and services listed. All information is given without guarantee. No part of this book is intended for navigation.

A: Located at Marina   B: Within Walking   C: Within 20 Miles   D: Not Available

PUBLIC SERVICES

	A	B	C	D		A	B	C	D		A	B	C	D
ACCOMMODATION			✓		GOLFING			✓		PUB			✓	
BAIT & TACKLE	✓				GROCERY	✓				PUMPOUT STN			✓	
BANK MACHINE			✓		HARDWARE	✓				RESTAURANT			✓	
BOAT CHARTER			✓		HOSPITAL			✓		RV FACILITIES			✓	
BOAT LAUNCH	✓				ICE	✓				SHOPS / MALL			✓	
BOAT RENTAL	✓				LAUNDRY			✓		SHOWER			✓	
CAMPING			✓		BOAT LIFT	✓				SWIM POOL				✓
CAR RENTAL			✓		LIQUOR STORE			✓		TAXI	✓			
CHARTS			✓		24 HR PARKING	✓				TELEPHONE	✓			
DIVE SHOP			✓		POST OFFICE			✓		TIDAL GRID				✓
FISH LICENSE	✓				PROPANE			✓		TOILETS	✓			

TEXACO

HOURS SUMMER
7:30-6 M-F 7-7 S,S

HOURS WINTER
SAME

TEL 459-1950

DIESEL	✓
GASOLINE	✓
STOVE OIL	
PROPANE	
AVIATION	

STORAGE, LAUNCHING, REPAIR - RAMP AND
SLING LAUNCH
BOAT SALES AND BROKERAGE.
MOSTLY BOATHOUSES.

ORCAS ISLAND

LOCALE

BRANDT'S LANDING
VHF:
TEL: 376-4477   CHART # 18423
FAX: N 48 43 W 122 54
Washington Area Codes 206, 360 & 509

PO BOX 79
EAST SOUND, WA.
98245

GENERAL

OFFICE HOURS
SUMMER:	9AM - 9PM
WINTER:	SAME

DAILY MOORAGE
SUMMER:	$10.00 PER DAY
WINTER:	SAME

MONTHLY MOORAGE
SUMMER:	INQUIRE
WINTER:	SAME

VISA ☐   MasterCard ☐
☐   DISCOVER ☐

ON THE DOCK SERVICES
POWER	✓	LIGHTING	
30 AMP	✓	CABLE	
WATER	✓	PHONE	
GARBAGE	✓	DERRICK	
WASTE OIL		LIVE ABRD	

Note: All marina information is subject to; change without notice, misinterpretation, misrepresentation and human error. In no way are the facilities mentioned in this book obligated to honor the rates and services listed. All information is given without guarantee. No part of this book is intended for navigation.

PUBLIC SERVICES

A: Located at Marina   B: Within Walking   C: Within 20 Miles   D: Not Available

	A	B	C	D
ACCOMMODATION	✓			
BAIT & TACKLE			✓	
BANK MACHINE			✓	
BOAT CHARTER			✓	
BOAT LAUNCH	✓			
BOAT RENTAL			✓	
CAMPING			✓	
CAR RENTAL			✓	
CHARTS			✓	
DIVE SHOP				✓
FISH LICENSE			✓	

	A	B	C	D
GOLFING			✓	
GROCERY			✓	
HARDWARE			✓	
HOSPITAL			✓	
ICE			✓	
LAUNDRY	✓			
BOAT LIFT			✓	
LIQUOR STORE			✓	
24 HR PARKING	✓			
POST OFFICE			✓	
PROPANE			✓	

	A	B	C	D
PUB			✓	
PUMPOUT STN			✓	
RESTAURANT			✓	
RV FACILITIES			✓	
SHOPS / MALL			✓	
SHOWER	✓			
SWIM POOL	✓			
TAXI	✓			
TELEPHONE	✓			
TIDAL GRID				✓
TOILETS	✓			

MOORAGE IS ONLY AVAILABLE THROUGH
SMUGGLER'S VILLA RESORT.

HOURS SUMMER	NO FUEL FLOAT	DIESEL	
HOURS WINTER		GASOLINE	
		STOVE OIL	
		PROPANE	
TEL		AVIATION	

LOCALE

CAYOU QUAY MARINA
VHF:
TEL: 376-4560   CHART # 18423
FAX: N 48 37 W 123 00
Washington Area Codes 206, 360 & 509

P.O. BOX 116
DEER HARBOR, WA.
98243

GENERAL

OFFICE HOURS
SUMMER:	
WINTER:	

DAILY MOORAGE
SUMMER:	PRIVATE
WINTER:	SAME

MONTHLY MOORAGE
SUMMER:	PRIVATE
WINTER:	SAME

VISA   MasterCard   DISCOVER

ON THE DOCK SERVICES
POWER	✓	LIGHTING	✓	
30 AMP	✓	CABLE	✓	
WATER	✓	PHONE	✓	
GARBAGE	✓	DERRICK		
WASTE OIL		LIVE ABRD	✓	

WHARVES\FLOATS   100 FT

Note: All marina information is subject to; change without notice, misrepresentation, misrepresentation and human error. In no way are the facilities mentioned in this book obligated to honor the rates and services listed. All information is given without guarantee. No part of this book is intended for navigation.

PUBLIC SERVICES

A: Located at Marina   B: Within Walking   C: Within 20 Miles   D: Not Available

	A	B	C	D
ACCOMMODATION		✓		
BAIT & TACKLE		✓		
BANK MACHINE			✓	
BOAT CHARTER				✓
BOAT LAUNCH			✓	
BOAT RENTAL		✓		
CAMPING			✓	
CAR RENTAL				✓
CHARTS		✓		
DIVE SHOP				✓
FISH LICENSE		✓		

	A	B	C	D
GOLFING			✓	
GROCERY		✓		
HARDWARE			✓	
HOSPITAL			✓	
ICE		✓		
LAUNDRY				✓
BOAT LIFT			✓	
LIQUOR STORE				✓
24 HR PARKING	✓			
POST OFFICE		✓		
PROPANE			✓	

	A	B	C	D
PUB		✓		
PUMPOUT STN			✓	
RESTAURANT		✓		
RV FACILITIES				✓
SHOPS / MALL			✓	
SHOWER	✓			
SWIM POOL	✓			
TAXI	✓			
TELEPHONE	✓			
TIDAL GRID				✓
TOILETS	✓			

THIS A PRIVATE MARINA, TRANSIENT MOORAGE IS NOT AVAILABLE.

HOURS SUMMER	NO FUEL FLOAT	DIESEL	
		GASOLINE	
HOURS WINTER		STOVE OIL	
		PROPANE	
TEL		AVIATION	

LOCALE

DEER HARBOR RESORT & MARINA
VHF: 16
TEL: 376-4420   CHART # 18423
FAX: N 48 37 W 123 00
Washington Area Codes 206, 360 & 509

P.O. BOX 200
DEER HARBOR, WA.
98243

GENERAL

OFFICE HOURS

| SUMMER: | 8AM - 8PM |
| WINTER: | CHECK IN HOTEL |

DAILY MOORAGE

| SUMMER: | INQUIRE |
| WINTER: | SEE COMMENTS |

MONTHLY MOORAGE

| SUMMER: | INQUIRE |
| WINTER: | SEE COMMENTS |

VISA	YES	MasterCard	YES
	YES	DISCOVER	YES

ON THE DOCK SERVICES

POWER	✓	LIGHTING	✓
30 AMP		CABLE	
WATER	✓	PHONE	
GARBAGE	✓	DERRICK	
WASTE OIL		LIVE ABRD	

Note: All marina information is subject to; change without notice, misinterpretation, misrepresentation and human error. In no way are the facilities mentioned in this book obligated to honor the rates and services listed. All information is given without guarantee. No part of this book is intended for navigation.

PUBLIC SERVICES

A: Located at Marina   B: Within Walking   C: Within 20 Miles   D: Not Available

	A	B	C	D
ACCOMMODATION	✓			
BAIT & TACKLE	✓			
BANK MACHINE				✓
BOAT CHARTER				✓
BOAT LAUNCH			✓	
BOAT RENTAL	✓			
CAMPING			✓	
CAR RENTAL				✓
CHARTS	✓			
DIVE SHOP				✓
FISH LICENSE	✓			

	A	B	C	D
GOLFING			✓	
GROCERY	✓			
HARDWARE		✓		
HOSPITAL			✓	
ICE	✓			
LAUNDRY				✓
BOAT LIFT	✓			
LIQUOR STORE				✓
24 HR PARKING				✓
POST OFFICE	✓			
PROPANE				✓

	A	B	C	D
PUB		✓		
PUMPOUT STN			✓	
RESTAURANT	✓			
RV FACILITIES				✓
SHOPS / MALL				✓
SHOWER	✓			
SWIM POOL	✓			
TAXI	✓			
TELEPHONE	✓			
TIDAL GRID				✓
TOILETS	✓			

RENOVATIONS AND MANY CHANGES
EXPECTED AT TIME OF PRINTING. SOME
SERVICES AND RATES MAY CHANGE.
FUEL FLOAT IS ALSO UNDER RENOVATIONS.

SHELL

HOURS SUMMER
INQUIRE
HOURS WINTER
SAME
TEL   376-4420

MARINE

DIESEL	✓
GASOLINE	✓
STOVE OIL	
PROPANE	
AVIATION	

ORCAS ISLAND

EAST SOUND PUBLIC DOCK

VHF:
TEL: CHART # 18423
FAX: N 48 41 W 122 54
Washington Area Codes 206, 360 & 509

MADRONA ST.
EAST SOUND, WA.

GENERAL

OFFICE HOURS
SUMMER:
WINTER:

DAILY MOORAGE
SUMMER:
WINTER:

MONTHLY MOORAGE
SUMMER:
WINTER:

VISA   MasterCard
         DISCOVER

ON THE DOCK SERVICES

POWER		LIGHTING	
30 AMP		CABLE	
WATER		PHONE	
GARBAGE		DERRICK	
WASTE OIL		LIVE ABRD	

Note: All marina information is subject to; change without notice, misrepresentation, misrepresentation and human error. In no way are the facilities mentioned in this book obligated to honor the rates and services listed. All information is given without guarantee. No part of this book is intended for navigation.

PUBLIC SERVICES

A: Located at Marina   B: Within Walking   C: Within 20 Miles   D: Not Available

	A	B	C	D		A	B	C	D		A	B	C	D
ACCOMMODATION		✓			GOLFING			✓		PUB		✓		
BAIT & TACKLE		✓			GROCERY		✓			PUMPOUT STN			✓	
BANK MACHINE		✓			HARDWARE			✓		RESTAURANT		✓		
BOAT CHARTER		✓			HOSPITAL		✓			RV FACILITIES			✓	
BOAT LAUNCH			✓		ICE			✓		SHOPS / MALL		✓		
BOAT RENTAL			✓		LAUNDRY			✓		SHOWER			✓	
CAMPING			✓		BOAT LIFT			✓		SWIM POOL			✓	
CAR RENTAL			✓		LIQUOR STORE		✓			TAXI	✓			
CHARTS		✓			24 HR PARKING	✓				TELEPHONE	✓			
DIVE SHOP				✓	POST OFFICE		✓			TIDAL GRID				✓
FISH LICENSE			✓		PROPANE			✓		TOILETS		✓		

HOURS SUMMER	NO FUEL FLOAT	DIESEL	
HOURS WINTER		GASOLINE	
		STOVE OIL	
		PROPANE	
TEL		AVIATION	

ORCAS ISLAND

LOCALE	
ISLAND PETROLEUM SERVICES	1 WATERFRONT ST.
VHF:	PO BOX 70
TEL: 376-3883 CHART # 18423	ORCAS, WA.
FAX: N 48 35 W 122 56	98280
Washington Area Codes 206, 360 & 509	

GENERAL

OFFICE HOURS

SUMMER:	8AM-5:30PM DAILY
WINTER:	SAME

DAILY MOORAGE

SUMMER:	$.50 PER FT
WINTER:	SAME

MONTHLY MOORAGE

SUMMER:	$2.50 PER FT
WINTER:	SAME

VISA — YES   MasterCard — YES
— YES   DISCOVER — YES

ON THE DOCK SERVICES

POWER		LIGHTING	
30 AMP		CABLE	
WATER	✓	PHONE	
GARBAGE	✓	DERRICK	
WASTE OIL		LIVE ABRD	

Note: All marina information is subject to; change without notice, misinterpretation, misrepresentation and human error. In no way are the facilities mentioned in this book obligated to honor the rates and services listed. All information is given without guarantee. No part of this book is intended for navigation.

PUBLIC SERVICES

A: Located at Marina   B: Within Walking   C: Within 20 Miles   D: Not Available

	A	B	C	D
ACCOMMODATION	✓			
BAIT & TACKLE	✓			
BANK MACHINE			✓	
BOAT CHARTER			✓	
BOAT LAUNCH			✓	
BOAT RENTAL			✓	
CAMPING			✓	
CAR RENTAL			✓	
CHARTS			✓	
DIVE SHOP			✓	
FISH LICENSE			✓	

	A	B	C	D
GOLFING			✓	
GROCERY	✓			
HARDWARE			✓	
HOSPITAL			✓	
ICE	✓			
LAUNDRY			✓	
BOAT LIFT			✓	
LIQUOR STORE	✓			
24 HR PARKING			✓	
POST OFFICE		✓		
PROPANE			✓	

	A	B	C	D
PUB		✓		
PUMPOUT STN			✓	
RESTAURANT	✓			
RV FACILITIES			✓	
SHOPS / MALL			✓	
SHOWER			✓	
SWIM POOL			✓	
TAXI	✓			
TELEPHONE	✓			
TIDAL GRID				✓
TOILETS	✓			

THIS DOCK PROVIDES FUEL & RELATED PRODUCTS. MOORAGE IS AVAILABLE AS SPACE PERMITS.
$10.00 CHARGE MAY APPLY IF TYING UP WITHOUT FUEL FILL.

TEXACO

HOURS SUMMER		DIESEL	✓
8AM-5:30PM	MARINE	GASOLINE	✓
HOURS WINTER		STOVE OIL	
CALL		PROPANE	
TEL 376-3883		AVIATION	

ORCAS ISLAND

LOCALE

LIEBERHAVEN MARINA
VHF:
TEL: 376-2472   CHART # 18423
FAX: N 48 36.20 W 122 48.90
Washington Area Codes 206, 360 & 509

PO BOX 127
OLGA , WA.
98279

GENERAL

OFFICE HOURS

SUMMER:	7AM-6PM APR-OCT
WINTER:	CLOSED

DAILY MOORAGE

SUMMER:	$.55 PER FT
WINTER:	

MONTHLY MOORAGE

SUMMER:	$4.50 PER FT
WINTER:	

VISA	YES	MasterCard	YES
		DISCOVER	

ON THE DOCK SERVICES

POWER	✓	LIGHTING	✓
30 AMP	✓	CABLE	
WATER	✓	PHONE	
GARBAGE	✓	DERRICK	
WASTE OIL		LIVE ABRD	

WHARVES\FLOATS   UP TO 70 FT

Note: All marina information is subject to; change without notice, misinterpretation, misrepresentation and human error. In no way are the facilities mentioned in this book obligated to honor the rates and services listed. All information is given without guarantee. No part of this book is intended for navigation.

PUBLIC SERVICES

A: Located at Marina   B: Within Walking   C: Within 20 Miles   D: Not Available

	A	B	C	D
ACCOMMODATION	✓			
BAIT & TACKLE	✓			
BANK MACHINE			✓	
BOAT CHARTER	✓			
BOAT LAUNCH	✓			
BOAT RENTAL	✓			
CAMPING			✓	
CAR RENTAL			✓	
CHARTS	✓			
DIVE SHOP			✓	
FISH LICENSE			✓	

	A	B	C	D
GOLFING			✓	
GROCERY	✓			
HARDWARE	✓			
HOSPITAL			✓	
ICE	✓			
LAUNDRY			✓	
BOAT LIFT			✓	
LIQUOR STORE			✓	
24 HR PARKING	✓			
POST OFFICE			✓	
PROPANE			✓	

	A	B	C	D
PUB			✓	
PUMPOUT STN			✓	
RESTAURANT			✓	
RV FACILITIES			✓	
SHOPS / MALL			✓	
SHOWER			✓	
SWIM POOL			✓	
TAXI	✓			
TELEPHONE	✓			
TIDAL GRID				✓
TOILETS	✓			

HOURS SUMMER	NO FUEL FLOAT	DIESEL	
		GASOLINE	
HOURS WINTER		STOVE OIL	
		PROPANE	
TEL		AVIATION	

MOORING BUOYS, ENGINE REPAIRS, SAILING, WHALE WATCHING, AND KAYAKING.

LOCALE

OLGA STATE DOCK
VHF:
TEL: CHART # 18423
FAX: N 48 37 W 122 50
Washington Area Codes 206, 360 & 509

GENERAL

OFFICE HOURS

SUMMER:	VARIES
WINTER:	N/A

DAILY MOORAGE

SUMMER:	
WINTER:	

MONTHLY MOORAGE

SUMMER:	
WINTER:	

VISA [ ]   MasterCard [ ]
[ ]   DISCOVER [ ]

ON THE DOCK SERVICES

POWER		LIGHTING	
30 AMP		CABLE	
WATER		PHONE	
GARBAGE	✓	DERRICK	
WASTE OIL		LIVE ABRD	

Note: All marina information is subject to; change without notice, misinterpretation, misrepresentation and human error. In no way are the facilities mentioned in this book obligated to honor the rates and services listed. All information is given without guarantee. No part of this book is intended for navigation.

PUBLIC SERVICES

A: Located at Marina   B: Within Walking   C: Within 20 Miles   D: Not Available

	A	B	C	D
ACCOMMODATION		✓		
BAIT & TACKLE				
BANK MACHINE			✓	
BOAT CHARTER			✓	
BOAT LAUNCH			✓	
BOAT RENTAL			✓	
CAMPING		✓		
CAR RENTAL			✓	
CHARTS			✓	
DIVE SHOP			✓	
FISH LICENSE				

	A	B	C	D
GOLFING			✓	
GROCERY	✓			
HARDWARE			✓	
HOSPITAL			✓	
ICE	✓			
LAUNDRY			✓	
BOAT LIFT			✓	
LIQUOR STORE			✓	
24 HR PARKING			✓	
POST OFFICE	✓			
PROPANE			✓	

	A	B	C	D
PUB			✓	
PUMPOUT STN			✓	
RESTAURANT	✓			
RV FACILITIES		✓		
SHOPS / MALL	✓			
SHOWER		✓		
SWIM POOL	✓			
TAXI	✓			
TELEPHONE	✓			
TIDAL GRID				✓
TOILETS		✓		

THIS IS A SEASONAL DOCK. BAIT & TACKLE, GROCERY, AND TAKE OUT ARE SEASONALLY AVAILABLE.

HOURS SUMMER		DIESEL [ ]
	NO	GASOLINE [ ]
HOURS WINTER	FUEL	STOVE OIL [ ]
	FLOAT	PROPANE [ ]
TEL		AVIATION [ ]

ORCAS ISLAND

ROSARIO RESORT MARINA

VHF: 78
TEL: 376-2222 CHART # 18423
FAX: 376-3680 N 48 38 W 122 52
Washington Area Codes 206, 360 & 509

1 ROSARIO WAY
EASTSOUND, WA.
98245

GENERAL

OFFICE HOURS

SUMMER:	8AM - 9PM
WINTER:	9AM - 5PM

DAILY MOORAGE

SUMMER:	VARIES BY LENGTH
WINTER:	SAME

MONTHLY MOORAGE

SUMMER:	LIMITED
WINTER:	SAME

VISA	YES	MasterCard	YES
(--o--)	YES	DISCOVER	YES

ON THE DOCK SERVICES

POWER	✓	LIGHTING	✓
30 AMP	✓	CABLE	
WATER	✓	PHONE	
GARBAGE	✓	DERRICK	
WASTE OIL		LIVE ABRD	

Note: All marina information is subject to; change without notice, misinterpretation, misrepresentation and human error. In no way are the facilities mentioned in this book obligated to honor the rates and services listed. All information is given without guarantee. No part of this book is intended for navigation.

PUBLIC SERVICES

A: Located at Marina B: Within Walking C: Within 20 Miles D: Not Available

	A	B	C	D
ACCOMMODATION	✓			
BAIT & TACKLE	✓			
BANK MACHINE			✓	
BOAT CHARTER			✓	
BOAT LAUNCH	✓			
BOAT RENTAL			✓	
CAMPING			✓	
CAR RENTAL	✓			
CHARTS	✓			
DIVE SHOP			✓	
FISH LICENSE	✓			

	A	B	C	D
GOLFING			✓	
GROCERY	✓			
HARDWARE			✓	
HOSPITAL			✓	
ICE	✓			
LAUNDRY	✓			
BOAT LIFT			✓	
LIQUOR STORE			✓	
24 HR PARKING	✓			
POST OFFICE			✓	
PROPANE			✓	

	A	B	C	D
PUB	✓			
PUMPOUT STN			✓	
RESTAURANT	✓			
RV FACILITIES			✓	
SHOPS / MALL			✓	
SHOWER	✓			
SWIM POOL	✓			
TAXI	✓			
TELEPHONE	✓			
TIDAL GRID				✓
TOILETS	✓			

INDEPENDENT

HOURS SUMMER		DIESEL	✓
8AM-9PM	MARINE	GASOLINE	✓
HOURS WINTER		STOVE OIL	
9AM-5PM		PROPANE	
TEL 376-2222		AVIATION	

MOORING BUOYS WITH SEASONAL WATER TAXI AVAILABLE ON CHANNEL 78

LOCALE

SMUGGLERS VILLA RESORT
VHF:
TEL: 376-2297   CHART # 18423
FAX: N 48 43 W 122 54
Washington Area Codes 206, 360 & 509

PO BOX 79
EAST SOUND, WA.
98245

GENERAL

OFFICE HOURS
SUMMER:	9AM - 9PM
WINTER:	SAME

DAILY MOORAGE
SUMMER:	$10/DAY SEMI PRIV.
WINTER:	SAME

MONTHLY MOORAGE
SUMMER:	INQUIRE*
WINTER:	SAME

VISA ☐   MasterCard ☐

☐   DISCOVER ☐

ON THE DOCK SERVICES
POWER	✓	LIGHTING	✓
30 AMP		CABLE	
WATER	✓	PHONE	
GARBAGE	✓	DERRICK	
WASTE OIL		LIVE ABRD	

WHARVES\FLOATS   UP TO 26 FT

Note: All marina information is subject to; change without notice, misinterpretation, misrepresentation and human error. In no way are the facilities mentioned in this book obligated to honor the rates and services listed. All information is given without guarantee. No part of this book is intended for navigation.

PUBLIC SERVICES

A: Located at Marina   B: Within Walking   C: Within 20 Miles   D: Not Available

	A	B	C	D
ACCOMMODATION	✓			
BAIT & TACKLE			✓	
BANK MACHINE			✓	
BOAT CHARTER			✓	
BOAT LAUNCH	✓			
BOAT RENTAL			✓	
CAMPING			✓	
CAR RENTAL			✓	
CHARTS			✓	
DIVE SHOP				✓
FISH LICENSE			✓	

	A	B	C	D
GOLFING			✓	
GROCERY			✓	
HARDWARE			✓	
HOSPITAL			✓	
ICE			✓	
LAUNDRY	✓			
BOAT LIFT			✓	
LIQUOR STORE			✓	
24 HR PARKING	✓			
POST OFFICE			✓	
PROPANE			✓	

	A	B	C	D
PUB			✓	
PUMPOUT STN			✓	
RESTAURANT			✓	
RV FACILITIES			✓	
SHOPS / MALL			✓	
SHOWER	✓			
SWIM POOL	✓			
TAXI	✓			
TELEPHONE	✓			
TIDAL GRID				✓
TOILETS	✓			

1-800-488-2097

HOURS SUMMER		DIESEL	☐
	NO	GASOLINE	☐
HOURS WINTER	FUEL	STOVE OIL	☐
	FLOAT	PROPANE	☐
TEL		AVIATION	☐

ORCAS ISLAND

WEST BEACH MARINA
VHF:
TEL: 376-2240   CHART # 18423
FAX: N 48 41 W 122 58
Washington Area Codes 206, 360 & 509

RT. 1, BOX 510
EASTSOUND, WA.
98245

OFFICE HOURS

SUMMER:	9AM - 8PM
WINTER:	9AM - 6PM

DAILY MOORAGE

SUMMER:	INQUIRE
WINTER:	N/A

MONTHLY MOORAGE

SUMMER:	N/A
WINTER:	N/A

VISA YES   MasterCard YES

ON THE DOCK SERVICES

POWER		LIGHTING	
30 AMP		CABLE	
WATER	✓	PHONE	
GARBAGE		DERRICK	
WASTE OIL		LIVE ABRD	

WHARVES\FLOATS   UP TO 30 FT

Note: All marina information is subject to; change without notice, misinterpretation, misrepresentation and human error. In no way are the facilities mentioned in this book obligated to honor the rates and services listed. All information is given without guarantee. No part of this book is intended for navigation.

A: Located at Marina   B: Within Walking   C: Within 20 Miles   D: Not Available

	A	B	C	D		A	B	C	D		A	B	C	D
ACCOMMODATION	✓				GOLFING			✓		PUB			✓	
BAIT & TACKLE	✓				GROCERY	✓				PUMPOUT STN			✓	
BANK MACHINE			✓		HARDWARE			✓		RESTAURANT			✓	
BOAT CHARTER				✓	HOSPITAL			✓		RV FACILITIES	✓			
BOAT LAUNCH	✓				ICE	✓				SHOPS / MALL			✓	
BOAT RENTAL		✓			LAUNDRY	✓				SHOWER	✓			
CAMPING	✓				BOAT LIFT			✓		SWIM POOL			✓	
CAR RENTAL			✓		LIQUOR STORE			✓		TAXI	✓			
CHARTS			✓		24 HR PARKING	✓				TELEPHONE	✓			
DIVE SHOP				✓	POST OFFICE			✓		TIDAL GRID			✓	
FISH LICENSE	✓				PROPANE	✓				TOILETS	✓			

SCUBA AIR

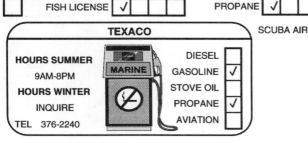

TEXACO

HOURS SUMMER
9AM-8PM
HOURS WINTER
INQUIRE
TEL   376-2240

MARINE

DIESEL	
GASOLINE	✓
STOVE OIL	
PROPANE	✓
AVIATION	

ORCAS ISLAND

WEST SOUND MARINA
VHF: 16
TEL: 376-2314   CHART # 18423
FAX: N 48 37 W 122 57
Washington Area Codes 206, 360 & 509

P.O. BOX 19
ORCAS, WA.
98280

GENERAL

OFFICE HOURS
SUMMER:	8-5M-F 9-4ST 10-3S
WINTER:	8-5 M - F 10-3 ST

DAILY MOORAGE
SUMMER:	$.50 PER FT
WINTER:	SAME

MONTHLY MOORAGE
SUMMER:	$3.00-$6.00 PER FT
WINTER:	SAME

VISA YES   MasterCard YES

ON THE DOCK SERVICES
POWER	√	LIGHTING	√
30 AMP	√	CABLE	
WATER	√	PHONE	
GARBAGE	√	DERRICK	√
WASTE OIL		LIVE ABRD	√

WHARVES\FLOATS   60 FT

Note: All marina information is subject to; change without notice, misinterpretation, misrepresentation and human error. In no way are the facilities mentioned in this book obligated to honor the rates and services listed. All information is given without guarantee. No part of this book is intended for navigation.

PUBLIC SERVICES

A: Located at Marina   B: Within Walking   C: Within 20 Miles   D: Not Available

	A	B	C	D
ACCOMMODATION			√	
BAIT & TACKLE	√			
BANK MACHINE			√	
BOAT CHARTER				√
BOAT LAUNCH			√	
BOAT RENTAL			√	
CAMPING			√	
CAR RENTAL				√
CHARTS	√			
DIVE SHOP				√
FISH LICENSE	√			

	A	B	C	D
GOLFING			√	
GROCERY		√		
HARDWARE	√			
HOSPITAL			√	
ICE	√			
LAUNDRY				√
BOAT LIFT	√			
LIQUOR STORE				√
24 HR PARKING	√			
POST OFFICE			√	
PROPANE	√			

	A	B	C	D
PUB			√	
PUMPOUT STN	√			
RESTAURANT		√		
RV FACILITIES				√
SHOPS / MALL			√	
SHOWER	√			
SWIM POOL			√	
TAXI	√			
TELEPHONE	√			
TIDAL GRID				√
TOILETS	√			

FULL SERVICE YARD.
24 HOUR EMERGENCY SERVICES.

INDEPENDENT

HOURS SUMMER
AS ABOVE
HOURS WINTER
SAME
TEL   376-2314

MARINE

DIESEL	√
GASOLINE	√
STOVE OIL	
PROPANE	√
AVIATION	

OREGON

HAMMOND MARINA
VHF: 16 & 11
TEL: 861-3197
FAX: 861-2351
Washington Area Codes 206, 360 & 509

CHART # 18521
N 46 10.3 W 124 00

IREDALE ST.
PO BOX 250
WARRENTON, OR.
97146

GENERAL

OFFICE HOURS
SUMMER:	6AM - 5PM DAILY
WINTER:	8AM - 5PM M - F

DAILY MOORAGE
SUMMER:	<30'$10 >30'$15
WINTER:	SAME

MONTHLY MOORAGE
SUMMER:	$150.00 / MONTH
WINTER:	SAME

ON THE DOCK SERVICES
POWER	✓	LIGHTING	✓
30 AMP	✓	CABLE	
WATER	✓	PHONE	
GARBAGE	✓	DERRICK	✓
WASTE OIL	✓	LIVE ABRD	✓

Note: All marina information is subject to; change without notice, misinterpretation, misrepresentation and human error. In no way are the facilities mentioned in this book obligated to honor the rates and services listed. All information is given without guarantee. No part of this book is intended for navigation.

PUBLIC SERVICES

A: Located at Marina   B: Within Walking   C: Within 20 Miles   D: Not Available

	A	B	C	D
ACCOMMODATION		✓		
BAIT & TACKLE	✓			
BANK MACHINE		✓		
BOAT CHARTER	✓			
BOAT LAUNCH	✓			
BOAT RENTAL				✓
CAMPING			✓	
CAR RENTAL			✓	
CHARTS			✓	
DIVE SHOP			✓	
FISH LICENSE	✓			

	A	B	C	D
GOLFING			✓	
GROCERY		✓		
HARDWARE			✓	
HOSPITAL			✓	
ICE	✓			
LAUNDRY		✓		
BOAT LIFT			✓	
LIQUOR STORE			✓	
24 HR PARKING	✓			
POST OFFICE		✓		
PROPANE		✓		

	A	B	C	D
PUB		✓		
PUMPOUT STN			✓	
RESTAURANT		✓		
RV FACILITIES		✓		
SHOPS / MALL		✓		
SHOWER	✓			
SWIM POOL				✓
TAXI	✓			
TELEPHONE	✓			
TIDAL GRID				✓
TOILETS	✓			

UNBRANDED

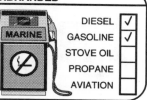

HOURS SUMMER	
7AM-5PM DAILY	
HOURS WINTER	
ON CALL	
TEL 325-5701	

DIESEL	✓
GASOLINE	✓
STOVE OIL	
PROPANE	
AVIATION	

LOCALE

SKIPANON MARINA
VHF:
TEL: 861-0362   CHART # 18521
FAX: N 46 10.3 W 123 50.5
Washington Area Codes 206, 360 & 509

200 N.E. SKIPANON DR.
PO BOX 100
WARRENTON, OR.
97146

GENERAL

OFFICE HOURS
SUMMER:	1PM - 5PM M -TH
WINTER:	SAME

DAILY MOORAGE
SUMMER:	$10.00 PER DAY
WINTER:	SAME

MONTHLY MOORAGE
SUMMER:	$4.50 PER FT
WINTER:	

VISA MasterCard DISCOVER

ON THE DOCK SERVICES
POWER	✓	LIGHTING	✓
30 AMP	✓	CABLE	✓
WATER	✓	PHONE	✓
GARBAGE	✓	DERRICK	
WASTE OIL		LIVE ABRD	✓

Note: All marina information is subject to; change without notice, misinterpretation, misrepresentation and human error. In no way are the facilities mentioned in this book obligated to honor the rates and services listed. All information is given without guarantee. No part of this book is intended for navigation.

PUBLIC SERVICES

A: Located at Marina   B: Within Walking   C: Within 20 Miles   D: Not Available

	A	B	C	D
ACCOMMODATION		✓		
BAIT & TACKLE		✓		
BANK MACHINE			✓	
BOAT CHARTER		✓		
BOAT LAUNCH		✓		
BOAT RENTAL				✓
CAMPING			✓	
CAR RENTAL			✓	
CHARTS			✓	
DIVE SHOP			✓	
FISH LICENSE		✓		

	A	B	C	D
GOLFING			✓	
GROCERY		✓		
HARDWARE		✓		
HOSPITAL			✓	
ICE		✓		
LAUNDRY		✓		
BOAT LIFT		✓		
LIQUOR STORE			✓	
24 HR PARKING	✓			
POST OFFICE		✓		
PROPANE		✓		

	A	B	C	D
PUB	✓			
PUMPOUT STN			✓	
RESTAURANT	✓			
RV FACILITIES			✓	
SHOPS / MALL		✓		
SHOWER	✓			
SWIM POOL				✓
TAXI	✓			
TELEPHONE	✓			
TIDAL GRID				✓
TOILETS	✓			

24 - 50 FT SLIPS.
RESTAURANT AND LOUNGE ADJACENT TO PARKING LOT.

NO FUEL FLOAT

HOURS SUMMER
HOURS WINTER
TEL

DIESEL
GASOLINE
STOVE OIL
PROPANE
AVIATION

OREGON

LOCALE

WARRENTON MARINA
VHF: 16 & 11
TEL: 861-3822   CHART # 18521
FAX: 861-2351   N 46 10.3 W 123 50.5
Washington Area Codes 206, 360 & 509

N.E. HARBOUR PLACE
PO BOX 250
WARRENTON, OR.
97146

GENERAL

OFFICE HOURS
SUMMER:	8AM - 5PM M - ST
WINTER:	8AM - 5PM M - F

DAILY MOORAGE
SUMMER:	<30'$10 >30'$15
WINTER:	SAME

MONTHLY MOORAGE
SUMMER:	$150.00 / MONTH
WINTER:	SAME

ON THE DOCK SERVICES

POWER	✓	LIGHTING	✓
30 AMP	✓	CABLE	
WATER	✓	PHONE	
GARBAGE	✓	DERRICK	✓
WASTE OIL	✓	LIVE ABRD	✓

Note: All marina information is subject to; change without notice, misinterpretation, misrepresentation and human error. In no way are the facilities mentioned in this book obligated to honor the rates and services listed. All information is given without guarantee. No part of this book is intended for navigation.

PUBLIC SERVICES

A: Located at Marina   B: Within Walking   C: Within 20 Miles   D: Not Available

	A	B	C	D
ACCOMMODATION			✓	
BAIT & TACKLE		✓		
BANK MACHINE			✓	
BOAT CHARTER	✓			
BOAT LAUNCH	✓			
BOAT RENTAL				✓
CAMPING			✓	
CAR RENTAL			✓	
CHARTS	✓			
DIVE SHOP			✓	
FISH LICENSE		✓		

	A	B	C	D
GOLFING			✓	
GROCERY		✓		
HARDWARE	✓			
HOSPITAL			✓	
ICE		✓		
LAUNDRY		✓		
BOAT LIFT			✓	
LIQUOR STORE			✓	
24 HR PARKING	✓			
POST OFFICE		✓		
PROPANE		✓		

	A	B	C	D
PUB		✓		
PUMPOUT STN				✓
RESTAURANT		✓		
RV FACILITIES			✓	
SHOPS / MALL			✓	
SHOWER	✓			
SWIM POOL				✓
TAXI	✓			
TELEPHONE	✓			
TIDAL GRID				✓
TOILETS	✓			✓

	HOURS SUMMER	NO FUEL FLOAT	DIESEL	
	HOURS WINTER		GASOLINE	
			STOVE OIL	
			PROPANE	
	TEL		AVIATION	

LEISURE CRAFT ENCOURAGED. NEW HARBOR MASTER.
FORT STEVENS HISTORICAL MUSEUM.
FUEL DOCK IN HAMMOND (2 MILES).

PACIFIC COAST

BAY CENTER MARINA

VHF:

TEL: 942-3422   CHART # 18504

FAX: 942-5865   N 46 40 W 124 00

Washington Area Codes 206, 360 & 509

SECOND STREET
1725 OCEAN AVE.
BAY CENTER, WA.
98577

OFFICE HOURS
| SUMMER: | UNATTENDED |
| WINTER: | |

DAILY MOORAGE
| SUMMER: | N/A |
| WINTER: | N/A |

MONTHLY MOORAGE
| SUMMER: | $20 PER MONTH |
| WINTER: | SAME |

ON THE DOCK SERVICES
POWER		LIGHTING	✓
30 AMP		CABLE	
WATER		PHONE	
GARBAGE	✓	DERRICK	
WASTE OIL		LIVE ABRD	

WHARVES\FLOATS   450 FT

Note: All marina information is subject to; change without notice, misinterpretation, misrepresentation and human error. In no way are the facilities mentioned in this book obligated to honor the rates and services listed. All information is given without guarantee. No part of this book is intended for navigation.

A: Located at Marina   B: Within Walking   C: Within 20 Miles   D: Not Available

	A	B	C	D
ACCOMMODATION			✓	
BAIT & TACKLE	✓			
BANK MACHINE			✓	
BOAT CHARTER				✓
BOAT LAUNCH	✓			
BOAT RENTAL				✓
CAMPING		✓		
CAR RENTAL				✓
CHARTS			✓	
DIVE SHOP				✓
FISH LICENSE			✓	

	A	B	C	D
GOLFING				✓
GROCERY		✓		
HARDWARE			✓	
HOSPITAL			✓	
ICE	✓			
LAUNDRY			✓	
BOAT LIFT			✓	
LIQUOR STORE			✓	
24 HR PARKING	✓			
POST OFFICE		✓		
PROPANE		✓		

	A	B	C	D
PUB	✓			
PUMPOUT STN				✓
RESTAURANT	✓			
RV FACILITIES		✓		
SHOPS / MALL			✓	
SHOWER				✓
SWIM POOL				✓
TAXI				✓
TELEPHONE	✓			
TIDAL GRID				✓
TOILETS		✓		

NO FUEL FLOAT

HOURS SUMMER
HOURS WINTER
TEL

DIESEL
GASOLINE
STOVE OIL
PROPANE
AVIATION

92

PACIFIC COAST

NAHCOTTA SMALL BOAT BASIN

LOCALE

VHF:
TEL: 665-4547
FAX:
Washington Area Codes 206, 360 & 509

CHART # 18504
N 46 30 W 124 00

3119 - 275 ST.
OCEAN PARK, WA.
98460

GENERAL

OFFICE HOURS

SUMMER:	7:30AM - 4PM
WINTER:	SAME

DAILY MOORAGE

SUMMER:	INQUIRE
WINTER:	SAME

MONTHLY MOORAGE

SUMMER:	INQUIRE
WINTER:	SAME

ON THE DOCK SERVICES

POWER	✓	LIGHTING	✓
30 AMP	✓	CABLE	
WATER	✓	PHONE	
GARBAGE	✓	DERRICK	✓
WASTE OIL		LIVE ABRD	

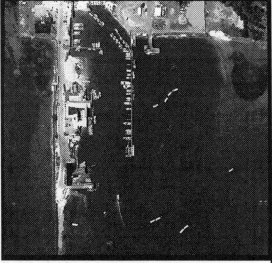

Note: All marina information is subject to; change without notice, misinterpretation, misrepresentation and human error. In no way are the facilities mentioned in this book obligated to honor the rates and services listed. All information is given without guarantee. No part of this book is intended for navigation.

PUBLIC SERVICES

A: Located at Marina   **B: Within Walking**   **C: Within 20 Miles**   **D: Not Available**

	A	B	C	D
ACCOMMODATION			✓	
BAIT & TACKLE			✓	
BANK MACHINE			✓	
BOAT CHARTER				
BOAT LAUNCH				
BOAT RENTAL				
CAMPING			✓	
CAR RENTAL				✓
CHARTS			✓	
DIVE SHOP			✓	
FISH LICENSE				

	A	B	C	D
GOLFING				✓
GROCERY			✓	
HARDWARE			✓	
HOSPITAL			✓	
ICE	✓			
LAUNDRY			✓	
BOAT LIFT			✓	
LIQUOR STORE			✓	
24 HR PARKING	✓			
POST OFFICE			✓	
PROPANE			✓	

	A	B	C	D
PUB	✓			
PUMPOUT STN	✓			
RESTAURANT	✓			
RV FACILITIES			✓	
SHOPS / MALL			✓	
SHOWER			✓	
SWIM POOL				✓
TAXI				✓
TELEPHONE	✓			
TIDAL GRID				✓
TOILETS	✓			

UNBRANDED

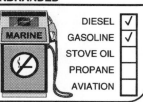

HOURS SUMMER
INQUIRE

HOURS WINTER
INQUIRE

TEL   665-4541

DIESEL	✓
GASOLINE	✓
STOVE OIL	
PROPANE	
AVIATION	

PACIFIC COAST

LOCALE

PORT OF CHINOOK

VHF: 88

TEL: 777-8797　　　　CHART # 18521

FAX:　　　　　　　　N 46 10.7 W 124 00

Washington Area Codes 206, 360 & 509

#1 PORTLAND ST.
PO BOX 185
CHINOOK, WA.
98614

GENERAL

OFFICE HOURS

SUMMER:	8AM - 5PM DAILY
WINTER:	8AM - 5PM M - F

DAILY MOORAGE

SUMMER:	$7.00 PER DAY
WINTER:	SAME

MONTHLY MOORAGE

SUMMER:	VARIES
WINTER:	CALL FOR RATES*

VISA　MasterCard　DISCOVER

ON THE DOCK SERVICES

POWER	✓	LIGHTING	✓
30 AMP		CABLE	
WATER	✓	PHONE	
GARBAGE	✓	DERRICK	✓
WASTE OIL	✓	LIVE ABRD	✓

Note: All marina information is subject to; change without notice, misinterpretation, misrepresentation and human error. In no way are the facilities mentioned in this book obligated to honor the rates and services listed. All information is given without guarantee. No part of this book is intended for navigation.

PUBLIC SERVICES

A: Located at Marina　B: Within Walking　C: Within 20 Miles　D: Not Available

	A	B	C	D
ACCOMMODATION		✓		
BAIT & TACKLE		✓		
BANK MACHINE			✓	
BOAT CHARTER		✓		
BOAT LAUNCH	✓			
BOAT RENTAL				✓
CAMPING		✓		
CAR RENTAL				✓
CHARTS				✓
DIVE SHOP				
FISH LICENSE		✓		

	A	B	C	D
GOLFING			✓	
GROCERY		✓		
HARDWARE			✓	
HOSPITAL			✓	
ICE		✓		
LAUNDRY			✓	
BOAT LIFT	✓			
LIQUOR STORE			✓	
24 HR PARKING	✓			
POST OFFICE		✓		
PROPANE			✓	

	A	B	C	D
PUB		✓		
PUMPOUT STN			✓	
RESTAURANT		✓		
RV FACILITIES	✓			
SHOPS / MALL		✓		
SHOWER		✓		
SWIM POOL				✓
TAXI	✓			
TELEPHONE	✓			
TIDAL GRID				✓
TOILETS	✓			

UNOCAL 76

HOURS SUMMER

8AM-4PM DAILY

HOURS WINTER

8AM-4PM M-F

TEL

MARINE

DIESEL	✓
GASOLINE	✓
STOVE OIL	
PROPANE	
AVIATION	

PACIFIC COAST

LOCALE

PORT OF ILWACO
VHF: 16 & 69
TEL: 642-3143   CHART # 18521
FAX: 642-3148   N 46 10.7 W 124 00
Washington Area Codes 206, 360 & 509

112 HOWARTON ST.
PO BOX 307
ILWACO, WA.
98624

GENERAL

OFFICE HOURS

SUMMER:	8AM - 5PM DAILY
WINTER:	8AM - 5PM M - F

DAILY MOORAGE

SUMMER:	$7 -$17.25 PER DAY
WINTER:	SAME

MONTHLY MOORAGE

SUMMER:	$4.50 PER FT REC.
WINTER:	$3.50 PER FT COM.

VISA   MasterCard   DISCOVER

ON THE DOCK SERVICES

POWER	✓	LIGHTING	✓
30 AMP		CABLE	
WATER	✓	PHONE	
GARBAGE	✓	DERRICK	✓
WASTE OIL	✓	LIVE ABRD	✓

WHARVES\FLOATS   16-180 FT

Note: All marina information is subject to; change without notice, misinterpretation, misrepresentation and human error. In no way are the facilities mentioned in this book obligated to honor the rates and services listed. All information is given without guarantee. No part of this book is intended for navigation.

PUBLIC SERVICES

A: Located at Marina   B: Within Walking   C: Within 20 Miles   D: Not Available

	A	B	C	D
ACCOMMODATION	✓			
BAIT & TACKLE	✓			
BANK MACHINE		✓		
BOAT CHARTER	✓			
BOAT LAUNCH	✓			
BOAT RENTAL			✓	
CAMPING	✓			
CAR RENTAL			✓	
CHARTS	✓			
DIVE SHOP			✓	
FISH LICENSE	✓			

	A	B	C	D
GOLFING			✓	
GROCERY	✓			
HARDWARE	✓			
HOSPITAL		✓		
ICE	✓			
LAUNDRY		✓		
BOAT LIFT	✓			
LIQUOR STORE		✓		
24 HR PARKING	✓			
POST OFFICE		✓		
PROPANE		✓		

	A	B	C	D
PUB	✓			
PUMPOUT STN	✓			
RESTAURANT	✓			
RV FACILITIES	✓			
SHOPS / MALL	✓			
SHOWER	✓			
SWIM POOL				✓
TAXI	✓			
TELEPHONE	✓			
TIDAL GRID				✓
TOILETS	✓			

NICHOL'S FUEL DOCK

HOURS SUMMER
6AM-6PM DAILY

HOURS WINTER
ON CALL

TEL   642-4159

DIESEL	✓
GASOLINE	✓
STOVE OIL	
PROPANE	
AVIATION	

SELF SERVICE BOATYARD. LARGE RECREATIONAL CRAFT ENCOURAGED. PORT OF CALL FOR OCEAN AS WELL AS RIVER CRUISING.
ROCKSIDE RESTAURANTS, FISHING CHARTERS, AND SEAFOOD.
NEARLY 1000 SLIPS.

LOCALE

PORT OF WILLAPA HARBOR
VHF:
TEL: 942-3422   CHART # 18504
FAX: 942-5865   N 46 40 W 124 00
Washington Area Codes 206, 360 & 509

1725 OCEAN AVE.
RAYMOND, WA.
98577

GENERAL

OFFICE HOURS

SUMMER:	8AM - 5PM M - F
WINTER:	SAME

DAILY MOORAGE

SUMMER:	$.20 PER FT
WINTER:	SAME

MONTHLY MOORAGE

SUMMER:	$1.25 PER FT
WINTER:	SAME

VISA   MasterCard   DISCOVER

ON THE DOCK SERVICES

POWER	✓	LIGHTING	✓
30 AMP	✓	CABLE	
WATER		PHONE	
GARBAGE	✓	DERRICK	
WASTE OIL	✓	LIVE ABRD	

Note: All marina information is subject to; change without notice, misinterpretation, misrepresentation and human error. In no way are the facilities mentioned in this book obligated to honor the rates and services listed. All information is given without guarantee. No part of this book is intended for navigation.

PUBLIC SERVICES

A: Located at Marina   B: Within Walking   C: Within 20 Miles   D: Not Available

	A	B	C	D
ACCOMMODATION			✓	
BAIT & TACKLE			✓	
BANK MACHINE			✓	
BOAT CHARTER				✓
BOAT LAUNCH			✓	
BOAT RENTAL				✓
CAMPING			✓	
CAR RENTAL				✓
CHARTS	✓			
DIVE SHOP				✓
FISH LICENSE			✓	

	A	B	C	D
GOLFING			✓	
GROCERY			✓	
HARDWARE	✓			
HOSPITAL		✓		
ICE	✓			
LAUNDRY			✓	
BOAT LIFT	✓			
LIQUOR STORE			✓	
24 HR PARKING	✓			
POST OFFICE			✓	
PROPANE	✓			

	A	B	C	D
PUB			✓	
PUMPOUT STN				✓
RESTAURANT			✓	
RV FACILITIES	✓			
SHOPS / MALL			✓	
SHOWER	✓			
SWIM POOL				✓
TAXI				✓
TELEPHONE	✓			
TIDAL GRID				✓
TOILETS			✓	

HOURS SUMMER		DIESEL	
	NO	GASOLINE	
HOURS WINTER	FUEL	STOVE OIL	
	FLOAT	PROPANE	
TEL		AVIATION	

PACIFIC COAST

LOCALE

SOUTH BEND BOAT HARBOR
VHF:
TEL: 875-5571   CHART # 18504
FAX: 875-9447   N 46 40 W 124 00
Washington Area Codes 206, 360 & 509

FT OF WILLAPA AVE & HWY 101
P.O. DRAWER 9
SOUTH BEND, WA.
98586

GENERAL

OFFICE HOURS
SUMMER:	CITY HALL
WINTER:	7:30AM - 5PM M - F

DAILY MOORAGE
SUMMER:	$5.20 - $7.20/DAY
WINTER:	SAME

MONTHLY MOORAGE
SUMMER:	$1.20 - $1.50/FT
WINTER:	SAME

ON THE DOCK SERVICES
POWER	✓	LIGHTING	✓	
30 AMP	✓	CABLE		
WATER	✓	PHONE		
GARBAGE	✓	DERRICK	✓	
WASTE OIL		LIVE ABRD		

WHARVES\FLOATS   700 FT

Note: All marina information is subject to; change without notice, misinterpretation, misrepresentation and human error. In no way are the facilities mentioned in this book obligated to honor the rates and services listed. All information is given without guarantee. No part of this book is intended for navigation.

PUBLIC SERVICES

A: Located at Marina   B: Within Walking   C: Within 20 Miles   D: Not Available

	A	B	C	D
ACCOMMODATION		✓		
BAIT & TACKLE				✓
BANK MACHINE		✓		
BOAT CHARTER				✓
BOAT LAUNCH	✓			
BOAT RENTAL				✓
CAMPING			✓	
CAR RENTAL				✓
CHARTS			✓	
DIVE SHOP				✓
FISH LICENSE			✓	

	A	B	C	D
GOLFING			✓	
GROCERY		✓		
HARDWARE			✓	
HOSPITAL		✓		
ICE		✓		
LAUNDRY		✓		
BOAT LIFT			✓	
LIQUOR STORE		✓		
24 HR PARKING	✓			
POST OFFICE		✓		
PROPANE		✓		

	A	B	C	D
PUB	✓			
PUMPOUT STN				✓
RESTAURANT	✓			
RV FACILITIES			✓	
SHOPS / MALL		✓		
SHOWER				✓
SWIM POOL				✓
TAXI	✓			
TELEPHONE	✓			
TIDAL GRID				✓
TOILETS	✓			

HOURS SUMMER	NO FUEL FLOAT	DIESEL
		GASOLINE
HOURS WINTER		STOVE OIL
		PROPANE
TEL		AVIATION

PACIFIC COAST

LOCALE

THE WESTPORT MARINA
VHF: 71
TEL: 268-9665   CHART # 18502
FAX: 268-9413   N 46 55 W 124 10
Washington Area Codes 206, 360 & 509

326 LAMB ST.
PORT OF GRAYS HARBOUR
PO BOX 1601
WESTPORT, WA . 98595

GENERAL

OFFICE HOURS
SUMMER:	8AM - 10PM DAILY
WINTER:	8AM - 5PM M - F

DAILY MOORAGE
SUMMER:	SEE
WINTER:	COMMENTS**

MONTHLY MOORAGE
SUMMER:	CALL FOR RATES*
WINTER:	

VISA   MasterCard   DISCOVER

ON THE DOCK SERVICES
POWER	✓	LIGHTING	✓
30 AMP	✓	CABLE	✓
WATER	✓	PHONE	✓
GARBAGE	✓	DERRICK	
WASTE OIL		LIVE ABRD	✓

WHARVES\FLOATS   680 SLIPS

Note: All marina information is subject to; change without notice, misinterpretation, misrepresentation and human error. In no way are the facilities mentioned in this book obligated to honor the rates and services listed. All information is given without guarantee. No part of this book is intended for navigation.

A: Located at Marina   B: Within Walking   C: Within 20 Miles   D: Not Available

PUBLIC SERVICES

	A	B	C	D
ACCOMMODATION		✓		
BAIT & TACKLE		✓		
BANK MACHINE		✓		
BOAT CHARTER	✓			
BOAT LAUNCH	✓			
BOAT RENTAL				✓
CAMPING		✓		
CAR RENTAL				✓
CHARTS		✓		
DIVE SHOP			✓	
FISH LICENSE		✓		

	A	B	C	D
GOLFING				✓
GROCERY		✓		
HARDWARE		✓		
HOSPITAL			✓	
ICE		✓		
LAUNDRY		✓		
BOAT LIFT				✓
LIQUOR STORE		✓		
24 HR PARKING		✓		
POST OFFICE		✓		
PROPANE		✓		

	A	B	C	D
PUB		✓		
PUMPOUT STN	✓			
RESTAURANT		✓		
RV FACILITIES		✓		
SHOPS / MALL		✓		
SHOWER		✓		
SWIM POOL				✓
TAXI	✓			
TELEPHONE	✓			
TIDAL GRID				✓
TOILETS	✓			

MARITIME MUSEUM, SURFING AND CHAINSAW
CARVING CONTESTS.

** DAILY MOORAGE YEAR ROUND
$6.00 - $12.00 UP TO 50 FT THEN $.25 PER FT.

CHEVRON

MARINE

HOURS SUMMER		DIESEL	✓
8AM-5PM M-SAT		GASOLINE	✓
HOURS WINTER		STOVE OIL	
8AM-5PM M-F		PROPANE	
TEL 268-0076		AVIATION	

POINT ROBERTS

LOCALE

POINT ROBERTS MARINA RESORT
VHF:
TEL: 945-2255   CHART # 18421
FAX: 945-0927   N 48 58.3 W 123 03.6
Washington Area Codes 206, 360 & 509

713 SIMUNDSON DRIVE
POINT ROBERTS, WA.
98281

GENERAL

OFFICE HOURS

SUMMER:	8:30 AM - 5 PM
WINTER:	8:30 AM - 5 PM

DAILY MOORAGE

SUMMER:	$.50 PER FT
WINTER:	$.50 PER FT

MONTHLY MOORAGE

SUMMER:	$5.30 PER FT
WINTER:	$5.30 PER FT

 YES   YES

ON THE DOCK SERVICES

POWER	✓	LIGHTING	
30 AMP	✓	CABLE	
WATER	✓	PHONE	
GARBAGE	✓	DERRICK	
WASTE OIL	✓	LIVE ABRD	✓

WHARVES\FLOATS   24' TO 125'

Note: All marina information is subject to; change without notice, misrepresentation, misrepresentation and human error. In no way are the facilities mentioned in this book obligated to honor the rates and services listed. All information is given without guarantee. No part of this book is intended for navigation.

PUBLIC SERVICES

A: Located at Marina   B: Within Walking   C: Within 20 Miles   D: Not Available

	A	B	C	D
ACCOMMODATION			✓	
BAIT & TACKLE	✓			
BANK MACHINE		✓		
BOAT CHARTER				✓
BOAT LAUNCH	✓			
BOAT RENTAL				✓
CAMPING		✓		
CAR RENTAL			✓	
CHARTS	✓			
DIVE SHOP				✓
FISH LICENSE		✓		

	A	B	C	D
GOLFING			✓	
GROCERY		✓		
HARDWARE	✓			
HOSPITAL			✓	
ICE	✓			
LAUNDRY	✓			
BOAT LIFT	✓			
LIQUOR STORE		✓		
24 HR PARKING	✓			
POST OFFICE		✓		
PROPANE	✓			

	A	B	C	D
PUB	✓			
PUMPOUT STN	✓			
RESTAURANT	✓			
RV FACILITIES		✓		
SHOPS / MALL		✓		
SHOWER	✓			
SWIM POOL			✓	
TAXI			✓	
TELEPHONE	✓			
TIDAL GRID				✓
TOILETS	✓			

TEXACO

HOURS SUMMER
7 AM - 9 PM
HOURS WINTER
8 AM - 5 PM
TEL   945-2255

DIESEL	✓
GASOLINE	✓
STOVE OIL	
PROPANE	✓
AVIATION	

POINT ROBERTS MARINA OFFERS THE MOST CONVENIENT ACCESS TO THE GULF AND SAN JUAN ISLANDS.
A NEW MARINA CLUB PROVIDES THE BOATER WITH A FIRST CLASS LOUNGING AND DINING FACILITY.
OUR FUEL DOCK PROVIDES EXCELLENT SERVICE AND OUR ON SITE REPAIR SERVICES CAN SERVE ALL YOUR NEEDS.

PORT ANGELES

PORT ANGELES MARINE INC.
VHF:
TEL: 457-4505   CHART # 18468
FAX: N 48 07 W 123 26
Washington Area Codes 206, 360 & 509

832 BOAT HAVEN DRIVE
PORT ANGLES, WA.
98363

LOCALE

GENERAL

OFFICE HOURS

SUMMER:	8-5 APR - OCT
WINTER:	8-5M-F 8-12S 10-12S

DAILY MOORAGE

SUMMER:	UP TO 30' $10
WINTER:	$.20/FT OVER

MONTHLY MOORAGE

SUMMER:	$2.50/FT PLUS TX
WINTER:	SAME

VISA *MasterCard* *DISCOVER*

ON THE DOCK SERVICES

POWER	✓	LIGHTING	✓
30 AMP		CABLE	
WATER	✓	PHONE	✓
GARBAGE	✓	DERRICK	✓
WASTE OIL	✓	LIVE ABRD	✓

WHARVES\FLOATS   750' TRANSIENT

Note: All marina information is subject to; change without notice, misinterpretation, misrepresentation and human error. In no way are the facilities mentioned in this book obligated to honor the rates and services listed. All information is given without guarantee. No part of this book is intended for navigation.

PUBLIC SERVICES

A: Located at Marina   B: Within Walking   C: Within 20 Miles   D: Not Available

	A	B	C	D
ACCOMMODATION		✓		
BAIT & TACKLE	✓			
BANK MACHINE		✓		
BOAT CHARTER	✓			
BOAT LAUNCH	✓			
BOAT RENTAL				✓
CAMPING			✓	
CAR RENTAL		✓		
CHARTS	✓			
DIVE SHOP		✓		
FISH LICENSE	✓			

	A	B	C	D
GOLFING			✓	
GROCERY		✓		
HARDWARE	✓			
HOSPITAL			✓	
ICE	✓			
LAUNDRY		✓		
BOAT LIFT	✓			
LIQUOR STORE		✓		
24 HR PARKING	✓			
POST OFFICE		✓		
PROPANE		✓		

	A	B	C	D
PUB		✓		
PUMPOUT STN	✓			
RESTAURANT	✓			
RV FACILITIES			✓	
SHOPS / MALL		✓		
SHOWER	✓			
SWIM POOL		✓		
TAXI	✓			
TELEPHONE	✓			
TIDAL GRID	✓			
TOILETS	✓			

SEE HAUL OUT SECTION OF THIS BOOK

WINTER FUEL FLOAT HOURS
8 - 5 M - F, 8 - 12 SAT, 8 - 10 SUN

CHEVRON

HOURS SUMMER
8AM - 5PM
HOURS WINTER
SEE COMMENTS
TEL   457-4505

MARINE

DIESEL	✓
GASOLINE	✓
STOVE OIL	
PROPANE	
AVIATION	

PORT HADLOCK

LOCALE

LOWER PORT HADLOCK
VHF:
TEL: CHART # 18423
FAX: N 48 02 W 122 45
Washington Area Codes 206, 360 & 509

WATER ST.
& LOWER HADLOCK RD.
PORT HADLOCK, WA.

GENERAL

OFFICE HOURS
SUMMER:	UNATTENDED
WINTER:	

DAILY MOORAGE
SUMMER:	12 HOUR MAX
WINTER:	

MONTHLY MOORAGE
SUMMER:	2 VISITS PER MTH
WINTER:	

VISA   MasterCard   DISCOVER

ON THE DOCK SERVICES
POWER		LIGHTING	
30 AMP		CABLE	
WATER		PHONE	
GARBAGE		DERRICK	
WASTE OIL		LIVE ABRD	

Note: All marina information is subject to; change without notice, misrepresentation, misrepresentation and human error. In no way are the facilities mentioned in this book obligated to honor the rates and services listed. All information is given without guarantee. No part of this book is intended for navigation.

PUBLIC SERVICES

A: Located at Marina   B: Within Walking   C: Within 20 Miles   D: Not Available

	A	B	C	D
ACCOMMODATION		✓		
BAIT & TACKLE		✓		
BANK MACHINE		✓		
BOAT CHARTER		✓		
BOAT LAUNCH	✓			
BOAT RENTAL				✓
CAMPING			✓	
CAR RENTAL				
CHARTS		✓		
DIVE SHOP		✓		
FISH LICENSE		✓		

	A	B	C	D
GOLFING			✓	
GROCERY		✓		
HARDWARE			✓	
HOSPITAL			✓	
ICE	✓			
LAUNDRY	✓			
BOAT LIFT			✓	
LIQUOR STORE	✓			
24 HR PARKING	✓			
POST OFFICE	✓			
PROPANE	✓			

	A	B	C	D
PUB		✓		
PUMPOUT STN		✓		
RESTAURANT	✓			
RV FACILITIES		✓		
SHOPS / MALL		✓		
SHOWER		✓		
SWIM POOL			✓	
TAXI		✓		
TELEPHONE	✓			
TIDAL GRID				✓
TOILETS	✓			

HOURS SUMMER		NO FUEL FLOAT	DIESEL	
HOURS WINTER			GASOLINE	
			STOVE OIL	
			PROPANE	
TEL			AVIATION	

ANCHORAGE IN DEEP WATER HARBOR - DEEP WATER PASSAGE TO PORT LUDLOW.

STOP FOR DINNER AFTER FIVE AT THE AJAX CAFE - THE COOLEST RESTAURANT EVER.

THE OLD ALCOHOL PLANT MARINA & LODGE

VHF:
TEL: 385-7030   CHART # 18423
FAX: 385-6955   N 48 02 W 122 45
Washington Area Codes 206, 360 & 509

310 ALCOHOL LOOP RD.
PORT HADLOCK, WA.
98339

GENERAL

OFFICE HOURS

SUMMER:	7AM - 10PM
WINTER:	SAME

DAILY MOORAGE

SUMMER:	<30'=$15 <45'=$20
WINTER:	>45=$25 PLUS PWR

MONTHLY MOORAGE

SUMMER:	$4.00 PER FT
WINTER:	SAME

VISA	YES	MasterCard	YES
	YES	DISCOVER	YES

ON THE DOCK SERVICES

POWER	√	LIGHTING	√
30 AMP	√	CABLE	
WATER	√	PHONE	√
GARBAGE	√	DERRICK	
WASTE OIL	√	LIVE ABRD	√

WHARVES\FLOATS   90 SLIP & BRKWTR

Note: All marina information is subject to; change without notice, misinterpretation, misrepresentation and human error. In no way are the facilities mentioned in this book obligated to honor the rates and services listed. All information is given without guarantee. No part of this book is intended for navigation.

PUBLIC SERVICES

A: Located at Marina   B: Within Walking   C: Within 20 Miles   D: Not Available

	A	B	C	D
ACCOMMODATION	√			
BAIT & TACKLE		√		
BANK MACHINE		√		
BOAT CHARTER	√			
BOAT LAUNCH		√		
BOAT RENTAL		√		
CAMPING		√		
CAR RENTAL		√		
CHARTS		√		
DIVE SHOP		√		
FISH LICENSE		√		

	A	B	C	D
GOLFING		√		
GROCERY		√		
HARDWARE		√		
HOSPITAL		√		
ICE		√		
LAUNDRY		√		
BOAT LIFT		√		
LIQUOR STORE		√		
24 HR PARKING	√			
POST OFFICE		√		
PROPANE		√		

	A	B	C	D
PUB	√			
PUMPOUT STN		√		
RESTAURANT	√			
RV FACILITIES	√			
SHOPS / MALL		√		
SHOWER	√			
SWIM POOL		√		
TAXI		√		
TELEPHONE	√			
TIDAL GRID		√		
TOILETS	√			

THE OLD ALCOHOL PLANT REALLY WAS AN ALCOHOL PLANT FROM 1911 TO 1913. IT WAS THE CLASSEN CHEMICAL CO., A FRANCHISE OF A FRENCH PROCESS TO MAKE ALCOHOL OUT OF SAWDUST. THE PLANT WAS FOUNDED BY OFFICERS OF THE WASHINGTON MILL CO., WHICH HAD CLOSED THE HADLOCK LUMBER MILL IN 1907.

HOURS SUMMER
HOURS WINTER
TEL

NO FUEL FLOAT

DIESEL	
GASOLINE	
STOVE OIL	
PROPANE	
AVIATION	

PORT LUDLOW

PORT LUDLOW MARINA
VHF: 16
TEL: 437-0513   CHART # 18445
FAX: 437-2824   N 47 55 W 122 40
Washington Area Codes 206, 360 & 509

1 GULL DRIVE
PORT LUDLOW, WA.
98365

GENERAL

OFFICE HOURS
SUMMER:	7AM - 9PM
WINTER:	9 - 5 CLOSED TUE

DAILY MOORAGE
SUMMER:	$.60 PER FT
WINTER:	$.50 PER FT

MONTHLY MOORAGE
SUMMER:	CALL FOR RATES*
WINTER:	

VISA	YES	MasterCard	YES
[AmEx]	YES	DISCOVER	

ON THE DOCK SERVICES
POWER	✓	LIGHTING	✓
30 AMP	✓	CABLE	
WATER	✓	PHONE	
GARBAGE	✓	DERRICK	✓
WASTE OIL	✓	LIVE ABRD	✓

WHARVES\FLOATS   300 SLIPS + 670 FT

Note: All marina information is subject to; change without notice, misinterpretation, misrepresentation and human error. In no way are the facilities mentioned in this book obligated to honor the rates and services listed. All information is given without guarantee. No part of this book is intended for navigation.

PUBLIC SERVICES

A: Located at Marina   B: Within Walking   C: Within 20 Miles   D: Not Available

	A	B	C	D
ACCOMMODATION	✓			
BAIT & TACKLE	✓			
BANK MACHINE	✓			
BOAT CHARTER				✓
BOAT LAUNCH		✓		
BOAT RENTAL	✓			
CAMPING		✓		
CAR RENTAL				✓
CHARTS	✓			
DIVE SHOP				✓
FISH LICENSE	✓			

	A	B	C	D
GOLFING	✓			
GROCERY	✓			
HARDWARE			✓	
HOSPITAL			✓	
ICE	✓			
LAUNDRY	✓			
BOAT LIFT				✓
LIQUOR STORE			✓	
24 HR PARKING	✓			
POST OFFICE	✓			
PROPANE	✓			

	A	B	C	D
PUB	✓			
PUMPOUT STN	✓			
RESTAURANT	✓			
RV FACILITIES		✓		
SHOPS / MALL		✓		
SHOWER	✓			
SWIM POOL				✓
TAXI				✓
TELEPHONE	✓			
TIDAL GRID				✓
TOILETS	✓			

TEXACO

HOURS SUMMER
7AM - 8PM
HOURS WINTER
9AM - 4PM
TEL   437-0513

DIESEL	✓
GASOLENE	✓
STOVE OIL	
PROPANE	✓
AVIATION	

SHUTTLE SERVICE ACROSS HARBOR TO GOLF COURSE. BEER & WINE AVAILABLE AT STORE. COMPRESSED NATURAL GAS AT FUEL FLOAT, PORT-A- POTTY DUMP.

LOCALE

CITY OF PORT ORCHARD PEDESTRIAN PIER

VHF:
TEL: CHART # 18445
FAX: N 47 32 W 122 38
Washington Area Codes 206, 360 & 509

509 BAY STREET
PORT ORCHARD, WA.

GENERAL

OFFICE HOURS

SUMMER:	UNATTENDED
WINTER:	

DAILY MOORAGE

SUMMER:	
WINTER:	

MONTHLY MOORAGE

SUMMER:	
WINTER:	

VISA   *MasterCard*
[card]   *DISCOVER*

ON THE DOCK SERVICES

POWER		LIGHTING	
30 AMP		CABLE	
WATER		PHONE	
GARBAGE		DERRICK	
WASTE OIL		LIVE ABRD	

Note: All marina information is subject to; change without notice, misinterpretation, misrepresentation and human error. In no way are the facilities mentioned in this book obligated to honor the rates and services listed. All information is given without guarantee. No part of this book is intended for navigation.

PUBLIC SERVICES

A: Located at Marina   B: Within Walking   C: Within 20 Miles   D: Not Available

	A	B	C	D
ACCOMMODATION		✓		
BAIT & TACKLE		✓		
BANK MACHINE		✓		
BOAT CHARTER				✓
BOAT LAUNCH		✓		
BOAT RENTAL				✓
CAMPING			✓	
CAR RENTAL		✓		
CHARTS		✓		
DIVE SHOP			✓	
FISH LICENSE		✓		

	A	B	C	D
GOLFING			✓	
GROCERY		✓		
HARDWARE		✓		
HOSPITAL			✓	
ICE		✓		
LAUNDRY		✓		
BOAT LIFT		✓		
LIQUOR STORE		✓		
24 HR PARKING		✓		
POST OFFICE		✓		
PROPANE			✓	

	A	B	C	D
PUB		✓		
PUMPOUT STN		✓		
RESTAURANT		✓		
RV FACILITIES				✓
SHOPS / MALL		✓		
SHOWER		✓		
SWIM POOL		✓		
TAXI		✓		
TELEPHONE		✓		
TIDAL GRID				✓
TOILETS		✓		

HOURS SUMMER	**NO**	DIESEL
HOURS WINTER	**FUEL**	GASOLINE
	FLOAT	STOVE OIL
TEL		PROPANE
		AVIATION

PORT ORCHARD

LOCALE	**DOCKSIDE SALES & SERVICE**		53 BAY ST. W.
	VHF:		P.O. BOX 1028
	TEL: 876-9016	CHART # 18445	PORT ORCHARD, WA.
	FAX: 876-6491	N 47 32 W 122 38	98366
	Washington Area Codes 206, 360 & 509		

GENERAL

OFFICE HOURS

SUMMER:	8 - 5 M - F 9 - 3 SAT
WINTER:	SAME

DAILY MOORAGE

SUMMER:	NONE
WINTER:	SAME

MONTHLY MOORAGE

SUMMER:	$3.50 / FT OPEN
WINTER:	$4.75 FT COVERED

VISA YES   MasterCard YES

ON THE DOCK SERVICES

POWER	✓	LIGHTING	✓
30 AMP	✓	CABLE	
WATER	✓	PHONE	✓
GARBAGE	✓	DERRICK	
WASTE OIL		LIVE ABRD	✓

WHARVES\FLOATS   800 FEET

Note: All marina information is subject to; change without notice, misinterpretation, misrepresentation and human error. In no way are the facilities mentioned in this book obligated to honor the rates and services listed. All information is given without guarantee. No part of this book is intended for navigation.

PUBLIC SERVICES

A: Located at Marina   B: Within Walking   C: Within 20 Miles   D: Not Available

	A	B	C	D
ACCOMMODATION		✓		
BAIT & TACKLE		✓		
BANK MACHINE		✓		
BOAT CHARTER			✓	
BOAT LAUNCH	✓			
BOAT RENTAL			✓	
CAMPING			✓	
CAR RENTAL		✓		
CHARTS		✓		
DIVE SHOP			✓	
FISH LICENSE			✓	

	A	B	C	D
GOLFING			✓	
GROCERY		✓		
HARDWARE	✓			
HOSPITAL			✓	
ICE	✓			
LAUNDRY	✓			
BOAT LIFT	✓			
LIQUOR STORE	✓			
24 HR PARKING	✓			
POST OFFICE	✓			
PROPANE			✓	

	A	B	C	D
PUB		✓		
PUMPOUT STN		✓		
RESTAURANT		✓		
RV FACILITIES			✓	
SHOPS / MALL		✓		
SHOWER	✓			
SWIM POOL		✓		
TAXI		✓		
TELEPHONE	✓			
TIDAL GRID				✓
TOILETS	✓			

SEE HAUL OUT SECTION OF THIS BOOK.

HOURS SUMMER	**NO FUEL FLOAT**	DIESEL	
HOURS WINTER		GASOLINE	
		STOVE OIL	
		PROPANE	
TEL		AVIATION	

LOCALE

KITSAP MARINA
VHF:
TEL: 895-2193   CHART # 18445
FAX: 876-1965   N 47 32 W 122 38
Washington Area Codes 206, 360 & 509

1595 S.W. BAY STREET
PORT ORCHARD, WA.
98366

GENERAL

OFFICE HOURS

SUMMER:	9-5:30 M - F 9-3 SAT
WINTER:	CLOSED SUN

DAILY MOORAGE

SUMMER:	N/A
WINTER:	N/A

MONTHLY MOORAGE

SUMMER:	$3.50 PER FT
WINTER:	SAME

VISA — YES   MasterCard — YES
— DISCOVER — YES

ON THE DOCK SERVICES

POWER	✓	LIGHTING	✓
30 AMP	✓	CABLE	
WATER	✓	PHONE	
GARBAGE	✓	DERRICK	
WASTE OIL		LIVE ABRD	✓

Note: All marina information is subject to; change without notice, misinterpretation, misrepresentation and human error. In no way are the facilities mentioned in this book obligated to honor the rates and services listed. All information is given without guarantee. No part of this book is intended for navigation.

PUBLIC SERVICES

A: Located at Marina   B: Within Walking   C: Within 20 Miles   D: Not Available

	A	B	C	D
ACCOMMODATION			✓	
BAIT & TACKLE	✓			
BANK MACHINE			✓	
BOAT CHARTER				✓
BOAT LAUNCH				✓
BOAT RENTAL				✓
CAMPING				✓
CAR RENTAL				✓
CHARTS			✓	
DIVE SHOP			✓	
FISH LICENSE			✓	

	A	B	C	D
GOLFING			✓	
GROCERY			✓	
HARDWARE	✓			
HOSPITAL			✓	
ICE			✓	
LAUNDRY			✓	
BOAT LIFT	✓			
LIQUOR STORE			✓	
24 HR PARKING	✓			
POST OFFICE			✓	
PROPANE				

	A	B	C	D
PUB			✓	
PUMPOUT STN			✓	
RESTAURANT			✓	
RV FACILITIES			✓	
SHOPS / MALL			✓	
SHOWER			✓	
SWIM POOL				
TAXI	✓			
TELEPHONE	✓			
TIDAL GRID				✓
TOILETS	✓			

HOURS SUMMER		DIESEL	
HOURS WINTER	NO FUEL FLOAT	GASOLINE	
		STOVE OIL	
		PROPANE	
TEL		AVIATION	

PORT ORCHARD

PORT ORCHARD MARINA
VHF: 15
TEL: 876-5535
FAX:
CHART # 18445
N 47 32.40 W 122 38.17
Washington Area Codes 206, 360 & 509

707 SIDNEY PARKWAY
8850 SW STATE HWY 3
PORT ORCHARD, WA.
98366

OFFICE HOURS

SUMMER:	7AM - 10PM
WINTER:	7AM - 7PM

DAILY MOORAGE

SUMMER:	$.25 PER FT
WINTER:	SAME

MONTHLY MOORAGE

SUMMER:	$2.30/FT OPEN
WINTER:	$3.50/FT COVERED

 YES   YES
 YES   YES

ON THE DOCK SERVICES

POWER	✓	LIGHTING	✓
30 AMP	✓	CABLE	
WATER	✓	PHONE	
GARBAGE	✓	DERRICK	
WASTE OIL	✓	LIVE ABRD	

WHARVES\FLOATS   1500 FT GUEST

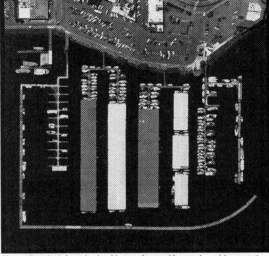

Note: All marina information is subject to; change without notice, misinterpretation, misrepresentation and human error. In no way are the facilities mentioned in this book obligated to honor the rates and services listed. All information is given without guarantee. No part of this book is intended for navigation.

A: Located at Marina   B: Within Walking   C: Within 20 Miles   D: Not Available

	A	B	C	D
ACCOMMODATION		✓		
BAIT & TACKLE		✓		
BANK MACHINE		✓		
BOAT CHARTER				✓
BOAT LAUNCH		✓		
BOAT RENTAL				✓
CAMPING			✓	
CAR RENTAL		✓		
CHARTS		✓		
DIVE SHOP			✓	
FISH LICENSE		✓		

	A	B	C	D
GOLFING			✓	
GROCERY		✓		
HARDWARE		✓		
HOSPITAL			✓	
ICE		✓		
LAUNDRY	✓			
BOAT LIFT		✓		
LIQUOR STORE		✓		
24 HR PARKING		✓		
POST OFFICE		✓		
PROPANE			✓	

	A	B	C	D
PUB		✓		
PUMPOUT STN	✓			
RESTAURANT		✓		
RV FACILITIES				✓
SHOPS / MALL		✓		
SHOWER	✓			
SWIM POOL		✓		
TAXI		✓		
TELEPHONE	✓			
TIDAL GRID				✓
TOILETS	✓			

TEXACO

HOURS SUMMER
7AM-9:30PM

HOURS WINTER
7AM-6:30PM

TEL   876-5535

DIESEL	✓
GASOLINE	✓
STOVE OIL	
PROPANE	
AVIATION	

RESERVATIONS ACCEPTED, EXCEPT MEMORIAL DAY, JULY 4, & LABOR DAY. LOCATED ONE BLOCK FROM DOWNTOWN. ANTIQUE CAPITAL OF PUGET SOUND. SEVEN RESTAURANTS WITHIN WALKING DISTANCE. CARD SECURITY.

CREDIT CARDS ACCEPTED AT FUEL FLOAT ONLY!

LOCALE

PORT ORCHARD YACHT CLUB
VHF:
TEL: 876-9010   CHART # 18445
FAX: N 47 32 W 122 38
Washington Area Codes 206, 360 & 509

P.O. BOX 3
PORT ORCHARD, WA.
98366

GENERAL

OFFICE HOURS

SUMMER:	
WINTER:	

DAILY MOORAGE

SUMMER:	RECIPROCAL
WINTER:	MEMBERS ONLY

MONTHLY MOORAGE

SUMMER:	MEMBERS
WINTER:	ONLY

VISA   MasterCard   DISCOVER

ON THE DOCK SERVICES

POWER	✓	LIGHTING	✓
30 AMP	✓	CABLE	
WATER	✓	PHONE	
GARBAGE		DERRICK	
WASTE OIL		LIVE ABRD	

Note: All marina information is subject to; change without notice, misinterpretation, misrepresentation and human error. In no way are the facilities mentioned in this book obligated to honor the rates and services listed. All information is given without guarantee. No part of this book is intended for navigation.

PUBLIC SERVICES

A: Located at Marina   B: Within Walking   C: Within 20 Miles   D: Not Available

	A	B	C	D
ACCOMMODATION		✓		
BAIT & TACKLE		✓		
BANK MACHINE		✓		
BOAT CHARTER			✓	
BOAT LAUNCH		✓		
BOAT RENTAL			✓	
CAMPING			✓	
CAR RENTAL		✓		
CHARTS		✓		
DIVE SHOP			✓	
FISH LICENSE		✓		

	A	B	C	D
GOLFING			✓	
GROCERY		✓		
HARDWARE		✓		
HOSPITAL			✓	
ICE	✓			
LAUNDRY		✓		
BOAT LIFT		✓		
LIQUOR STORE		✓		
24 HR PARKING	✓			
POST OFFICE		✓		
PROPANE			✓	

	A	B	C	D
PUB		✓		
PUMPOUT STN	✓			
RESTAURANT		✓		
RV FACILITIES			✓	
SHOPS / MALL		✓		
SHOWER	✓			
SWIM POOL		✓		
TAXI		✓		
TELEPHONE	✓			
TIDAL GRID				✓
TOILETS	✓			

HOURS SUMMER

HOURS WINTER

TEL

NO FUEL FLOAT

DIESEL	
GASOLINE	
STOVE OIL	
PROPANE	
AVIATION	

PORT ORCHARD

LOCALE

SINCLAIR INLET MARINA
VHF:
TEL: 895-5167
FAX: 876-3171
Washington Area Codes 206, 360 & 509

CHART # 18445
N 47 32 W 122 38

501 BAY ST.
PORT ORCHARD, WA.
98366

GENERAL

OFFICE HOURS
SUMMER:	9:30AM - 4:30PM
WINTER:	SAME

DAILY MOORAGE
SUMMER:	NO TRANSIENT
WINTER:	SAME

MONTHLY MOORAGE
SUMMER:	$3.95 FT OPEN
WINTER:	$5.95 FT COVERED

ON THE DOCK SERVICES
POWER	✓	LIGHTING	✓
30 AMP	✓	CABLE	✓
WATER	✓	PHONE	✓
GARBAGE	✓	DERRICK	
WASTE OIL		LIVE ABRD	✓

WHARVES\FLOATS   58 SLIPS PLUS*

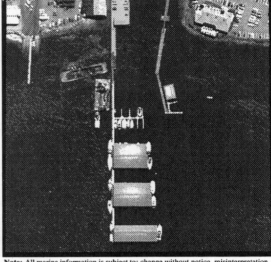

Note: All marina information is subject to; change without notice, misinterpretation, misrepresentation and human error. In no way are the facilities mentioned in this book obligated to honor the rates and services listed. All information is given without guarantee. No part of this book is intended for navigation.

PUBLIC SERVICES

A: Located at Marina   B: Within Walking   C: Within 20 Miles   D: Not Available

	A	B	C	D
ACCOMMODATION		✓		
BAIT & TACKLE		✓		
BANK MACHINE		✓		
BOAT CHARTER		✓		
BOAT LAUNCH		✓		
BOAT RENTAL				✓
CAMPING			✓	
CAR RENTAL				
CHARTS		✓		
DIVE SHOP			✓	
FISH LICENSE		✓		

	A	B	C	D
GOLFING			✓	
GROCERY		✓		
HARDWARE		✓		
HOSPITAL			✓	
ICE		✓		
LAUNDRY	✓			
BOAT LIFT		✓		
LIQUOR STORE		✓		
24 HR PARKING	✓			
POST OFFICE		✓		
PROPANE		✓		

	A	B	C	D
PUB		✓		
PUMPOUT STN		✓		
RESTAURANT		✓		
RV FACILITIES			✓	
SHOPS / MALL		✓		
SHOWER	✓			
SWIM POOL			✓	
TAXI		✓		
TELEPHONE	✓			
TIDAL GRID				✓
TOILETS	✓			

HOURS SUMMER	**NO FUEL FLOAT**	DIESEL
		GASOLINE
HOURS WINTER		STOVE OIL
		PROPANE
TEL		AVIATION

PORT ORCHARD

LOCALE

SULDAN'S BOATWORKS
VHF:
TEL: 876-4435   CHART # 18445
FAX: 876-9575   N 47 32 W 122 38
Washington Area Codes 206, 360 & 509

1343 S.W. BAY STREET
PORT ORCHARD, WA.
98366

GENERAL

OFFICE HOURS
| SUMMER: | 8:30-5 M-F 9-2 SAT |
| WINTER: | SAME |

DAILY MOORAGE
| SUMMER: | NONE |
| WINTER: | NONE |

MONTHLY MOORAGE
| SUMMER: | $3.50 PER FT |
| WINTER: | SAME |

VISA YES   MasterCard YES

ON THE DOCK SERVICES
POWER	✓	LIGHTING	✓
30 AMP		CABLE	
WATER	✓	PHONE	
GARBAGE	✓	DERRICK	✓
WASTE OIL	✓	LIVE ABRD	

Note: All marina information is subject to; change without notice, misinterpretation, misrepresentation and human error. In no way are the facilities mentioned in this book obligated to honor the rates and services listed. All information is given without guarantee. No part of this book is intended for navigation.

A: Located at Marina   B: Within Walking   C: Within 20 Miles   D: Not Available

PUBLIC SERVICES

	A	B	C	D
ACCOMMODATION			✓	
BAIT & TACKLE			✓	
BANK MACHINE			✓	
BOAT CHARTER				✓
BOAT LAUNCH			✓	
BOAT RENTAL				✓
CAMPING			✓	
CAR RENTAL			✓	
CHARTS	✓			
DIVE SHOP			✓	
FISH LICENSE			✓	

	A	B	C	D
GOLFING			✓	
GROCERY			✓	
HARDWARE	✓			
HOSPITAL			✓	
ICE			✓	
LAUNDRY			✓	
BOAT LIFT	✓			
LIQUOR STORE			✓	
24 HR PARKING	✓			
POST OFFICE			✓	
PROPANE		✓		

	A	B	C	D
PUB			✓	
PUMPOUT STN			✓	
RESTAURANT			✓	
RV FACILITIES			✓	
SHOPS / MALL			✓	
SHOWER			✓	
SWIM POOL			✓	
TAXI			✓	
TELEPHONE	✓			
TIDAL GRID				✓
TOILETS			✓	

SPECIALIZING IN WOODEN BOAT REPAIR.
FAMILY OWNED BUSINESS SINCE 1946.
FULL MECHANICAL SHIPWRIGHT SERVICES.

HOURS SUMMER
HOURS WINTER
TEL
NO FUEL FLOAT
DIESEL
GASOLINE
STOVE OIL
PROPANE
AVIATION

PORT TOWNSEND

CAPE GEORGE MARINA
VHF:
TEL: 385-1177   CHART # 18423
FAX: N 48 06 W 122 53
Washington Area Codes 206, 360 & 509

CAPE GEORGE COLONY
PORT TOWNSEND, WA.
98368

GENERAL

OFFICE HOURS
SUMMER:	9AM - 12PM
WINTER:	

DAILY MOORAGE
SUMMER:	GUESTS & EMERG.
WINTER:	

MONTHLY MOORAGE
SUMMER:	MEMBERS ONLY
WINTER:	

VISA   MasterCard
DISCOVER

ON THE DOCK SERVICES
POWER	✓	LIGHTING	✓
30 AMP		CABLE	
WATER	✓	PHONE	
GARBAGE		DERRICK	
WASTE OIL		LIVE ABRD	

Note: All marina information is subject to; change without notice, misinterpretation, misrepresentation and human error. In no way are the facilities mentioned in this book obligated to honor the rates and services listed. All information is given without guarantee. No part of this book is intended for navigation.

A: Located at Marina   B: Within Walking   C: Within 20 Miles   D: Not Available

PUBLIC SERVICES

	A	B	C	D
ACCOMMODATION			✓	
BAIT & TACKLE			✓	
BANK MACHINE			✓	
BOAT CHARTER			✓	
BOAT LAUNCH	✓			
BOAT RENTAL			✓	
CAMPING			✓	
CAR RENTAL			✓	
CHARTS			✓	
DIVE SHOP			✓	
FISH LICENSE			✓	

	A	B	C	D
GOLFING			✓	
GROCERY			✓	
HARDWARE			✓	
HOSPITAL			✓	
ICE			✓	
LAUNDRY			✓	
BOAT LIFT			✓	
LIQUOR STORE			✓	
24 HR PARKING	✓			
POST OFFICE			✓	
PROPANE			✓	

	A	B	C	D
PUB			✓	
PUMPOUT STN			✓	
RESTAURANT			✓	
RV FACILITIES			✓	
SHOPS / MALL			✓	
SHOWER			✓	
SWIM POOL			✓	
TAXI			✓	
TELEPHONE	✓			
TIDAL GRID			✓	
TOILETS	✓			

HOURS SUMMER	NO FUEL FLOAT	DIESEL	
		GASOLINE	
HOURS WINTER		STOVE OIL	
		PROPANE	
TEL		AVIATION	

PORT TOWNSEND

LOCALE

POINT HUDSON RESORT & MARINA
VHF:
TEL: 385-2828   CHART # 18423
FAX: 385-7331   N 48 07.25 W 122 45.01
Washington Area Codes 206, 360 & 509

103 HUDSON ST.
PORT TOWNSEND, WA.
98368

GENERAL

OFFICE HOURS
SUMMER:	8AM - 10:30PM
WINTER:	SAME

DAILY MOORAGE
SUMMER:	$5 1-4HRS $0.50/FT*
WINTER:	31'+ BEAM $0.75/FT*

MONTHLY MOORAGE
SUMMER:	NONE*
WINTER:	$4.60 - $6.90/FT*

VISA YES   MasterCard YES
DISCOVER

ON THE DOCK SERVICES
POWER	✓	LIGHTING	✓
30 AMP	✓	CABLE	
WATER	✓	PHONE	
GARBAGE	✓	DERRICK	
WASTE OIL		LIVE ABRD	✓

WHARVES\FLOATS   600' & 60 SLIPS

Note: All marina information is subject to; change without notice, misinterpretation, misrepresentation and human error. In no way are the facilities mentioned in this book obligated to honor the rates and services listed. All information is given without guarantee. No part of this book is intended for navigation.

PUBLIC SERVICES

A: Located at Marina   B: Within Walking   C: Within 20 Miles   D: Not Available

	A	B	C	D
ACCOMMODATION	✓			
BAIT & TACKLE	✓			
BANK MACHINE		✓		
BOAT CHARTER		✓		
BOAT LAUNCH	✓			
BOAT RENTAL		✓		
CAMPING			✓	
CAR RENTAL				
CHARTS	✓			
DIVE SHOP		✓		
FISH LICENSE	✓			

	A	B	C	D
GOLFING			✓	
GROCERY	✓			
HARDWARE	✓			
HOSPITAL			✓	
ICE	✓			
LAUNDRY	✓			
BOAT LIFT	✓			
LIQUOR STORE		✓		
24 HR PARKING	✓			
POST OFFICE		✓		
PROPANE	✓			

	A	B	C	D
PUB		✓		
PUMPOUT STN		✓		
RESTAURANT	✓			
RV FACILITIES	✓			
SHOPS / MALL		✓		
SHOWER	✓			
SWIM POOL			✓	
TAXI	✓			
TELEPHONE	✓			
TIDAL GRID				✓
TOILETS	✓			

MOORAGE SLIPS ARE LIMITED TO VESSELS
40 FT IN LENGTH OVERALL (LOA*), OR LESS.

* LOA (LENGTH OVERALL) INCLUDES BOW
SPRIT, SWIM STEP, DINGHY / DAVITS, PULPITS,
ETC.
CONTACT MARINA FOR MOORAGE TYPES,
POWER & LIVE ABOARD RATES.

HOURS SUMMER		DIESEL	
	NO	GASOLINE	
HOURS WINTER	FUEL	STOVE OIL	
	FLOAT	PROPANE	
TEL		AVIATION	

PORT TOWNSEND

PORT OF PORT TOWNSEND

LOCALE

VHF:
TEL: 385-2355   CHART # 18423
FAX: 385-3988   N 48 07 W 122 45
Washington Area Codes 206, 360 & 509

2601 WASHINGTON ST.
PO BOX 1180
PORT TOWNSEND, WA.
98368

OFFICE HOURS

SUMMER:	8 - 5:30 DAILY
WINTER:	8 - 4:30 M - F

DAILY MOORAGE

SUMMER:	$9.00 - $15.00
WINTER:	PLUS PWR

MONTHLY MOORAGE

SUMMER:	$142 - $373
WINTER:	$85 - $226

VISA	YES	MasterCard	YES
[card]		DISCOVER	

ON THE DOCK SERVICES

POWER	✓	LIGHTING	✓
30 AMP	✓	CABLE	
WATER	✓	PHONE	
GARBAGE	✓	DERRICK	
WASTE OIL	✓	LIVE ABRD	✓

WHARVES\FLOATS   300 SLIPS

Note: All marina information is subject to; change without notice, misinterpretation, misrepresentation and human error. In no way are the facilities mentioned in this book obligated to honor the rates and services listed. All information is given without guarantee. No part of this book is intended for navigation.

PUBLIC SERVICES

A: Located at Marina   B: Within Walking   C: Within 20 Miles   D: Not Available

	A	B	C	D
ACCOMMODATION	✓			
BAIT & TACKLE	✓			
BANK MACHINE		✓		
BOAT CHARTER	✓			
BOAT LAUNCH	✓			
BOAT RENTAL	✓			
CAMPING			✓	
CAR RENTAL		✓		
CHARTS	✓			
DIVE SHOP	✓			
FISH LICENSE	✓			

	A	B	C	D
GOLFING		✓		
GROCERY		✓		
HARDWARE	✓			
HOSPITAL			✓	
ICE	✓			
LAUNDRY	✓			
BOAT LIFT	✓			
LIQUOR STORE		✓		
24 HR PARKING	✓			
POST OFFICE	✓			
PROPANE		✓		

	A	B	C	D
PUB		✓		
PUMPOUT STN	✓			
RESTAURANT		✓		
RV FACILITIES			✓	
SHOPS / MALL		✓		
SHOWER	✓			
SWIM POOL			✓	
TAXI	✓			
TELEPHONE	✓			
TIDAL GRID				✓
TOILETS	✓			

UNBRANDED

HOURS SUMMER
8AM-8PM

HOURS WINTER
8AM-5PM

TEL   385-7031

MARINE

DIESEL	✓
GASOLINE	✓
STOVE OIL	
PROPANE	
AVIATION	

ALL MARINE TRADES ON SITE.
HAUL OUTS AND STORAGE AVAILABLE.

SEE HAUL OUT SECTION OF THIS BOOK.

LOCALE

BAY MARINE ON MILLER BAY

VHF:
TEL: 598-4900
FAX: 598-3439
Washington Area Codes 206, 360 & 509

CHART # 18445
N 47 45 W 122 33

20622 MILLER BAY RD.
PO BOX 396
SUQUAMISH, WA.
98392

GENERAL

OFFICE HOURS

SUMMER:	9AM - 5PM DAILY
WINTER:	9AM - 5PM T - SAT

DAILY MOORAGE

SUMMER:	NO TRANSIENT
WINTER:	SAME

MONTHLY MOORAGE

SUMMER:	$1.75 PER FT
WINTER:	SAME

VISA YES
MasterCard YES
[diners]
DISCOVER YES

ON THE DOCK SERVICES

POWER		LIGHTING	✓
30 AMP		CABLE	
WATER		PHONE	
GARBAGE		DERRICK	
WASTE OIL	✓	LIVE ABRD	✓

Note: All marina information is subject to; change without notice, misinterpretation, misrepresentation and human error. In no way are the facilities mentioned in this book obligated to honor the rates and services listed. All information is given without guarantee. No part of this book is intended for navigation.

PUBLIC SERVICES

A: Located at Marina   B: Within Walking   C: Within 20 Miles   D: Not Available

	A	B	C	D
ACCOMMODATION			✓	
BAIT & TACKLE			✓	
BANK MACHINE			✓	
BOAT CHARTER				✓
BOAT LAUNCH	✓			
BOAT RENTAL				✓
CAMPING			✓	
CAR RENTAL			✓	
CHARTS			✓	
DIVE SHOP			✓	
FISH LICENSE			✓	

	A	B	C	D
GOLFING			✓	
GROCERY			✓	
HARDWARE	✓			
HOSPITAL			✓	
ICE			✓	
LAUNDRY			✓	
BOAT LIFT	✓			
LIQUOR STORE			✓	
24 HR PARKING			✓	
POST OFFICE			✓	
PROPANE			✓	

	A	B	C	D
PUB			✓	
PUMPOUT STN			✓	
RESTAURANT			✓	
RV FACILITIES			✓	
SHOPS / MALL		✓		
SHOWER			✓	
SWIM POOL			✓	
TAXI	✓			
TELEPHONE		✓		
TIDAL GRID			✓	
TOILETS				

ENTER MILLER BAY AT HIGH TIDE ONLY.
SAND BAR AT ENTRANCE, DRIES AT MINUS
TIDES.

HOURS SUMMER	NO FUEL FLOAT	DIESEL	
HOURS WINTER		GASOLINE	
		STOVE OIL	
		PROPANE	
TEL		AVIATION	

POULSBO

LOCALE

LIBERTY BAY MARINA

VHF:

TEL: 779-7762   CHART # 18445

FAX: 598-3663   N 47 43 W 122 38

Washington Area Codes 206, 360 & 509

17791 FJORD DR. N.E.
POULSBO, WA.
98110

GENERAL

OFFICE HOURS

SUMMER:	APPT. ONLY
WINTER:	SAME

DAILY MOORAGE

SUMMER:	NO TRANSIENT
WINTER:	SAME

MONTHLY MOORAGE

SUMMER:	$4.00 PER FT
WINTER:	SAME

VISA   MasterCard   DISCOVER

ON THE DOCK SERVICES

POWER	✓	LIGHTING	✓
30 AMP	✓	CABLE	
WATER	✓	PHONE	✓
GARBAGE	✓	DERRICK	
WASTE OIL		LIVE ABRD	✓

WHARVES\FLOATS 7800 FT

Note: All marina information is subject to; change without notice, misinterpretation, misrepresentation and human error. In no way are the facilities mentioned in this book obligated to honor the rates and services listed. All information is given without guarantee. No part of this book is intended for navigation.

PUBLIC SERVICES

A: Located at Marina   B: Within Walking   C: Within 20 Miles   D: Not Available

	A	B	C	D		A	B	C	D		A	B	C	D
ACCOMMODATION		✓			GOLFING			✓		PUB		✓		
BAIT & TACKLE		✓			GROCERY		✓			PUMPOUT STN	✓			
BANK MACHINE		✓			HARDWARE		✓			RESTAURANT		✓		
BOAT CHARTER			✓		HOSPITAL			✓		RV FACILITIES			✓	
BOAT LAUNCH	✓				ICE		✓			SHOPS / MALL		✓		
BOAT RENTAL			✓		LAUNDRY	✓				SHOWER	✓			
CAMPING			✓		BOAT LIFT	✓				SWIM POOL			✓	
CAR RENTAL		✓			LIQUOR STORE		✓			TAXI	✓			
CHARTS		✓			24 HR PARKING	✓				TELEPHONE	✓			
DIVE SHOP		✓			POST OFFICE	✓				TIDAL GRID				✓
FISH LICENSE		✓			PROPANE			✓		TOILETS	✓			

30, 50 & 220, PLUS 3 PHASE POWER.

PRIVATE MARINA - WE TRY TO KEEP IT NICE.
QUITE SELECTIVE.

HOURS SUMMER	DIESEL
	GASOLINE
NO FUEL FLOAT	STOVE OIL
HOURS WINTER	PROPANE
TEL	AVIATION

POULSBO

LOCALE

PORT OF POULSBO
VHF:
TEL: 779-9905   CHART # 18445
FAX: 779-3505   N 47 43 W 122 38
Washington Area Codes 206, 360 & 509

18809 FRONT ST
PO BOX 732
POULSBO, WA.
98370

GENERAL

OFFICE HOURS
SUMMER:	8AM-8PM
WINTER:	8AM-4:30PM

DAILY MOORAGE
SUMMER:	$.25 PER FT
WINTER:	SAME

MONTHLY MOORAGE
SUMMER:	$2.27 PER FT
WINTER:	SAME

VISA	YES	MasterCard	YES
	YES	DISCOVER	YES

ON THE DOCK SERVICES
POWER	✓	LIGHTING	✓
30 AMP		CABLE	
WATER	✓	PHONE	
GARBAGE	✓	DERRICK	
WASTE OIL		LIVE ABRD	✓

WHARVES\FLOATS   17X40' 115X30'

Note: All marina information is subject to; change without notice, misinterpretation, misrepresentation and human error. In no way are the facilities mentioned in this book obligated to honor the rates and services listed. All information is given without guarantee. No part of this book is intended for navigation.

PUBLIC SERVICES

A: Located at Marina   B: Within Walking   C: Within 20 Miles   D: Not Available

	A	B	C	D
ACCOMMODATION		✓		
BAIT & TACKLE		✓		
BANK MACHINE		✓		
BOAT CHARTER			✓	
BOAT LAUNCH	✓			
BOAT RENTAL			✓	
CAMPING			✓	
CAR RENTAL		✓		
CHARTS	✓			
DIVE SHOP	✓			
FISH LICENSE	✓			

	A	B	C	D
GOLFING			✓	
GROCERY		✓		
HARDWARE		✓		
HOSPITAL			✓	
ICE	✓			
LAUNDRY	✓			
BOAT LIFT			✓	
LIQUOR STORE		✓		
24 HR PARKING		✓		
POST OFFICE		✓		
PROPANE		✓		

	A	B	C	D
PUB	✓			
PUMPOUT STN	✓			
RESTAURANT	✓			
RV FACILITIES			✓	
SHOPS / MALL		✓		
SHOWER	✓			
SWIM POOL		✓		
TAXI	✓			
TELEPHONE	✓			
TIDAL GRID	✓			
TOILETS	✓			

$7.50 MINIMUM CHARGE FOR OVERNIGHT MOORAGE.
POULSBO - "A LITTLE NORWAY." ANTIQUE SHOPS LOCATED IN HISTORIC DOWNTOWN. NORTHERN MOST TWO DOCKS ARE GUEST MOORAGE.

TEXACO CARD ACCEPTED AT FUEL FLOAT.

TEXACO

HOURS SUMMER		DIESEL	✓
8AM-8PM	MARINE	GASOLINE	✓
HOURS WINTER		STOVE OIL	
8AM-4:30PM		PROPANE	
TEL 779-9905		AVIATION	

QUILCENE BAY

LOCALE

QUILCENE MARINA
VHF:
TEL: 765-3131   CHART # 18445
FAX: N 47 46 W 122 51
Washington Area Codes 206, 360 & 509

1731 LINGER LONGER RD.
QUILCENE, WA.
98376

GENERAL

OFFICE HOURS
SUMMER:	4 - 6 M - F 10 - 5 S,S
WINTER:	RESTROOM 8 - 8

DAILY MOORAGE
SUMMER:	
WINTER:	

MONTHLY MOORAGE
SUMMER:	
WINTER:	

VISA — YES   MasterCard — YES
 — [ ]   DISCOVER — [ ]

ON THE DOCK SERVICES
POWER	✓	LIGHTING	✓
30 AMP	✓	CABLE	
WATER	✓	PHONE	
GARBAGE	✓	DERRICK	
WASTE OIL	✓	LIVE ABRD	

Note: All marina information is subject to; change without notice, misinterpretation, misrepresentation and human error. In no way are the facilities mentioned in this book obligated to honor the rates and services listed. All information is given without guarantee. No part of this book is intended for navigation.

PUBLIC SERVICES

A: Located at Marina   B: Within Walking   C: Within 20 Miles   D: Not Available

	A	B	C	D
ACCOMMODATION			✓	
BAIT & TACKLE			✓	
BANK MACHINE			✓	
BOAT CHARTER				✓
BOAT LAUNCH	✓			
BOAT RENTAL				✓
CAMPING			✓	
CAR RENTAL				✓
CHARTS				
DIVE SHOP				✓
FISH LICENSE	✓			

	A	B	C	D
GOLFING				
GROCERY			✓	
HARDWARE			✓	
HOSPITAL				
ICE			✓	
LAUNDRY				
BOAT LIFT				
LIQUOR STORE			✓	
24 HR PARKING	✓			
POST OFFICE			✓	
PROPANE				

	A	B	C	D
PUB				✓
PUMPOUT STN	✓			
RESTAURANT			✓	
RV FACILITIES				✓
SHOPS / MALL				✓
SHOWER	✓			
SWIM POOL				
TAXI				
TELEPHONE	✓			
TIDAL GRID				
TOILETS	✓			

UNBRANDED

HOURS SUMMER

HOURS WINTER

TEL

MARINE

DIESEL	✓
GASOLINE	✓
STOVE OIL	
PROPANE	
AVIATION	

CREDIT CARDS ONLY ACCEPTED AT FUEL FLOAT.
ADJACENT TO OLYMPIC NATIONAL FOREST.

LOCALE

ALBERT JENSEN & SONS
VHF:
TEL: 378-4343   CHART # 18423
FAX: N 48 32 W 123 00
Washington Area Codes 206, 360 & 509

880 TURN POINT RD
PO BOX 666
FRIDAY HARBOR, WA.
98250

GENERAL

OFFICE HOURS
SUMMER:	8AM-4:30PM M-F
WINTER:	SAME

DAILY MOORAGE
SUMMER:	NO TRANSIENT
WINTER:	SAME

MONTHLY MOORAGE
SUMMER:	$3.85-$6.50/FT
WINTER:	SAME

VISA YES   MasterCard YES
[ ]   DISCOVER [ ]

ON THE DOCK SERVICES
POWER	✓	LIGHTING	✓
30 AMP		CABLE	
WATER	✓	PHONE	
GARBAGE	✓	DERRICK	✓
WASTE OIL		LIVE ABRD	

Note: All marina information is subject to; change without notice, misinterpretation, misrepresentation and human error. In no way are the facilities mentioned in this book obligated to honor the rates and services listed. All information is given without guarantee. No part of this book is intended for navigation.

PUBLIC SERVICES

A: Located at Marina   B: Within Walking   C: Within 20 Miles   D: Not Available

	A	B	C	D
ACCOMMODATION			✓	
BAIT & TACKLE			✓	
BANK MACHINE			✓	
BOAT CHARTER			✓	
BOAT LAUNCH	✓			
BOAT RENTAL			✓	
CAMPING			✓	
CAR RENTAL			✓	
CHARTS			✓	
DIVE SHOP			✓	
FISH LICENSE			✓	

	A	B	C	D
GOLFING			✓	
GROCERY			✓	
HARDWARE	✓			
HOSPITAL			✓	
ICE			✓	
LAUNDRY			✓	
BOAT LIFT	✓			
LIQUOR STORE			✓	
24 HR PARKING	✓			
POST OFFICE			✓	
PROPANE				✓

	A	B	C	D
PUB			✓	
PUMPOUT STN			✓	
RESTAURANT			✓	
RV FACILITIES			✓	
SHOPS / MALL			✓	
SHOWER	✓			
SWIM POOL			✓	
TAXI	✓			
TELEPHONE	✓			
TIDAL GRID			✓	
TOILETS	✓			

FULL SERVICE BOAT YARD.
MACHINE AND FABRICATION WORK, ENGINE
REPAIRS, AND OFF SEASON STORAGE.

HOURS SUMMER

HOURS WINTER

TEL

NO FUEL FLOAT

DIESEL	[ ]
GASOLINE	[ ]
STOVE OIL	[ ]
PROPANE	[ ]
AVIATION	[ ]

SAN JUAN ISLAND

CAPRON'S LANDING

VHF:

TEL: 378-4581   CHART # 18423

FAX: N 48 32 W 123 00

Washington Area Codes 206, 360 & 509

620 WABBASS
FRIDAY HARBOR, WA.

GENERAL

OFFICE HOURS

SUMMER:	VARIES
WINTER:	SAME

DAILY MOORAGE

SUMMER:	N/A
WINTER:	N/A

MONTHLY MOORAGE

SUMMER:	INQUIRE
WINTER:	SAME

VISA   MasterCard

DISCOVER

ON THE DOCK SERVICES

POWER	✓	LIGHTING	✓
30 AMP	✓	CABLE	✓
WATER	✓	PHONE	✓
GARBAGE	✓	DERRICK	
WASTE OIL	✓	LIVE ABRD	✓

Note: All marina information is subject to; change without notice, misinterpretation, misrepresentation and human error. In no way are the facilities mentioned in this book obligated to honor the rates and services listed. All information is given without guarantee. No part of this book is intended for navigation.

PUBLIC SERVICES

A: Located at Marina   B: Within Walking   C: Within 20 Miles   D: Not Available

	A	B	C	D
ACCOMMODATION		✓		
BAIT & TACKLE		✓		
BANK MACHINE		✓		
BOAT CHARTER		✓		
BOAT LAUNCH		✓		
BOAT RENTAL		✓		
CAMPING			✓	
CAR RENTAL		✓		
CHARTS		✓		
DIVE SHOP		✓		
FISH LICENSE		✓		

	A	B	C	D
GOLFING			✓	
GROCERY		✓		
HARDWARE		✓		
HOSPITAL		✓		
ICE		✓		
LAUNDRY	✓			
BOAT LIFT			✓	
LIQUOR STORE		✓		
24 HR PARKING		✓		
POST OFFICE		✓		
PROPANE		✓		

	A	B	C	D
PUB		✓		
PUMPOUT STN		✓		
RESTAURANT		✓		
RV FACILITIES			✓	
SHOPS / MALL		✓		
SHOWER	✓			
SWIM POOL		✓		
TAXI	✓			
TELEPHONE	✓			
TIDAL GRID				✓
TOILETS	✓			

PRIVATE DOCK. TRANSIENT MOORAGE IS ONLY AVAILABLE FROM SLIP OWNERS.

HOURS SUMMER

HOURS WINTER

TEL

NO FUEL FLOAT

DIESEL	
GASOLINE	
STOVE OIL	
PROPANE	
AVIATION	

LOCALE

PORT OF FRIDAY HARBOR MARINA

VHF: 66

TEL: 378-2688   CHART # 18423

FAX: 378-6114   N 48 32.12 W 123 00.55

Washington Area Codes 206, 360 & 509

204 FRONT STREET
PO BOX 889
FRIDAY HARBOR, WA.
98250

GENERAL

OFFICE HOURS

SUMMER:	7AM-9PM
WINTER:	8AM-5PM

DAILY MOORAGE

SUMMER:	$.55/FT $.65/RES.
WINTER:	$.45 PER FT

MONTHLY MOORAGE

SUMMER:	N/A
WINTER:	$4.61 PER FT

VISA — YES

MasterCard — YES

ON THE DOCK SERVICES

POWER	✓	LIGHTING	✓
30 AMP	✓	CABLE	
WATER	✓	PHONE	
GARBAGE	✓	DERRICK	✓
WASTE OIL	✓	LIVE ABRD	✓

WHARVES\FLOATS   20-60 FT

Note: All marina information is subject to; change without notice, misinterpretation, misrepresentation and human error. In no way are the facilities mentioned in this book obligated to honor the rates and services listed. All information is given without guarantee. No part of this book is intended for navigation.

PUBLIC SERVICES

A: Located at Marina   B: Within Walking   C: Within 20 Miles   D: Not Available

	A	B	C	D
ACCOMMODATION		✓		
BAIT & TACKLE		✓		
BANK MACHINE		✓		
BOAT CHARTER	✓			
BOAT LAUNCH		✓		
BOAT RENTAL	✓			
CAMPING			✓	
CAR RENTAL		✓		
CHARTS		✓		
DIVE SHOP	✓			
FISH LICENSE		✓		

	A	B	C	D
GOLFING			✓	
GROCERY		✓		
HARDWARE		✓		
HOSPITAL		✓		
ICE	✓			
LAUNDRY		✓		
BOAT LIFT			✓	
LIQUOR STORE		✓		
24 HR PARKING		✓		
POST OFFICE		✓		
PROPANE	✓			

	A	B	C	D
PUB		✓		
PUMPOUT STN	✓			
RESTAURANT		✓		
RV FACILITIES			✓	
SHOPS / MALL		✓		
SHOWER	✓			
SWIM POOL		✓		
TAXI	✓			
TELEPHONE	✓			
TIDAL GRID				✓
TOILETS	✓			

CHEVRON

HOURS SUMMER		
7AM-7PM	DIESEL	✓
HOURS WINTER	GASOLINE	✓
	STOVE OIL	✓
8AM-5PM	PROPANE	✓
TEL 378-2464	AVIATION	

MARINE

SAN JUAN ISLAND

LOCALE

ROCHE HARBOR RESORT & MARINA
VHF: 78 a USA
TEL: 378-2155
FAX: 378-6809
Washington Area Codes 206, 360 & 509

CHART # 18423
N 48 36.45 W 123 09.30

REUBEN TARTE MEM. DR.
PO BOX 4001
ROCHE HARBOR, WA.
98250

GENERAL

OFFICE HOURS
SUMMER:	7:30AM-9PM
WINTER:	9AM-5PM

DAILY MOORAGE
SUMMER:	$1.00 PER FT
WINTER:	$.50 PER FT

MONTHLY MOORAGE
SUMMER:	$198.00
WINTER:	SAME

VISA MasterCard DISCOVER

ON THE DOCK SERVICES
POWER	✓	LIGHTING	✓
30 AMP	✓	CABLE	
WATER	✓	PHONE	
GARBAGE	✓	DERRICK	
WASTE OIL		LIVE ABRD	✓

WHARVES\FLOATS   30 - 120 FT

Note: All marina information is subject to; change without notice, misinterpretation, misrepresentation and human error. In no way are the facilities mentioned in this book obligated to honor the rates and services listed. All information is given without guarantee. No part of this book is intended for navigation.

PUBLIC SERVICES

A: Located at Marina   B: Within Walking   C: Within 20 Miles   D: Not Available

	A	B	C	D
ACCOMMODATION	✓			
BAIT & TACKLE	✓			
BANK MACHINE			✓	
BOAT CHARTER	✓			
BOAT LAUNCH	✓			
BOAT RENTAL	✓			
CAMPING	✓			
CAR RENTAL	✓			
CHARTS	✓			
DIVE SHOP			✓	
FISH LICENSE	✓			

	A	B	C	D
GOLFING			✓	
GROCERY	✓			
HARDWARE	✓			
HOSPITAL			✓	
ICE	✓			
LAUNDRY	✓			
BOAT LIFT			✓	
LIQUOR STORE	✓			
24 HR PARKING	✓			
POST OFFICE	✓			
PROPANE	✓			

	A	B	C	D
PUB	✓			
PUMPOUT STN	✓			
RESTAURANT	✓			
RV FACILITIES			✓	
SHOPS / MALL	✓			
SHOWER	✓			
SWIM POOL	✓			
TAXI	✓			
TELEPHONE	✓			
TIDAL GRID				✓
TOILETS	✓			

TEXACO

HOURS SUMMER	
8AM-7PM	
HOURS WINTER	
9AM-5PM	
TEL 378-2155	

MARINE

DIESEL	✓
GASOLINE	✓
STOVE OIL	
PROPANE	✓
AVIATION	

MOORING BUOYS.
NIGHTLY COLOR CEREMONY & CANNON
SALUTE DURING SUMMER MONTHS.

SAN JUAN ISLAND

LOCALE

SHIPYARD COVE MARINA
VHF:
TEL: 378-5101   CHART # 18423
FAX: 378-3855   N 48 31.37 W 123 00.00
Washington Area Codes 206, 360 & 509

740 TURN POINT ROAD
FRIDAY HARBOR, WA.
98250

GENERAL

OFFICE HOURS
SUMMER:	VARIES
WINTER:	VARIES

DAILY MOORAGE
SUMMER:	N/A
WINTER:	N/A

MONTHLY MOORAGE
SUMMER:	$6.50 PER FT
WINTER:	$4.50 PER FT

VISA   MasterCard
DISCOVER

ON THE DOCK SERVICES
POWER	✓	LIGHTING	✓
30 AMP	✓	CABLE	
WATER	✓	PHONE	✓
GARBAGE	✓	DERRICK	
WASTE OIL		LIVE ABRD	✓

WHARVES\FLOATS   200 FT

Note: All marina information is subject to; change without notice, misinterpretation, misrepresentation and human error. In no way are the facilities mentioned in this book obligated to honor the rates and services listed. All information is given without guarantee. No part of this book is intended for navigation.

PUBLIC SERVICES

A: Located at Marina   B: Within Walking   C: Within 20 Miles   D: Not Available

	A	B	C	D
ACCOMMODATION			✓	
BAIT & TACKLE			✓	
BANK MACHINE			✓	
BOAT CHARTER			✓	
BOAT LAUNCH	✓			
BOAT RENTAL			✓	
CAMPING			✓	
CAR RENTAL			✓	
CHARTS			✓	
DIVE SHOP			✓	
FISH LICENSE			✓	

	A	B	C	D
GOLFING			✓	
GROCERY			✓	
HARDWARE		✓		
HOSPITAL			✓	
ICE			✓	
LAUNDRY	✓			
BOAT LIFT		✓		
LIQUOR STORE			✓	
24 HR PARKING	✓			
POST OFFICE			✓	
PROPANE			✓	

	A	B	C	D
PUB			✓	
PUMPOUT STN			✓	
RESTAURANT			✓	
RV FACILITIES			✓	
SHOPS / MALL			✓	
SHOWER	✓			
SWIM POOL				
TAXI	✓			
TELEPHONE	✓			
TIDAL GRID			✓	
TOILETS	✓			

MAINLY TIE UP DOCK WITH LIMITED SERVICES.
GUESTS WELCOME BY PRE-ARRANGEMENT
ONLY. PETS DISCOURAGED. CANADIAN FUNDS
ACCEPTED.

HOURS SUMMER

HOURS WINTER

TEL

NO FUEL FLOAT

DIESEL	
GASOLINE	
STOVE OIL	
PROPANE	
AVIATION	

SAN JUAN ISLAND

SNUG HARBOR RESORT

VHF:
TEL: 378-4762   CHART # 18423
FAX: N 48 34 W 123 11
Washington Area Codes 206, 360 & 509

2371 MITCHELL BAY RD.
FRIDAY HARBOR, WA.
98250

GENERAL

OFFICE HOURS

SUMMER:	8AM-8PM
WINTER:	9AM-5PM

DAILY MOORAGE

SUMMER:	$15.00MIN. $.75/FT
WINTER:	$9.45MIN $.45/FT

MONTHLY MOORAGE

SUMMER:	$20/FT ANNUAL AV*
WINTER:	$3.75/FT

VISA **YES**   MasterCard **YES**
(Amex) [ ]   DISCOVER [ ]

ON THE DOCK SERVICES

POWER	✓	LIGHTING	✓
30 AMP	✓	CABLE	
WATER	✓	PHONE	
GARBAGE	✓	DERRICK	
WASTE OIL	✓	LIVE ABRD	✓

WHARVES\FLOATS   UP TO 50 FT

Note: All marina information is subject to; change without notice, misinterpretation, misrepresentation and human error. In no way are the facilities mentioned in this book obligated to honor the rates and services listed. All information is given without guarantee. No part of this book is intended for navigation.

PUBLIC SERVICES

A: Located at Marina   B: Within Walking   C: Within 20 Miles   D: Not Available

	A	B	C	D
ACCOMMODATION	✓			
BAIT & TACKLE	✓			
BANK MACHINE			✓	
BOAT CHARTER	✓			
BOAT LAUNCH	✓			
BOAT RENTAL	✓			
CAMPING	✓			
CAR RENTAL			✓	
CHARTS	✓			
DIVE SHOP	✓			
FISH LICENSE	✓			

	A	B	C	D
GOLFING			✓	
GROCERY	✓			
HARDWARE	✓			
HOSPITAL			✓	
ICE	✓			
LAUNDRY	✓			
BOAT LIFT	✓			
LIQUOR STORE			✓	
24 HR PARKING	✓			
POST OFFICE			✓	
PROPANE	✓			

	A	B	C	D
PUB			✓	
PUMPOUT STN			✓	
RESTAURANT			✓	
RV FACILITIES	✓			
SHOPS / MALL	✓			
SHOWER	✓			
SWIM POOL			✓	
TAXI	✓			
TELEPHONE	✓			
TIDAL GRID	✓			
TOILETS	✓			

SNUG GAS

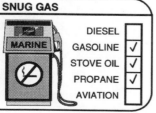

HOURS SUMMER		
8AM-8PM	DIESEL	
HOURS WINTER	GASOLINE	✓
9AM-5PM	STOVE OIL	✓
TEL 378-4762	PROPANE	✓
	AVIATION	

SCUBA TANKS REFILLED.
KAYAKS AND SWIMMING POND.

SEATTLE

LOCALE

AGC MARINA
VHF:
TEL: 284-4204   CHART # 18477
FAX: 286-1111
Washington Area Codes 206, 360 & 509

1200 WESTLAKE AVE. N.
SEATTLE, WA.
98109

GENERAL

OFFICE HOURS

SUMMER:	8 AM - 5 PM M-F
WINTER:	

DAILY MOORAGE

SUMMER:	N/A
WINTER:	

MONTHLY MOORAGE

SUMMER:	$6.25 - $8.25 / FT*
WINTER:	$6.25 - $8.25 / FT*

ON THE DOCK SERVICES

POWER	✓	LIGHTING	✓
30 AMP	✓	CABLE	
WATER	✓	PHONE	✓
GARBAGE	✓	DERRICK	
WASTE OIL		LIVE ABRD	✓

WHARVES\FLOATS   UP TO 114 FT

Note: All marina information is subject to; change without notice, misrepresentation, misrepresentation and human error. In no way are the facilities mentioned in this book obligated to honor the rates and services listed. All information is given without guarantee. No part of this book is intended for navigation.

PUBLIC SERVICES

A: Located at Marina   B: Within Walking   C: Within 20 Miles   D: Not Available

	A	B	C	D
ACCOMMODATION		✓		
BAIT & TACKLE			✓	
BANK MACHINE	✓			
BOAT CHARTER		✓		
BOAT LAUNCH			✓	
BOAT RENTAL		✓		
CAMPING				✓
CAR RENTAL			✓	
CHARTS			✓	
DIVE SHOP			✓	
FISH LICENSE			✓	

	A	B	C	D
GOLFING				✓
GROCERY			✓	
HARDWARE			✓	
HOSPITAL			✓	
ICE	✓			
LAUNDRY	✓			
BOAT LIFT			✓	
LIQUOR STORE			✓	
24 HR PARKING	✓			
POST OFFICE			✓	
PROPANE			✓	

	A	B	C	D
PUB	✓			
PUMPOUT STN			✓	
RESTAURANT	✓			
RV FACILITIES				✓
SHOPS / MALL		✓		
SHOWER	✓			
SWIM POOL				✓
TAXI	✓			
TELEPHONE	✓			
TIDAL GRID				✓
TOILETS	✓			

50 AMP AVAILABLE.

HOURS SUMMER		DIESEL
	NO FUEL FLOAT	GASOLINE
HOURS WINTER		STOVE OIL
		PROPANE
TEL		AVIATION

124

SEATTLE

LOCALE

BALLARD MILL MARINA
VHF:
TEL: 789-4777   CHART # 18447
FAX: 782-0469
Washington Area Codes 206, 360 & 509

4733 SHILSHOLE AVE. N.W.
SEATTLE, WA.
98107

GENERAL

OFFICE HOURS
SUMMER:	9 AM - 5 PM M - F
WINTER:	

DAILY MOORAGE
SUMMER:	CALL
WINTER:	

MONTHLY MOORAGE
SUMMER:	$6.40 PER FT*
WINTER:	

ON THE DOCK SERVICES
POWER	✓	LIGHTING	✓
30 AMP	✓	CABLE	✓
WATER	✓	PHONE	✓
GARBAGE	✓	DERRICK	
WASTE OIL	✓	LIVE ABRD	✓

Note: All marina information is subject to; change without notice, misinterpretation, misrepresentation and human error. In no way are the facilities mentioned in this book obligated to honor the rates and services listed. All information is given without guarantee. No part of this book is intended for navigation.

PUBLIC SERVICES

A: Located at Marina   B: Within Walking   C: Within 20 Miles   D: Not Available

	A	B	C	D
ACCOMMODATION			✓	
BAIT & TACKLE		✓		
BANK MACHINE		✓		
BOAT CHARTER			✓	
BOAT LAUNCH	✓			
BOAT RENTAL			✓	
CAMPING			✓	
CAR RENTAL			✓	
CHARTS	✓			
DIVE SHOP			✓	
FISH LICENSE		✓		

	A	B	C	D
GOLFING			✓	
GROCERY		✓		
HARDWARE		✓		
HOSPITAL		✓		
ICE		✓		
LAUNDRY	✓			
BOAT LIFT		✓		
LIQUOR STORE		✓		
24 HR PARKING	✓			
POST OFFICE		✓		
PROPANE		✓		

	A	B	C	D
PUB		✓		
PUMPOUT STN	✓			
RESTAURANT	✓			
RV FACILITIES			✓	
SHOPS / MALL		✓		
SHOWER	✓			
SWIM POOL			✓	
TAXI	✓			
TELEPHONE	✓			
TIDAL GRID				✓
TOILETS	✓			

HOURS SUMMER	**NO FUEL FLOAT** DIESEL / GASOLINE / STOVE OIL / PROPANE / AVIATION
HOURS WINTER	
TEL	

2 PUMPOUT STATIONS, PORTABLE AND STATIONARY.

CLOSE TO SHOPPING FACILITIES
RESTAURANTS AND BARS IN BALLARD.

PETS ON APPROVAL*

BRANCHFLOWER MARINA

VHF:
TEL: 783-5961   CHART # 18447
FAX:
Washington Area Codes 206, 360 & 509

4507 SHILSHOLE AVE. N.W.
P.O. BOX 17015
SEATTLE, WA.
98107

GENERAL

OFFICE HOURS

SUMMER:	9 AM - 3 PM
WINTER:	

DAILY MOORAGE

SUMMER:	N/A
WINTER:	

MONTHLY MOORAGE

SUMMER:	$6.00 TO $8.25 / FT
WINTER:	

VISA   MasterCard   DISCOVER

ON THE DOCK SERVICES

POWER	✓	LIGHTING	✓
30 AMP	✓	CABLE	
WATER	✓	PHONE	✓
GARBAGE	✓	DERRICK	
WASTE OIL		LIVE ABRD	✓

WHARVES\FLOATS   UP TO 100 FT

Note: All marina information is subject to; change without notice, misinterpretation, misrepresentation and human error. In no way are the facilities mentioned in this book obligated to honor the rates and services listed. All information is given without guarantee. No part of this book is intended for navigation.

A: Located at Marina   B: Within Walking   C: Within 20 Miles   D: Not Available

PUBLIC SERVICES

	A	B	C	D
ACCOMMODATION				✓
BAIT & TACKLE		✓		
BANK MACHINE		✓		
BOAT CHARTER			✓	
BOAT LAUNCH		✓		
BOAT RENTAL			✓	
CAMPING				✓
CAR RENTAL		✓		
CHARTS		✓		
DIVE SHOP			✓	
FISH LICENSE		✓		

	A	B	C	D
GOLFING				✓
GROCERY		✓		
HARDWARE		✓		
HOSPITAL			✓	
ICE		✓		
LAUNDRY		✓		
BOAT LIFT		✓		
LIQUOR STORE			✓	
24 HR PARKING	✓			
POST OFFICE		✓		
PROPANE		✓		

	A	B	C	D
PUB		✓		
PUMPOUT STN		✓		
RESTAURANT		✓		
RV FACILITIES				✓
SHOPS / MALL		✓		
SHOWER	✓			
SWIM POOL				✓
TAXI	✓			
TELEPHONE		✓		
TIDAL GRID				✓
TOILETS	✓			

50 AMP POWER AVAILABLE

HOURS SUMMER

HOURS WINTER

TEL

NO FUEL FLOAT

DIESEL	
GASOLINE	
STOVE OIL	
PROPANE	
AVIATION	

SEATTLE

LOCALE

CANAL MARINA
VHF:
TEL: 282-6767   CHART # 18447
FAX:
Washington Area Codes 206, 360 & 509

360 W. EWING ST.
SEATTLE, WA.
98119

GENERAL

OFFICE HOURS
SUMMER:	8 AM - 3 PM M - F
WINTER:	SAME

DAILY MOORAGE
SUMMER:	N/A
WINTER:	N/A

MONTHLY MOORAGE
SUMMER:	$5.50 - $6.00 / FT*
WINTER:	SAME

ON THE DOCK SERVICES
POWER	✓	LIGHTING	✓
30 AMP	✓	CABLE	
WATER	✓	PHONE	✓
GARBAGE	✓	DERRICK	
WASTE OIL		LIVE ABRD	

WHARVES\FLOATS   UP TO 45 FT

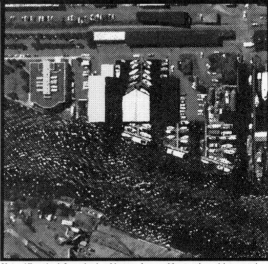

Note: All marina information is subject to; change without notice, misinterpretation, misrepresentation and human error. In no way are the facilities mentioned in this book obligated to honor the rates and services listed. All information is given without guarantee. No part of this book is intended for navigation.

PUBLIC SERVICES

A: Located at Marina   B: Within Walking   C: Within 20 Miles   D: Not Available

	A	B	C	D
ACCOMMODATION	✓			
BAIT & TACKLE				
BANK MACHINE				
BOAT CHARTER				
BOAT LAUNCH				
BOAT RENTAL				
CAMPING				
CAR RENTAL				
CHARTS				
DIVE SHOP				
FISH LICENSE				

	A	B	C	D
GOLFING				
GROCERY				
HARDWARE	✓			
HOSPITAL				
ICE				
LAUNDRY				
BOAT LIFT				
LIQUOR STORE				
24 HR PARKING	✓			
POST OFFICE				
PROPANE				

	A	B	C	D
PUB				
PUMPOUT STN	✓			
RESTAURANT				
RV FACILITIES				
SHOPS / MALL				
SHOWER				
SWIM POOL				
TAXI				
TELEPHONE				
TIDAL GRID				
TOILETS	✓			

SEE HAUL OUT SECTION OF THIS BOOK.

HOURS SUMMER	**NO FUEL FLOAT**	DIESEL
		GASOLINE
HOURS WINTER		STOVE OIL
		PROPANE
TEL		AVIATION

LOCALE

CHRIS BERG INC.
VHF:
TEL: 285-2250   CHART # 18447
FAX:
Washington Area Codes 206, 360 & 509

2730 WESTLAKE AVE. N.
SEATTLE, WA.
98109

GENERAL

OFFICE HOURS

SUMMER:	8 AM - 5 PM M - F
WINTER:	SAME

DAILY MOORAGE

SUMMER:	N/A
WINTER:	N/A

MONTHLY MOORAGE

SUMMER:	VARIES*
WINTER:	

VISA ☐   MasterCard ☐

☐   DISCOVER ☐

ON THE DOCK SERVICES

POWER	✓	LIGHTING	✓
30 AMP	✓	CABLE	
WATER	✓	PHONE	✓
GARBAGE	✓	DERRICK	
WASTE OIL	✓	LIVE ABRD	

Note: All marina information is subject to; change without notice, misinterpretation, misrepresentation and human error. In no way are the facilities mentioned in this book obligated to honor the rates and services listed. All information is given without guarantee. No part of this book is intended for navigation.

PUBLIC SERVICES

A: Located at Marina   B: Within Walking   C: Within 20 Miles   D: Not Available

	A	B	C	D
ACCOMMODATION			✓	
BAIT & TACKLE			✓	
BANK MACHINE		✓		
BOAT CHARTER		✓		
BOAT LAUNCH			✓	
BOAT RENTAL			✓	
CAMPING				✓
CAR RENTAL			✓	
CHARTS			✓	
DIVE SHOP			✓	
FISH LICENSE			✓	

	A	B	C	D
GOLFING			✓	
GROCERY		✓		
HARDWARE			✓	
HOSPITAL			✓	
ICE	✓			
LAUNDRY			✓	
BOAT LIFT			✓	
LIQUOR STORE			✓	
24 HR PARKING	✓			
POST OFFICE			✓	
PROPANE			✓	

	A	B	C	D
PUB		✓		
PUMPOUT STN		✓		
RESTAURANT		✓		
RV FACILITIES				✓
SHOPS / MALL			✓	
SHOWER		✓		
SWIM POOL			✓	
TAXI	✓			
TELEPHONE	✓			
TIDAL GRID				✓
TOILETS	✓			

SECURITY GATES.
50 AMP AVAILABLE.

UNOCAL 76

HOURS SUMMER		
8 AM - 8 PM DAILY	MARINE	DIESEL ✓
HOURS WINTER		GASOLINE ✓
9 AM - 5 PM DAILY		STOVE OIL ✓
TEL 284-6600		PROPANE ✓
		AVIATION ☐

DIESEL ✓
GASOLINE ✓
STOVE OIL ✓
PROPANE ✓
AVIATION ☐

SEATTLE

LOCALE

CITY DOCK
VHF:
TEL: 343-5600   CHART # 18447
FAX:
Washington Area Codes 206, 360 & 509

1301 N. NORTHLAKE WAY
#202 85 S. WASHINGTON ST.
SEATTLE, WA.
98104

GENERAL

OFFICE HOURS
SUMMER:	8 AM - 5 PM
WINTER:	

DAILY MOORAGE
SUMMER:	N/A
WINTER:	

MONTHLY MOORAGE
SUMMER:	$8.00 PER FT*
WINTER:	

VISA   MasterCard   DISCOVER

ON THE DOCK SERVICES
POWER	✓	LIGHTING	✓
30 AMP	✓	CABLE	✓
WATER	✓	PHONE	✓
GARBAGE	✓	DERRICK	
WASTE OIL		LIVE ABRD	✓

WHARVES\FLOATS   UP TO130 FT

Note: All marina information is subject to; change without notice, misinterpretation, misrepresentation and human error. In no way are the facilities mentioned in this book obligated to honor the rates and services listed. All information is given without guarantee. No part of this book is intended for navigation.

PUBLIC SERVICES

A: Located at Marina   B: Within Walking   C: Within 20 Miles   D: Not Available

	A	B	C	D
ACCOMMODATION		✓		
BAIT & TACKLE			✓	
BANK MACHINE		✓		
BOAT CHARTER			✓	
BOAT LAUNCH		✓		
BOAT RENTAL		✓		
CAMPING				✓
CAR RENTAL			✓	
CHARTS		✓		
DIVE SHOP			✓	
FISH LICENSE			✓	

	A	B	C	D
GOLFING				✓
GROCERY			✓	
HARDWARE		✓		
HOSPITAL			✓	
ICE		✓		
LAUNDRY		✓		
BOAT LIFT		✓		
LIQUOR STORE		✓		
24 HR PARKING	✓			
POST OFFICE			✓	
PROPANE			✓	

	A	B	C	D
PUB		✓		
PUMPOUT STN		✓		
RESTAURANT		✓		
RV FACILITIES			✓	
SHOPS / MALL		✓		
SHOWER			✓	
SWIM POOL			✓	
TAXI	✓			
TELEPHONE	✓			
TIDAL GRID				✓
TOILETS	✓			

50 AMP AVAILABLE.

HOURS SUMMER	**NO**	DIESEL
	FUEL	GASOLINE
HOURS WINTER		STOVE OIL
	FLOAT	PROPANE
TEL		AVIATION

LOCALE

ELLIOT BAY MARINA

VHF: 78
TEL: 285-4817 CHART # 18445
FAX: 282-0626 N 47 37.60 W 122 23.50
Washington Area Codes 206, 360 & 509

2601 W. MARINA PLACE
SEATTLE, WA.
98199

GENERAL

OFFICE HOURS

| SUMMER: | 9 AM - 6 PM* |
| WINTER: | SAME |

DAILY MOORAGE

| SUMMER: | $.75 PER FT* |
| WINTER: | $.50 PER FT* |

MONTHLY MOORAGE

| SUMMER: | VARIES* |
| WINTER: | |

VISA YES MasterCard YES
[key icon] [ ] DISCOVER [ ]

ON THE DOCK SERVICES

POWER	✓	LIGHTING	✓
30 AMP	✓	CABLE	✓
WATER	✓	PHONE	✓
GARBAGE	✓	DERRICK	
WASTE OIL	✓	LIVE ABRD	✓

WHARVES\FLOATS   UP TO 100 FT

Note: All marina information is subject to; change without notice, misrepresentation, misrepresentation and human error. In no way are the facilities mentioned in this book obligated to honor the rates and services listed. All information is given without guarantee. No part of this book is intended for navigation.

PUBLIC SERVICES

A: Located at Marina   B: Within Walking   C: Within 20 Miles   D: Not Available

	A	B	C	D
ACCOMMODATION			✓	
BAIT & TACKLE	✓			
BANK MACHINE		✓		
BOAT CHARTER	✓			
BOAT LAUNCH		✓		
BOAT RENTAL	✓			
CAMPING			✓	
CAR RENTAL	✓			
CHARTS		✓		
DIVE SHOP		✓		
FISH LICENSE	✓			

	A	B	C	D
GOLFING			✓	
GROCERY	✓			
HARDWARE		✓		
HOSPITAL			✓	
ICE	✓			
LAUNDRY	✓			
BOAT LIFT			✓	
LIQUOR STORE	✓			
24 HR PARKING	✓			
POST OFFICE			✓	
PROPANE		✓		

	A	B	C	D
PUB	✓			
PUMPOUT STN	✓			
RESTAURANT	✓			
RV FACILITIES				✓
SHOPS / MALL	✓			
SHOWER	✓			
SWIM POOL			✓	
TAXI	✓			
TELEPHONE	✓			
TIDAL GRID				✓
TOILETS	✓			

NO PETS

50 AMP AVAILABLE

CHEVRON

HOURS SUMMER	
8 AM - 8 PM	
HOURS WINTER	
8 AM - 5 PM	
TEL 282-8424	

DIESEL	✓
GASOLINE	✓
STOVE OIL	
PROPANE	
AVIATION	

LOCALE

EWING ST. MOORING
VHF:
TEL: 283-1075   CHART # 18447
FAX:
Washington Area Codes 206, 360 & 509

624 W. EWING
SEATTLE, WA.

GENERAL

OFFICE HOURS

SUMMER:	8 AM - 5 PM
WINTER:	SAME

DAILY MOORAGE

SUMMER:	N/A
WINTER:	N/A

MONTHLY MOORAGE

SUMMER:	VARIES
WINTER:	VARIES

VISA   MasterCard   DISCOVER

ON THE DOCK SERVICES

POWER	✓	LIGHTING	✓
30 AMP	✓	CABLE	
WATER	✓	PHONE	✓
GARBAGE	✓	DERRICK	
WASTE OIL		LIVE ABRD	✓

WHARVES\FLOATS   UP TO 40 FT

Note: All marina information is subject to; change without notice, misinterpretation, misrepresentation and human error. In no way are the facilities mentioned in this book obligated to honor the rates and services listed. All information is given without guarantee. No part of this book is intended for navigation.

PUBLIC SERVICES

A: Located at Marina   B: Within Walking   C: Within 20 Miles   D: Not Available

	A	B	C	D
ACCOMMODATION			✓	
BAIT & TACKLE			✓	
BANK MACHINE			✓	
BOAT CHARTER			✓	
BOAT LAUNCH			✓	
BOAT RENTAL			✓	
CAMPING				✓
CAR RENTAL		✓		
CHARTS			✓	
DIVE SHOP			✓	
FISH LICENSE			✓	

	A	B	C	D
GOLFING				✓
GROCERY		✓		
HARDWARE	✓			
HOSPITAL			✓	
ICE	✓			
LAUNDRY	✓			
BOAT LIFT	✓			
LIQUOR STORE			✓	
24 HR PARKING	✓			
POST OFFICE		✓		
PROPANE			✓	

	A	B	C	D
PUB		✓		
PUMPOUT STN	✓			
RESTAURANT		✓		
RV FACILITIES				✓
SHOPS / MALL			✓	
SHOWER	✓			
SWIM POOL				✓
TAXI	✓			
TELEPHONE	✓			
TIDAL GRID				✓
TOILETS		✓		

HOURS SUMMER	NO FUEL FLOAT	DIESEL	
HOURS WINTER		GASOLINE	
		STOVE OIL	
		PROPANE	
TEL		AVIATION	

LOCALE

FREMONT BOAT CO.
VHF: 19
TEL: 632-0152 CHART # 18447
FAX:
Washington Area Codes 206, 360 & 509

1059 N. NORTHLAKE WAY
SEATTLE, WA.
98103

GENERAL

OFFICE HOURS

SUMMER:	8 AM - 6 PM M-F
WINTER:	VARIES S & S

DAILY MOORAGE

SUMMER:	INQUIRE*
WINTER:	

MONTHLY MOORAGE

SUMMER:	$6.50 - $7.50/FT *
WINTER:	SAME

VISA   MasterCard
        DISCOVER

ON THE DOCK SERVICES

POWER	✓	LIGHTING	✓
30 AMP		CABLE	
WATER	✓	PHONE	✓
GARBAGE	✓	DERRICK	
WASTE OIL		LIVE ABRD	✓

WHARVES\FLOATS   UP TO 65 FT

Note: All marina information is subject to; change without notice, misinterpretation, misrepresentation and human error. In no way are the facilities mentioned in this book obligated to honor the rates and services listed. All information is given without guarantee. No part of this book is intended for navigation.

PUBLIC SERVICES

A: Located at Marina   B: Within Walking   C: Within 20 Miles   D: Not Available

	A	B	C	D		A	B	C	D		A	B	C	D
ACCOMMODATION		✓			GOLFING			✓		PUB		✓		
BAIT & TACKLE			✓		GROCERY		✓			PUMPOUT STN	✓			
BANK MACHINE		✓			HARDWARE	✓				RESTAURANT		✓		
BOAT CHARTER			✓		HOSPITAL			✓		RV FACILITIES				✓
BOAT LAUNCH		✓			ICE	✓				SHOPS / MALL		✓		
BOAT RENTAL		✓			LAUNDRY	✓				SHOWER				✓
CAMPING				✓	BOAT LIFT	✓				SWIM POOL				✓
CAR RENTAL			✓		LIQUOR STORE	✓				TAXI	✓			
CHARTS	✓				24 HR PARKING	✓				TELEPHONE	✓			
DIVE SHOP			✓		POST OFFICE			✓		TIDAL GRID				✓
FISH LICENSE			✓		PROPANE			✓		TOILETS	✓			

SECURED DOCKS.
20 MINUTES TO LOCKS & LAKE WASHINGTON.
EST. 1916. OFFICE IS ADORNED WITH
PICTURES OF ALL TUGS THAT HAVE TRAVELED
PUGET SOUND SINCE 1916.
PLEASE NOTE THIS PHOTO SHOWS FROM LEFT
TO RIGHT NORTHLAKE MARINA, LEE'S
MOORING, FREEMONT BOAT CO. AND LAKE
UNION WATER WORKS.

HOURS SUMMER
HOURS WINTER
TEL

NO
FUEL
FLOAT

DIESEL
GASOLINE
STOVE OIL
PROPANE
AVIATION

LOCALE

H.C. HENRY PIER
VHF:
TEL: N/A   CHART # 18447
FAX:
Washington Area Codes 206, 360 & 509

809 FAIRVIEW PLACE N.
SEATTLE, WA.
98109

GENERAL

OFFICE HOURS

| SUMMER: | N/A |
| WINTER: | N/A |

DAILY MOORAGE

| SUMMER: | N/A |
| WINTER: | N/A |

MONTHLY MOORAGE

| SUMMER: | $7.30 PER FT |
| WINTER: | SAME |

VISA   MasterCard

DISCOVER

ON THE DOCK SERVICES

POWER	✓	LIGHTING	✓
30 AMP	✓	CABLE	
WATER	✓	PHONE	✓
GARBAGE	✓	DERRICK	
WASTE OIL		LIVE ABRD	

WHARVES\FLOATS   UP TO 105 FT

Note: All marina information is subject to; change without notice, misinterpretation, misrepresentation and human error. In no way are the facilities mentioned in this book obligated to honor the rates and services listed. All information is given without guarantee. No part of this book is intended for navigation.

PUBLIC SERVICES

A: Located at Marina   B: Within Walking   C: Within 20 Miles   D: Not Available

	A	B	C	D
ACCOMMODATION		✓		
BAIT & TACKLE			✓	
BANK MACHINE		✓		
BOAT CHARTER		✓		
BOAT LAUNCH				✓
BOAT RENTAL		✓		
CAMPING				✓
CAR RENTAL			✓	
CHARTS		✓		
DIVE SHOP				✓
FISH LICENSE				✓

	A	B	C	D
GOLFING				✓
GROCERY			✓	
HARDWARE		✓		
HOSPITAL			✓	
ICE	✓			
LAUNDRY			✓	
BOAT LIFT	✓			
LIQUOR STORE			✓	
24 HR PARKING	✓			
POST OFFICE			✓	
PROPANE				✓

	A	B	C	D
PUB		✓		
PUMPOUT STN	✓			
RESTAURANT	✓			
RV FACILITIES				✓
SHOPS / MALL	✓			
SHOWER				
SWIM POOL				✓
TAXI	✓			
TELEPHONE	✓			
TIDAL GRID				✓
TOILETS		✓		

BOAT MUSEUM AND MARITIME CENTRE NEXT DOOR.

HOURS SUMMER		DIESEL	
	NO	GASOLINE	
HOURS WINTER	FUEL	STOVE OIL	
	FLOAT	PROPANE	
TEL		AVIATION	

SEATTLE

HARBOR ISLAND MARINA

VHF:
TEL: 467-9400   CHART # 18445
FAX: 233-0304   N 47 34 W 122 21
Washington Area Codes 206, 360 & 509

1001 KLICKITAT WAY S.W.
SEATTLE, WA.
98134

LOCALE

GENERAL

OFFICE HOURS
SUMMER:	8AM - 6PM W-SUN
WINTER:	SAME

DAILY MOORAGE
SUMMER:	
WINTER:	

MONTHLY MOORAGE
SUMMER:	$6.50 PER FT
WINTER:	SAME

VISA   MasterCard
          DISCOVER

ON THE DOCK SERVICES
POWER	✓	LIGHTING	✓
30 AMP	✓	CABLE	✓
WATER	✓	PHONE	✓
GARBAGE	✓	DERRICK	
WASTE OIL	✓	LIVE ABRD	✓

WHARVES\FLOATS   UP TO 200 FT

Note: All marina information is subject to; change without notice, misinterpretation, misrepresentation and human error. In no way are the facilities mentioned in this book obligated to honor the rates and services listed. All information is given without guarantee. No part of this book is intended for navigation.

PUBLIC SERVICES

A: Located at Marina   B: Within Walking   C: Within 20 Miles   D: Not Available

	A	B	C	D
ACCOMMODATION			✓	
BAIT & TACKLE	✓			
BANK MACHINE			✓	
BOAT CHARTER	✓			
BOAT LAUNCH		✓		
BOAT RENTAL		✓		
CAMPING				✓
CAR RENTAL			✓	
CHARTS	✓			
DIVE SHOP		✓		
FISH LICENSE			✓	

	A	B	C	D
GOLFING			✓	
GROCERY	✓			
HARDWARE			✓	
HOSPITAL			✓	
ICE	✓			
LAUNDRY			✓	
BOAT LIFT		✓		
LIQUOR STORE			✓	
24 HR PARKING	✓			
POST OFFICE			✓	
PROPANE			✓	

	A	B	C	D
PUB	✓			
PUMPOUT STN	✓			
RESTAURANT	✓			
RV FACILITIES				✓
SHOPS / MALL			✓	
SHOWER	✓			
SWIM POOL			✓	
TAXI	✓			
TELEPHONE	✓			
TIDAL GRID				✓
TOILETS	✓			

50 AMP AVAILABLE

TEXACO
HOURS SUMMER	DIESEL	✓
8 AM - 6 PM	GASOLINE	✓
HOURS WINTER	STOVE OIL	
8 AM - 6 PM	PROPANE	
TEL	AVIATION	

134

SEATTLE

LOCALE

LAKE UNION LANDING
VHF:
TEL: 623-4924   CHART # 18447
FAX:
Washington Area Codes 206, 360 & 509

1171 FAIRVIEW AVE. N.
SEATTLE, WA.
98109

GENERAL

OFFICE HOURS
SUMMER:	9 - 6 M-S 12 - 4 SUN
WINTER:	9 - 6 M-S 12 - 4 SUN

DAILY MOORAGE
SUMMER:	N/A
WINTER:	

MONTHLY MOORAGE
SUMMER:	$6.25 - $7.25 / FT
WINTER:	$6.25 - $7.25 / FT

ON THE DOCK SERVICES
POWER	✓	LIGHTING	✓
30 AMP	✓	CABLE	✓
WATER	✓	PHONE	✓
GARBAGE	✓	DERRICK	
WASTE OIL		LIVE ABRD	✓

WHARVES\FLOATS   UP TO 46 FT

Note: All marina information is subject to; change without notice, misinterpretation, misrepresentation and human error. In no way are the facilities mentioned in this book obligated to honor the rates and services listed. All information is given without guarantee. No part of this book is intended for navigation.

PUBLIC SERVICES

A: Located at Marina   B: Within Walking   C: Within 20 Miles   D: Not Available

	A	B	C	D
ACCOMMODATION		✓		
BAIT & TACKLE			✓	
BANK MACHINE		✓		
BOAT CHARTER	✓			
BOAT LAUNCH			✓	
BOAT RENTAL			✓	
CAMPING				✓
CAR RENTAL			✓	
CHARTS		✓		
DIVE SHOP			✓	
FISH LICENSE		✓		

	A	B	C	D
GOLFING			✓	
GROCERY		✓		
HARDWARE		✓		
HOSPITAL			✓	
ICE		✓		
LAUNDRY		✓		
BOAT LIFT	✓			
LIQUOR STORE			✓	
24 HR PARKING	✓			
POST OFFICE			✓	
PROPANE			✓	

	A	B	C	D
PUB		✓		
PUMPOUT STN		✓		
RESTAURANT	✓			
RV FACILITIES				✓
SHOPS / MALL		✓		
SHOWER	✓			
SWIM POOL				✓
TAXI	✓			
TELEPHONE	✓			
TIDAL GRID				✓
TOILETS	✓			

HOURS SUMMER		NO	DIESEL	
HOURS WINTER		FUEL	GASOLINE	
		FLOAT	STOVE OIL	
TEL			PROPANE	
			AVIATION	

LOCALE

LAKE UNION WATERWORKS
VHF:
TEL: 547-1654   CHART # 18447
FAX:
Washington Area Codes 206, 360 & 509

1101 N. NORTHLAKE WAY
SEATTLE, WA.
98103

GENERAL

OFFICE HOURS
SUMMER:	9 AM - 5 PM
WINTER:	9 AM - 5 PM

DAILY MOORAGE
SUMMER:	N/A
WINTER:	N/A

MONTHLY MOORAGE
SUMMER:	$6.50 PER FT
WINTER:	SAME

VISA   MasterCard   DISCOVER

ON THE DOCK SERVICES
POWER	✓	LIGHTING	✓
30 AMP	✓	CABLE	
WATER	✓	PHONE	✓
GARBAGE	✓	DERRICK	
WASTE OIL		LIVE ABRD	

WHARVES\FLOATS   UP TO 36 FT

Note: All marina information is subject to; change without notice, misinterpretation, misrepresentation and human error. In no way are the facilities mentioned in this book obligated to honor the rates and services listed. All information is given without guarantee. No part of this book is intended for navigation.

PUBLIC SERVICES

A: Located at Marina   B: Within Walking   C: Within 20 Miles   D: Not Available

	A	B	C	D
ACCOMMODATION		✓		
BAIT & TACKLE			✓	
BANK MACHINE		✓		
BOAT CHARTER			✓	
BOAT LAUNCH		✓		
BOAT RENTAL		✓		
CAMPING				✓
CAR RENTAL			✓	
CHARTS		✓		
DIVE SHOP			✓	
FISH LICENSE			✓	

	A	B	C	D
GOLFING			✓	
GROCERY		✓		
HARDWARE		✓		
HOSPITAL			✓	
ICE		✓		
LAUNDRY		✓		
BOAT LIFT		✓		
LIQUOR STORE		✓		
24 HR PARKING		✓		
POST OFFICE			✓	
PROPANE			✓	

	A	B	C	D
PUB		✓		
PUMPOUT STN		✓		
RESTAURANT		✓		
RV FACILITIES			✓	
SHOPS / MALL		✓		
SHOWER			✓	
SWIM POOL			✓	
TAXI	✓			
TELEPHONE		✓		
TIDAL GRID				✓
TOILETS	✓			

PLEASE NOTE THIS PHOTO SHOWS FROM LEFT TO RIGHT NORTHLAKE MARINA, LEE'S MOORING, FREEMONT BOAT CO. AND LAKE UNION WATER WORKS.

HOURS SUMMER		DIESEL
	NO FUEL FLOAT	GASOLINE
HOURS WINTER		STOVE OIL
		PROPANE
TEL		AVIATION

SEATTLE

LOCALE

LAKE UNION YACHT HARBOR
VHF:
TEL: 284-0080   CHART # 18477
FAX:
Washington Area Codes 206, 360 & 509

1530 WESTLAKE AVE. N.
SEATTLE, WA.

GENERAL

OFFICE HOURS
SUMMER:	9 - 5 M-S 12 - 4 SUN
WINTER:	SAME

DAILY MOORAGE
SUMMER:	N/A
WINTER:	N/A

MONTHLY MOORAGE
SUMMER:	YEARLY LEASES
WINTER:	INQUIRE*

ON THE DOCK SERVICES
POWER	✓	LIGHTING	✓
30 AMP	✓	CABLE	
WATER	✓	PHONE	
GARBAGE		DERRICK	
WASTE OIL		LIVE ABRD	

WHARVES\FLOATS   UP TO 76 FT

Note: All marina information is subject to; change without notice, misinterpretation, misrepresentation and human error. In no way are the facilities mentioned in this book obligated to honor the rates and services listed. All information is given without guarantee. No part of this book is intended for navigation.

PUBLIC SERVICES

A: Located at Marina   B: Within Walking   C: Within 20 Miles   D: Not Available

	A	B	C	D
ACCOMMODATION			✓	
BAIT & TACKLE			✓	
BANK MACHINE		✓		
BOAT CHARTER		✓		
BOAT LAUNCH			✓	
BOAT RENTAL		✓		
CAMPING				✓
CAR RENTAL			✓	
CHARTS		✓		
DIVE SHOP			✓	
FISH LICENSE			✓	

	A	B	C	D
GOLFING			✓	
GROCERY		✓		
HARDWARE		✓		
HOSPITAL			✓	
ICE		✓		
LAUNDRY			✓	
BOAT LIFT		✓		
LIQUOR STORE			✓	
24 HR PARKING	✓			
POST OFFICE			✓	
PROPANE			✓	

	A	B	C	D
PUB	✓			
PUMPOUT STN	✓			
RESTAURANT	✓			
RV FACILITIES				✓
SHOPS / MALL		✓		
SHOWER		✓		
SWIM POOL			✓	
TAXI	✓			
TELEPHONE	✓			
TIDAL GRID				✓
TOILETS	✓			

YACHT BROKERAGE AT THE MARINA.
DAY CHARTERS AVAILABLE.

HOURS SUMMER	**NO FUEL FLOAT**	DIESEL
		GASOLINE
HOURS WINTER		STOVE OIL
		PROPANE
TEL		AVIATION

137

LOCALE

LAKESIDE COASTAL GRILL & MARINA
VHF:
TEL: 547-3961   CHART # 18447
FAX:
Washington Area Codes 206, 360 & 509

2501 N. NORTHLAKE WAY
SEATTLE, WA.

GENERAL

OFFICE HOURS

SUMMER:	4 PM - 2 AM M - SAT
WINTER:	3 PM - 12 AM SUN

DAILY MOORAGE

SUMMER:	RESTAURANT
WINTER:	PATRONS ONLY

MONTHLY MOORAGE

SUMMER:	N/A
WINTER:	N/A

ON THE DOCK SERVICES

POWER		LIGHTING	
30 AMP		CABLE	
WATER		PHONE	
GARBAGE		DERRICK	
WASTE OIL		LIVE ABRD	

Note: All marina information is subject to; change without notice, misinterpretation, misrepresentation and human error. In no way are the facilities mentioned in this book obligated to honor the rates and services listed. All information is given without guarantee. No part of this book is intended for navigation.

PUBLIC SERVICES

A: Located at Marina   B: Within Walking   C: Within 20 Miles   D: Not Available

	A	B	C	D
ACCOMMODATION			✓	
BAIT & TACKLE			✓	
BANK MACHINE			✓	
BOAT CHARTER		✓		
BOAT LAUNCH		✓		
BOAT RENTAL	✓			
CAMPING		✓		
CAR RENTAL			✓	
CHARTS			✓	
DIVE SHOP			✓	
FISH LICENSE			✓	

	A	B	C	D
GOLFING			✓	
GROCERY			✓	
HARDWARE		✓		
HOSPITAL			✓	
ICE	✓			
LAUNDRY	✓			
BOAT LIFT	✓			
LIQUOR STORE			✓	
24 HR PARKING			✓	
POST OFFICE			✓	
PROPANE			✓	

	A	B	C	D
PUB	✓			
PUMPOUT STN			✓	
RESTAURANT	✓			
RV FACILITIES		✓		
SHOPS / MALL			✓	
SHOWER		✓		
SWIM POOL			✓	
TAXI	✓			
TELEPHONE	✓			
TIDAL GRID				✓
TOILETS	✓			

HOURS SUMMER	**NO**	DIESEL	
	FUEL	GASOLINE	
HOURS WINTER		STOVE OIL	
	FLOAT	PROPANE	
TEL		AVIATION	

SEATTLE

LOCALE

LECO MARINE INC.
VHF:
TEL: 285-0477   CHART # 18447
FAX: 285-0478
Washington Area Codes 206, 360 & 509

1080 W. EWING ST.
SEATTLE, WA.
98119

GENERAL

OFFICE HOURS

SUMMER:	8 - 5 M - F 8 - 11 SAT
WINTER:	SAME

DAILY MOORAGE

SUMMER:	N/A
WINTER:	

MONTHLY MOORAGE

SUMMER:	VARIES*
WINTER:	

VISA   MasterCard
[card]   DISCOVER

ON THE DOCK SERVICES

POWER	✓	LIGHTING	✓
30 AMP	✓	CABLE	
WATER	✓	PHONE	✓
GARBAGE	✓	DERRICK	
WASTE OIL		LIVE ABRD	✓

WHARVES\FLOATS   UP TO 62 FT

Note: All marina information is subject to; change without notice, misinterpretation, misrepresentation and human error. In no way are the facilities mentioned in this book obligated to honor the rates and services listed. All information is given without guarantee. No part of this book is intended for navigation.

A: Located at Marina   B: Within Walking   C: Within 20 Miles   D: Not Available

PUBLIC SERVICES

	A	B	C	D
ACCOMMODATION	✓			
BAIT & TACKLE		✓		
BANK MACHINE			✓	
BOAT CHARTER			✓	
BOAT LAUNCH			✓	
BOAT RENTAL			✓	
CAMPING				✓
CAR RENTAL			✓	
CHARTS			✓	
DIVE SHOP			✓	
FISH LICENSE		✓		

	A	B	C	D
GOLFING				✓
GROCERY		✓		
HARDWARE			✓	
HOSPITAL			✓	
ICE	✓			
LAUNDRY	✓			
BOAT LIFT	✓			
LIQUOR STORE			✓	
24 HR PARKING	✓			
POST OFFICE	✓			
PROPANE			✓	

	A	B	C	D
PUB		✓		
PUMPOUT STN	✓			
RESTAURANT		✓		
RV FACILITIES				✓
SHOPS / MALL			✓	
SHOWER	✓			
SWIM POOL				✓
TAXI	✓			
TELEPHONE		✓		
TIDAL GRID				✓
TOILETS	✓			

3 MINUTES FROM LOCKS

HOURS SUMMER	**NO FUEL FLOAT**	DIESEL	
		GASOLINE	
HOURS WINTER		STOVE OIL	
		PROPANE	
TEL		AVIATION	

LOCALE

LEE'S MOORING
VHF:
TEL: 547-5050   CHART # 18447
FAX: 547-5053
Washington Area Codes 206, 360 & 509

933 N. NORTHLAKE WAY
SEATTLE, WA.
98103

GENERAL

OFFICE HOURS
| SUMMER: | 8 AM - 5 PM M - F |
| WINTER: | SAME |

DAILY MOORAGE
| SUMMER: | N/A |
| WINTER: | N/A |

MONTHLY MOORAGE
| SUMMER: | $6.00 PER FT |
| WINTER: | SAME |

VISA MasterCard Discover

ON THE DOCK SERVICES
POWER	✓	LIGHTING	
30 AMP	✓	CABLE	
WATER	✓	PHONE	
GARBAGE		DERRICK	
WASTE OIL		LIVE ABRD	

WHARVES\FLOATS UP TO 50 FT

Note: All marina information is subject to; change without notice, misinterpretation, misrepresentation and human error. In no way are the facilities mentioned in this book obligated to honor the rates and services listed. All information is given without guarantee. No part of this book is intended for navigation.

PUBLIC SERVICES

A: Located at Marina   B: Within Walking   C: Within 20 Miles   D: Not Available

	A	B	C	D
ACCOMMODATION		✓		
BAIT & TACKLE			✓	
BANK MACHINE		✓		
BOAT CHARTER			✓	
BOAT LAUNCH			✓	
BOAT RENTAL			✓	
CAMPING				✓
CAR RENTAL			✓	
CHARTS		✓		
DIVE SHOP			✓	
FISH LICENSE			✓	

	A	B	C	D
GOLFING			✓	
GROCERY		✓		
HARDWARE		✓		
HOSPITAL		✓		
ICE		✓		
LAUNDRY		✓		
BOAT LIFT		✓		
LIQUOR STORE			✓	
24 HR PARKING	✓			
POST OFFICE			✓	
PROPANE			✓	

	A	B	C	D
PUB		✓		
PUMPOUT STN		✓		
RESTAURANT		✓		
RV FACILITIES				✓
SHOPS / MALL		✓		
SHOWER			✓	
SWIM POOL			✓	
TAXI	✓			
TELEPHONE		✓		
TIDAL GRID				✓
TOILETS	✓			

50 AMP AVAILABLE.

PLEASE NOTE THIS PHOTO SHOWS FROM LEFT TO RIGHT NORTHLAKE MARINA, LEE'S MOORING, FREEMONT BOAT CO. AND LAKE UNION WATER WORKS.

HOURS SUMMER
HOURS WINTER
TEL

NO FUEL FLOAT

DIESEL	
GASOLINE	
STOVE OIL	
PROPANE	
AVIATION	

SEATTLE

LOCKHAVEN MARINA INC.
VHF:
TEL: 283-6260   CHART # 18447
FAX: 283-0334
Washington Area Codes 206, 360 & 509

3030 W. COMMODORE WAY
SEATTLE, WA.
98199

GENERAL

OFFICE HOURS

SUMMER:	7 AM - 5 PM
WINTER:	7 AM - 5 PM

DAILY MOORAGE

SUMMER:	N/A
WINTER:	

MONTHLY MOORAGE

SUMMER:	$6.25 - $7.50 / FT*
WINTER:	SAME

ON THE DOCK SERVICES

POWER	✓	LIGHTING	✓
30 AMP	✓	CABLE	✓
WATER	✓	PHONE	✓
GARBAGE	✓	DERRICK	✓
WASTE OIL		LIVE ABRD	

WHARVES\FLOATS   UP TO 50 FT

Note: All marina information is subject to; change without notice, misinterpretation, misrepresentation and human error. In no way are the facilities mentioned in this book obligated to honor the rates and services listed. All information is given without guarantee. No part of this book is intended for navigation.

PUBLIC SERVICES

A: Located at Marina   B: Within Walking   C: Within 20 Miles   D: Not Available

	A	B	C	D
ACCOMMODATION			✓	
BAIT & TACKLE			✓	
BANK MACHINE			✓	
BOAT CHARTER			✓	
BOAT LAUNCH			✓	
BOAT RENTAL			✓	
CAMPING				✓
CAR RENTAL			✓	
CHARTS			✓	
DIVE SHOP			✓	
FISH LICENSE			✓	

	A	B	C	D
GOLFING				✓
GROCERY			✓	
HARDWARE			✓	
HOSPITAL			✓	
ICE			✓	
LAUNDRY			✓	
BOAT LIFT	✓			
LIQUOR STORE			✓	
24 HR PARKING	✓			
POST OFFICE			✓	
PROPANE			✓	

	A	B	C	D
PUB			✓	
PUMPOUT STN	✓			
RESTAURANT			✓	
RV FACILITIES				✓
SHOPS / MALL			✓	
SHOWER	✓			
SWIM POOL				✓
TAXI	✓			
TELEPHONE	✓			
TIDAL GRID				✓
TOILETS	✓			

HOURS SUMMER	NO FUEL FLOAT	DIESEL
		GASOLINE
HOURS WINTER		STOVE OIL
		PROPANE
TEL		AVIATION

LOCALE

MARINA MART MOORINGS
VHF:
TEL: 281-8260   CHART # 18477
FAX: 281-8362
Washington Area Codes 206, 360 & 509

1505 WESTLAKE AVE. N. #105
SEATTLE, WA.
98109

GENERAL

OFFICE HOURS

SUMMER:	8 AM - 5 PM M - F
WINTER:	SAME

DAILY MOORAGE

SUMMER:	INQUIRE
WINTER:	

MONTHLY MOORAGE

SUMMER:	$5.00 - $7.00 / FT*
WINTER:	SAME

VISA   MasterCard
DISCOVER

ON THE DOCK SERVICES

POWER	✓	LIGHTING	✓
30 AMP	✓	CABLE	
WATER	✓	PHONE	✓
GARBAGE	✓	DERRICK	
WASTE OIL		LIVE ABRD	

WHARVES\FLOATS   UP TO 94 FT

Note: All marina information is subject to; change without notice, misrepresentation, and human error. In no way are the facilities mentioned in this book obligated to honor the rates and services listed. All information is given without guarantee. No part of this book is intended for navigation.

PUBLIC SERVICES

A: Located at Marina   B: Within Walking   C: Within 20 Miles   D: Not Available

	A	B	C	D		A	B	C	D		A	B	C	D
ACCOMMODATION			✓		GOLFING				✓	PUB	✓			
BAIT & TACKLE			✓		GROCERY		✓			PUMPOUT STN	✓			
BANK MACHINE	✓				HARDWARE			✓		RESTAURANT	✓			
BOAT CHARTER		✓			HOSPITAL			✓		RV FACILITIES			✓	
BOAT LAUNCH			✓		ICE	✓				SHOPS / MALL			✓	
BOAT RENTAL			✓		LAUNDRY					SHOWER	✓			
CAMPING				✓	BOAT LIFT			✓		SWIM POOL			✓	
CAR RENTAL			✓		LIQUOR STORE			✓		TAXI	✓			
CHARTS			✓		24 HR PARKING	✓				TELEPHONE	✓			
DIVE SHOP			✓		POST OFFICE			✓		TIDAL GRID				✓
FISH LICENSE				✓	PROPANE			✓		TOILETS	✓			

50 AMP AVAILABLE.

HOURS SUMMER

HOURS WINTER

TEL

NO FUEL FLOAT

DIESEL
GASOLINE
STOVE OIL
PROPANE
AVIATION

SEATTLE

LOCALE

MCGINNIS MARINE INC.
VHF:
TEL: 782-5777   CHART # 18447
FAX:
Washington Area Codes 206, 360 & 509

5320 28TH AVE. N.W.
SEATTLE, WA.
98107

GENERAL

OFFICE HOURS
SUMMER:	10 AM - 3:30 PM
WINTER:	

DAILY MOORAGE
SUMMER:	CALL FOR INFO*
WINTER:	

MONTHLY MOORAGE
SUMMER:	$4.70 - $6.50*
WINTER:	

VISA   MasterCard   DISCOVER

ON THE DOCK SERVICES
POWER	✓	LIGHTING	✓
30 AMP	✓	CABLE	
WATER	✓	PHONE	✓
GARBAGE	✓	DERRICK	
WASTE OIL		LIVE ABRD	✓

WHARVES\FLOATS   UP TO 60 FT

Note: All marina information is subject to; change without notice, misrepresentation, misrepresentation and human error. In no way are the facilities mentioned in this book obligated to honor the rates and services listed. All information is given without guarantee. No part of this book is intended for navigation.

PUBLIC SERVICES

A: Located at Marina   B: Within Walking   C: Within 20 Miles   D: Not Available

	A	B	C	D
ACCOMMODATION		✓		
BAIT & TACKLE		✓		
BANK MACHINE		✓		
BOAT CHARTER		✓		
BOAT LAUNCH		✓		
BOAT RENTAL				
CAMPING			✓	
CAR RENTAL			✓	
CHARTS		✓		
DIVE SHOP			✓	
FISH LICENSE		✓		

	A	B	C	D
GOLFING			✓	
GROCERY		✓		
HARDWARE	✓			
HOSPITAL			✓	
ICE		✓		
LAUNDRY			✓	
BOAT LIFT			✓	
LIQUOR STORE		✓		
24 HR PARKING	✓			
POST OFFICE		✓		
PROPANE	✓			

	A	B	C	D
PUB		✓		
PUMPOUT STN	✓			
RESTAURANT	✓			
RV FACILITIES			✓	
SHOPS / MALL		✓		
SHOWER				
SWIM POOL			✓	
TAXI	✓			
TELEPHONE	✓			
TIDAL GRID				✓
TOILETS		✓		

PRIVATE MOORAGE, TRANSIENT ONLY WHEN SLIPS AVAILABLE.

HOURS SUMMER		DIESEL	
	NO	GASOLINE	
HOURS WINTER	FUEL	STOVE OIL	
	FLOAT	PROPANE	
TEL		AVIATION	

LOCALE

NORTHLAKE MARINA

VHF:
TEL: 633-2114   CHART # 18447
FAX: 547-8595
Washington Area Codes 206, 360 & 509

927 N. NORTHLAKE WAY
SEATTLE, WA.
98103

GENERAL

OFFICE HOURS

SUMMER:	OCCASIONALLY
WINTER:	

DAILY MOORAGE

SUMMER:	N/A
WINTER:	N/A

MONTHLY MOORAGE

SUMMER:	$6.00 PER FT
WINTER:	SAME

VISA   MasterCard   (card)   DISCOVER

ON THE DOCK SERVICES

POWER	✓	LIGHTING	✓
30 AMP	✓	CABLE	
WATER	✓	PHONE	
GARBAGE	✓	DERRICK	
WASTE OIL		LIVE ABRD	

WHARVES\FLOATS   UP TO 40 FT

Note: All marina information is subject to; change without notice, misinterpretation, misrepresentation and human error. In no way are the facilities mentioned in this book obligated to honor the rates and services listed. All information is given without guarantee. No part of this book is intended for navigation.

PUBLIC SERVICES

A: Located at Marina   B: Within Walking   C: Within 20 Miles   D: Not Available

	A	B	C	D
ACCOMMODATION		✓		
BAIT & TACKLE			✓	
BANK MACHINE		✓		
BOAT CHARTER			✓	
BOAT LAUNCH			✓	
BOAT RENTAL			✓	
CAMPING				✓
CAR RENTAL			✓	
CHARTS		✓		
DIVE SHOP			✓	
FISH LICENSE			✓	

	A	B	C	D
GOLFING			✓	
GROCERY		✓		
HARDWARE		✓		
HOSPITAL			✓	
ICE		✓		
LAUNDRY		✓		
BOAT LIFT		✓		
LIQUOR STORE			✓	
24 HR PARKING	✓			
POST OFFICE			✓	
PROPANE			✓	

	A	B	C	D
PUB		✓		
PUMPOUT STN		✓		
RESTAURANT		✓		
RV FACILITIES				✓
SHOPS / MALL		✓		
SHOWER				✓
SWIM POOL				✓
TAXI	✓			
TELEPHONE		✓		
TIDAL GRID				✓
TOILETS	✓			

LONG TERM MOORAGE.

PLEASE NOTE THIS PHOTO SHOWS FROM LEFT TO RIGHT NORTHLAKE MARINA, LEE'S MOORING, FREEMONT BOAT CO. AND LAKE UNION WATER WORKS.

HOURS SUMMER		DIESEL	
	NO FUEL FLOAT	GASOLINE	
HOURS WINTER		STOVE OIL	
		PROPANE	
TEL		AVIATION	

SEATTLE

NORTHLAKE MARITIME CENTER
VHF:
TEL: 547-7852   CHART # 18447
FAX: 548-9171
Washington Area Codes 206, 360 & 509

2309 N. NORTHLAKE WAY
SEATTLE, WA.
98103

LOCALE

GENERAL

OFFICE HOURS

SUMMER:	6 - 6 M - F 9 - 5 S,S
WINTER:	8 - 6 M - F 12 - 5 S,S

DAILY MOORAGE

SUMMER:	N/A
WINTER:	N/A

MONTHLY MOORAGE

SUMMER:	VARIES*
WINTER:	

VISA — YES
MasterCard — YES
⬤ —
DISCOVER — YES

ON THE DOCK SERVICES

POWER	✓	LIGHTING	✓
30 AMP	✓	CABLE	
WATER	✓	PHONE	✓
GARBAGE	✓	DERRICK	
WASTE OIL		LIVE ABRD	✓

WHARVES\FLOATS   300 FT

Note: All marina information is subject to; change without notice, misinterpretation, misrepresentation and human error. In no way are the facilities mentioned in this book obligated to honor the rates and services listed. All information is given without guarantee. No part of this book is intended for navigation.

PUBLIC SERVICES

A: Located at Marina   B: Within Walking   C: Within 20 Miles   D: Not Available

	A	B	C	D
ACCOMMODATION			✓	
BAIT & TACKLE				✓
BANK MACHINE			✓	
BOAT CHARTER			✓	
BOAT LAUNCH	✓			
BOAT RENTAL	✓			
CAMPING				✓
CAR RENTAL			✓	
CHARTS			✓	
DIVE SHOP			✓	
FISH LICENSE			✓	

	A	B	C	D
GOLFING				✓
GROCERY			✓	
HARDWARE	✓			
HOSPITAL			✓	
ICE	✓			
LAUNDRY	✓			
BOAT LIFT	✓			
LIQUOR STORE			✓	
24 HR PARKING	✓			
POST OFFICE		✓		
PROPANE			✓	

	A	B	C	D
PUB			✓	
PUMPOUT STN	✓			
RESTAURANT		✓		
RV FACILITIES				✓
SHOPS / MALL			✓	
SHOWER				✓
SWIM POOL				✓
TAXI	✓			
TELEPHONE	✓			
TIDAL GRID				✓
TOILETS	✓			

SHIPYARD REPAIR FACILITY.
50 AMP AVAILABLE.

	NO FUEL FLOAT	
HOURS SUMMER		DIESEL
		GASOLINE
HOURS WINTER		STOVE OIL
		PROPANE
TEL		AVIATION

SEATTLE

LOCALE

PORT OF SEATTLE
VHF: 17
TEL: 728-3000   CHART # 18447
FAX: 728-3393
Washington Area Codes 206, 360 & 509

3919 18TH AVE. W.
SEATTLE, WA.
98119

GENERAL

OFFICE HOURS
SUMMER:	8 AM - 4:30 PM
WINTER:	SAME

DAILY MOORAGE
SUMMER:	COMMERCIAL
WINTER:	ONLY

MONTHLY MOORAGE
SUMMER:	COMMERCIAL
WINTER:	ONLY

VISA   MasterCard   DISCOVER

ON THE DOCK SERVICES
POWER	✓	LIGHTING	✓
30 AMP	✓	CABLE	
WATER	✓	PHONE	
GARBAGE	✓	DERRICK	✓
WASTE OIL	✓	LIVE ABRD	✓

WHARVES\FLOATS   UP TO 400 FT

Note: All marina information is subject to; change without notice, misinterpretation, misrepresentation and human error. In no way are the facilities mentioned in this book obligated to honor the rates and services listed. All information is given without guarantee. No part of this book is intended for navigation.

PUBLIC SERVICES

A: Located at Marina   B: Within Walking   C: Within 20 Miles   D: Not Available

	A	B	C	D		A	B	C	D		A	B	C	D
ACCOMMODATION		✓			GOLFING				✓	PUB	✓			
BAIT & TACKLE	✓				GROCERY	✓				PUMPOUT STN		✓		
BANK MACHINE	✓				HARDWARE	✓				RESTAURANT	✓			
BOAT CHARTER			✓		HOSPITAL			✓		RV FACILITIES				✓
BOAT LAUNCH			✓		ICE	✓				SHOPS / MALL				
BOAT RENTAL			✓		LAUNDRY	✓				SHOWER	✓			
CAMPING				✓	BOAT LIFT	✓				SWIM POOL				✓
CAR RENTAL			✓		LIQUOR STORE			✓		TAXI	✓			
CHARTS		✓			24 HR PARKING	✓				TELEPHONE	✓			
DIVE SHOP			✓		POST OFFICE			✓		TIDAL GRID				✓
FISH LICENSE	✓				PROPANE			✓		TOILETS	✓			

DELTA WESTERN

HOURS SUMMER	MARINE	DIESEL ✓
		GASOLINE
HOURS WINTER		STOVE OIL
		PROPANE
TEL 282-1567		AVIATION

146

SEATTLE

LOCALE

QUEEN CITY YACHT CLUB

VHF:
TEL: 523-6085   CHART # 18447
FAX: 655-0444   N 47 38 W 122 18
Washington Area Codes 206, 360 & 509

1232 WESTLAKE AVE. N.
SEATTLE, WA.
98109

GENERAL

OFFICE HOURS

SUMMER:	VARIES
WINTER:	SAME

DAILY MOORAGE

SUMMER:	RECIPRICAL
WINTER:	ONLY

MONTHLY MOORAGE

SUMMER:	RECIPRICAL
WINTER:	ONLY

VISA ☐   MasterCard ☐
☐   DISCOVER ☐

ON THE DOCK SERVICES

POWER	✓	LIGHTING	✓
30 AMP	✓	CABLE	✓
WATER	✓	PHONE	✓
GARBAGE	✓	DERRICK	
WASTE OIL		LIVE ABRD	✓

Note: All marina information is subject to; change without notice, misrepresentation, misrepresentation and human error. In no way are the facilities mentioned in this book obligated to honor the rates and services listed. All information is given without guarantee. No part of this book is intended for navigation.

PUBLIC SERVICES

A: Located at Marina   B: Within Walking   C: Within 20 Miles   D: Not Available

	A	B	C	D
ACCOMMODATION		✓		
BAIT & TACKLE			✓	
BANK MACHINE			✓	
BOAT CHARTER			✓	
BOAT LAUNCH				
BOAT RENTAL				
CAMPING				
CAR RENTAL				
CHARTS				
DIVE SHOP				
FISH LICENSE				

	A	B	C	D
GOLFING				
GROCERY		✓		
HARDWARE			✓	
HOSPITAL			✓	
ICE	✓			
LAUNDRY			✓	
BOAT LIFT			✓	
LIQUOR STORE			✓	
24 HR PARKING	✓			
POST OFFICE			✓	
PROPANE			✓	

	A	B	C	D
PUB		✓		
PUMPOUT STN			✓	
RESTAURANT		✓		
RV FACILITIES				
SHOPS / MALL		✓		
SHOWER	✓			
SWIM POOL				✓
TAXI	✓			
TELEPHONE	✓			
TIDAL GRID				✓
TOILETS	✓			

HOURS SUMMER			DIESEL	
	NO		GASOLINE	
HOURS WINTER	FUEL		STOVE OIL	
	FLOAT		PROPANE	
TEL			AVIATION	

147

SEATTLE

LOCALE

SAGSTAD MARINA
VHF:
TEL: 784-6500   CHART # 18447
FAX: 784-9229
Washington Area Codes 206, 360 & 509

5109 SHILSHOLE N.W.
SEATTLE, WA.
98107

GENERAL

OFFICE HOURS
SUMMER:	9 AM - 5:30 PM
WINTER:	

DAILY MOORAGE
SUMMER:	N/A
WINTER:	

MONTHLY MOORAGE
SUMMER:	$172 - $310 / MTH
WINTER:	

VISA   MasterCard   DISCOVER

ON THE DOCK SERVICES
POWER	✓	LIGHTING	✓
30 AMP	✓	CABLE	
WATER	✓	PHONE	
GARBAGE	✓	DERRICK	
WASTE OIL		LIVE ABRD	

WHARVES\FLOATS   UP TO 40 FT

Note: All marina information is subject to; change without notice, misinterpretation, misrepresentation and human error. In no way are the facilities mentioned in this book obligated to honor the rates and services listed. All information is given without guarantee. No part of this book is intended for navigation.

PUBLIC SERVICES

A: Located at Marina   B: Within Walking   C: Within 20 Miles   D: Not Available

	A	B	C	D
ACCOMMODATION			✓	
BAIT & TACKLE			✓	
BANK MACHINE			✓	
BOAT CHARTER			✓	
BOAT LAUNCH		✓		
BOAT RENTAL			✓	
CAMPING			✓	
CAR RENTAL			✓	
CHARTS			✓	
DIVE SHOP		✓		
FISH LICENSE		✓		

	A	B	C	D
GOLFING			✓	
GROCERY		✓		
HARDWARE			✓	
HOSPITAL		✓		
ICE		✓		
LAUNDRY		✓		
BOAT LIFT	✓			
LIQUOR STORE		✓		
24 HR PARKING	✓			
POST OFFICE		✓		
PROPANE		✓		

	A	B	C	D
PUB		✓		
PUMPOUT STN	✓			
RESTAURANT		✓		
RV FACILITIES			✓	
SHOPS / MALL		✓		
SHOWER			✓	
SWIM POOL			✓	
TAXI	✓			
TELEPHONE	✓			
TIDAL GRID				✓
TOILETS	✓			

HOURS SUMMER	NO FUEL FLOAT	DIESEL	
		GASOLINE	
HOURS WINTER		STOVE OIL	
		PROPANE	
TEL		AVIATION	

148

SEATTLE

SALMON BAY MARINA
VHF:
TEL: 282-5555   CHART # 18447
FAX: 282-8482
Washington Area Codes 206, 360 & 509

2100 W. COMMODORE WAY
SEATTLE, WA.
98199

GENERAL

OFFICE HOURS
SUMMER:	8:30 - 4 TUES-SAT
WINTER:	SAME

DAILY MOORAGE
SUMMER:	$15.00 PER NIGHT
WINTER:	SAME

MONTHLY MOORAGE
SUMMER:	$5.25 - $8.00 / FT*
WINTER:	SAME

ON THE DOCK SERVICES
POWER	✓	LIGHTING	✓
30 AMP	✓	CABLE	
WATER	✓	PHONE	✓
GARBAGE	✓	DERRICK	
WASTE OIL		LIVE ABRD	✓

WHARVES\FLOATS   UP TO 60 FT

Note: All marina information is subject to; change without notice, misinterpretation, misrepresentation and human error. In no way are the facilities mentioned in this book obligated to honor the rates and services listed. All information is given without guarantee. No part of this book is intended for navigation.

PUBLIC SERVICES

A: Located at Marina   B: Within Walking   C: Within 20 Miles   D: Not Available

	A	B	C	D
ACCOMMODATION				
BAIT & TACKLE		✓		
BANK MACHINE		✓		
BOAT CHARTER				
BOAT LAUNCH				
BOAT RENTAL				
CAMPING				
CAR RENTAL				
CHARTS				
DIVE SHOP				
FISH LICENSE		✓		

	A	B	C	D
GOLFING				
GROCERY		✓		
HARDWARE		✓		
HOSPITAL				
ICE				
LAUNDRY	✓			
BOAT LIFT				
LIQUOR STORE				
24 HR PARKING	✓			
POST OFFICE				
PROPANE				

	A	B	C	D
PUB		✓		
PUMPOUT STN				✓
RESTAURANT		✓		
RV FACILITIES				
SHOPS / MALL				
SHOWER	✓			
SWIM POOL				
TAXI				
TELEPHONE	✓			
TIDAL GRID				
TOILETS	✓			

HOURS SUMMER	NO FUEL FLOAT	DIESEL	
		GASOLINE	
HOURS WINTER		STOVE OIL	
		PROPANE	
TEL		AVIATION	

SEATTLE MARINA INC.
VHF:
TEL: 632-9427   CHART # 18447
FAX:
Washington Area Codes 206, 360 & 509

2401 N. NORTHLAKE WAY
SEATTLE, WA.
98103

LOCALE

GENERAL

OFFICE HOURS

SUMMER:	
WINTER:	

DAILY MOORAGE

SUMMER:	$6.25 TO $6.50 / FT
WINTER:	SAME

MONTHLY MOORAGE

SUMMER:	$150.00 TO $350.00
WINTER:	SAME

VISA ☐   MasterCard ☐
☐   DISCOVER ☐

ON THE DOCK SERVICES

POWER	✓	LIGHTING	✓
30 AMP	✓	CABLE	
WATER	✓	PHONE	✓
GARBAGE		DERRICK	✓
WASTE OIL		LIVE ABRD	✓

WHARVES\FLOATS   20 TO 50 FT

Note: All marina information is subject to; change without notice, misinterpretation, misrepresentation and human error. In no way are the facilities mentioned in this book obligated to honor the rates and services listed. All information is given without guarantee. No part of this book is intended for navigation.

PUBLIC SERVICES

A: Located at Marina   B: Within Walking   C: Within 20 Miles   D: Not Available

	A	B	C	D
ACCOMMODATION			✓	
BAIT & TACKLE			✓	
BANK MACHINE			✓	
BOAT CHARTER		✓		
BOAT LAUNCH	✓			
BOAT RENTAL				
CAMPING		✓		
CAR RENTAL				
CHARTS				
DIVE SHOP				
FISH LICENSE				

	A	B	C	D
GOLFING				
GROCERY			✓	
HARDWARE	✓			
HOSPITAL				
ICE	✓			
LAUNDRY	✓			
BOAT LIFT	✓			
LIQUOR STORE			✓	
24 HR PARKING				
POST OFFICE			✓	
PROPANE				

	A	B	C	D
PUB		✓		
PUMPOUT STN			✓	
RESTAURANT	✓			
RV FACILITIES		✓		
SHOPS / MALL				
SHOWER	✓			
SWIM POOL				
TAXI		✓		
TELEPHONE		✓		
TIDAL GRID				
TOILETS	✓			

SEE HAUL OUT SECTION OF THIS BOOK.

HOURS SUMMER

HOURS WINTER

TEL

NO FUEL FLOAT

DIESEL	☐
GASOLINE	☐
STOVE OIL	☐
PROPANE	☐
AVIATION	☐

SEATTLE

LOCALE

SHILSHOLE BAY MARINA
VHF: 17
TEL: 728-3385
FAX: 728-3391
Washington Area Codes 206, 360 & 509

CHART # 18445 / 447
N 47 41 W 122 24.50

7001 SEAVIEW AVE. N.W.
SEATTLE, WA.
98117

GENERAL

OFFICE HOURS
SUMMER:	M-F 8 - 4:30 S,S 8 - 1
WINTER:	YEAR ROUND

DAILY MOORAGE
SUMMER:	$.40 PER FT
WINTER:	SAME

MONTHLY MOORAGE
SUMMER:	$5.75 - $7.17 + TAX
WINTER:	SAME

 YES
 YES
YES
YES

ON THE DOCK SERVICES
POWER	✓	LIGHTING	✓
30 AMP	✓	CABLE	
WATER	✓	PHONE	✓
GARBAGE	✓	DERRICK	✓
WASTE OIL	✓	LIVE ABRD	✓

Note: All marina information is subject to; change without notice, misinterpretation, misrepresentation and human error. In no way are the facilities mentioned in this book obligated to honor the rates and services listed. All information is given without guarantee. No part of this book is intended for navigation.

PUBLIC SERVICES

A: Located at Marina   B: Within Walking   C: Within 20 Miles   D: Not Available

	A	B	C	D
ACCOMMODATION			✓	
BAIT & TACKLE		✓		
BANK MACHINE		✓		
BOAT CHARTER	✓			
BOAT LAUNCH		✓		
BOAT RENTAL		✓		
CAMPING			✓	
CAR RENTAL			✓	
CHARTS			✓	
DIVE SHOP			✓	
FISH LICENSE		✓		

	A	B	C	D
GOLFING			✓	
GROCERY	✓			
HARDWARE		✓		
HOSPITAL			✓	
ICE	✓			
LAUNDRY	✓			
BOAT LIFT	✓			
LIQUOR STORE		✓		
24 HR PARKING	✓			
POST OFFICE			✓	
PROPANE	✓			

	A	B	C	D
PUB	✓			
PUMPOUT STN	✓			
RESTAURANT	✓			
RV FACILITIES			✓	
SHOPS / MALL			✓	
SHOWER	✓			
SWIM POOL			✓	
TAXI	✓			
TELEPHONE	✓			
TIDAL GRID				✓
TOILETS	✓			

TEXACO

HOURS SUMMER
M-F 9 - 5 S,S 8 - 7
HOURS WINTER
9 AM - 5 PM
TEL   783-7555

DIESEL	✓
GASOLINE	✓
STOVE OIL	✓
PROPANE	
AVIATION	

- DRY STORAGE
- RECYCLING & DISPOSAL SERVICES
PROVIDED. PLEASE USE !

SEATTLE

LOCALE

SOUTH PARK MARINA
VHF:
TEL: 762-3880
FAX: 762-5144
Washington Area Codes 206, 360 & 509

CHART # 18445
N 47 31.7 W 122 18.7

8604 DALLAS AVE. S.
SEATTLE, WA.
98108

GENERAL

OFFICE HOURS
SUMMER:	8:30 - 5 TUES-SAT
WINTER:	SAME

DAILY MOORAGE
SUMMER:	$10.00 PER DAY*
WINTER:	

MONTHLY MOORAGE
SUMMER:	$5.25 PER FT
WINTER:	SAME

VISA   MasterCard

DISCOVER

ON THE DOCK SERVICES
POWER	√	LIGHTING	√
30 AMP	√	CABLE	
WATER	√	PHONE	√
GARBAGE	√	DERRICK	
WASTE OIL	√	LIVE ABRD	√

WHARVES\FLOATS   4000 FT

Note: All marina information is subject to; change without notice, misinterpretation, misrepresentation and human error. In no way are the facilities mentioned in this book obligated to honor the rates and services listed. All information is given without guarantee. No part of this book is intended for navigation.

PUBLIC SERVICES

A: Located at Marina   B: Within Walking   C: Within 20 Miles   D: Not Available

	A	B	C	D
ACCOMMODATION			√	
BAIT & TACKLE			√	
BANK MACHINE			√	
BOAT CHARTER			√	
BOAT LAUNCH	√			
BOAT RENTAL			√	
CAMPING				√
CAR RENTAL			√	
CHARTS			√	
DIVE SHOP			√	
FISH LICENSE			√	

	A	B	C	D
GOLFING			√	
GROCERY		√		
HARDWARE	√			
HOSPITAL			√	
ICE			√	
LAUNDRY	√			
BOAT LIFT	√			
LIQUOR STORE			√	
24 HR PARKING	√			
POST OFFICE		√		
PROPANE			√	

	A	B	C	D
PUB		√		
PUMPOUT STN			√	
RESTAURANT		√		
RV FACILITIES	√			
SHOPS / MALL		√		
SHOWER	√			
SWIM POOL			√	
TAXI	√			
TELEPHONE	√			
TIDAL GRID				√
TOILETS	√			

SEE HAUL OUT SECTION OF THIS BOOK,

HOURS SUMMER

HOURS WINTER

TEL

NO FUEL FLOAT

DIESEL
GASOLINE
STOVE OIL
PROPANE
AVIATION

SEATTLE

LOCALE

STIMSON MARINA
VHF:
TEL: 784-3100   CHART # 18447
FAX: 784-3174
Washington Area Codes 206, 360 & 509

5265 SHILSHOLE AVE. N.W.
P.O. BOX 17705
SEATTLE, WA.
98107

GENERAL

OFFICE HOURS
SUMMER:	8:30 AM - 5 PM M - F
WINTER:	

DAILY MOORAGE
SUMMER:	N/A
WINTER:	

MONTHLY MOORAGE
SUMMER:	$6.30 PER FT
WINTER:	

ON THE DOCK SERVICES
POWER	✓	LIGHTING	✓
30 AMP	✓	CABLE	
WATER	✓	PHONE	✓
GARBAGE	✓	DERRICK	
WASTE OIL	✓	LIVE ABRD	

WHARVES\FLOATS   UP TO 80 FT

Note: All marina information is subject to; change without notice, misinterpretation, misrepresentation and human error. In no way are the facilities mentioned in this book obligated to honor the rates and services listed. All information is given without guarantee. No part of this book is intended for navigation.

PUBLIC SERVICES

A: Located at Marina   B: Within Walking   C: Within 20 Miles   D: Not Available

	A	B	C	D
ACCOMMODATION			✓	
BAIT & TACKLE		✓		
BANK MACHINE		✓		
BOAT CHARTER			✓	
BOAT LAUNCH		✓		
BOAT RENTAL			✓	
CAMPING				✓
CAR RENTAL				
CHARTS		✓		
DIVE SHOP				
FISH LICENSE		✓		

	A	B	C	D
GOLFING			✓	
GROCERY		✓		
HARDWARE	✓			
HOSPITAL		✓		
ICE		✓		
LAUNDRY				
BOAT LIFT		✓		
LIQUOR STORE		✓		
24 HR PARKING	✓			
POST OFFICE		✓		
PROPANE		✓		

	A	B	C	D
PUB		✓		
PUMPOUT STN		✓		
RESTAURANT		✓		
RV FACILITIES			✓	
SHOPS / MALL		✓		
SHOWER			✓	
SWIM POOL			✓	
TAXI	✓			
TELEPHONE	✓			
TIDAL GRID				✓
TOILETS	✓			

CHEVRON

HOURS SUMMER	
8 AM - 5 PM	
HOURS WINTER	
8 AM - 5 PM	
TEL 784-0171	

DIESEL	✓
GASOLINE	✓
STOVE OIL	
PROPANE	
AVIATION	

GAS DOCK LOCATED NEXT TO MARINA

LOCALE

TILLICUM MARINA

VHF:
TEL: 633-5454   CHART # 18447
FAX:
Washington Area Codes 206, 360 & 509

1331 N. NORTHLAKE WAY
SEATTLE, WA.
98103

GENERAL

OFFICE HOURS

SUMMER:	VARIES
WINTER:	

DAILY MOORAGE

SUMMER:	N/A
WINTER:	.

MONTHLY MOORAGE

SUMMER:	$6.40 TO $7.20 / FT
WINTER:	SAME

VISA ☐   MasterCard ☐
⊖ ☐   DISCOVER ☐

ON THE DOCK SERVICES

POWER	✓	LIGHTING	✓
30 AMP	✓	CABLE	
WATER	✓	PHONE	✓
GARBAGE	✓	DERRICK	
WASTE OIL		LIVE ABRD	

Note: All marina information is subject to; change without notice, misinterpretation, misrepresentation and human error. In no way are the facilities mentioned in this book obligated to honor the rates and services listed. All information is given without guarantee. No part of this book is intended for navigation.

PUBLIC SERVICES

A: Located at Marina   B: Within Walking   C: Within 20 Miles   D: Not Available

	A	B	C	D
ACCOMMODATION		✓		
BAIT & TACKLE			✓	
BANK MACHINE		✓		
BOAT CHARTER			✓	
BOAT LAUNCH		✓		
BOAT RENTAL		✓		
CAMPING				✓
CAR RENTAL			✓	
CHARTS		✓		
DIVE SHOP			✓	
FISH LICENSE			✓	

	A	B	C	D
GOLFING				✓
GROCERY			✓	
HARDWARE		✓		
HOSPITAL			✓	
ICE		✓		
LAUNDRY		✓		
BOAT LIFT		✓		
LIQUOR STORE		✓		
24 HR PARKING	✓			
POST OFFICE			✓	
PROPANE			✓	

	A	B	C	D
PUB		✓		
PUMPOUT STN		✓		
RESTAURANT		✓		
RV FACILITIES				✓
SHOPS / MALL		✓		
SHOWER				✓
SWIM POOL				✓
TAXI	✓			
TELEPHONE	✓			
TIDAL GRID				✓
TOILETS	✓			

NO FUEL FLOAT

HOURS SUMMER		DIESEL	☐
		GASOLINE	☐
HOURS WINTER		STOVE OIL	☐
		PROPANE	☐
TEL		AVIATION	☐

SEATTLE

UNIVERSITY BOAT MART MARINA

VHF:
TEL: 634-2050   CHART # 18447
FAX: 634-2209
Washington Area Codes 206, 360 & 509

1401 N.E. BOAT ST.
SEATTLE, WA.
98105

GENERAL

OFFICE HOURS

SUMMER:	VARIES*
WINTER:	

DAILY MOORAGE

SUMMER:	N/A
WINTER:	

MONTHLY MOORAGE

SUMMER:	$4.75 - $6.00 / FT *
WINTER:	SAME

VISA   MasterCard   DISCOVER

ON THE DOCK SERVICES

POWER	✓	LIGHTING	✓
30 AMP		CABLE	
WATER	✓	PHONE	
GARBAGE	✓	DERRICK	
WASTE OIL		LIVE ABRD	

WHARVES\FLOATS   UP TO 35 FT

Note: All marina information is subject to; change without notice, misinterpretation, misrepresentation and human error. In no way are the facilities mentioned in this book obligated to honor the rates and services listed. All information is given without guarantee. No part of this book is intended for navigation.

PUBLIC SERVICES

A: Located at Marina   B: Within Walking   C: Within 20 Miles   D: Not Available

	A	B	C	D
ACCOMMODATION		✓		
BAIT & TACKLE				✓
BANK MACHINE				✓
BOAT CHARTER				✓
BOAT LAUNCH	✓			
BOAT RENTAL				✓
CAMPING				✓
CAR RENTAL			✓	
CHARTS				✓
DIVE SHOP				✓
FISH LICENSE				✓

	A	B	C	D
GOLFING				✓
GROCERY		✓		
HARDWARE				✓
HOSPITAL		✓		
ICE		✓		
LAUNDRY		✓		
BOAT LIFT				✓
LIQUOR STORE		✓		
24 HR PARKING	✓			
POST OFFICE		✓		
PROPANE		✓		

	A	B	C	D
PUB		✓		
PUMPOUT STN			✓	
RESTAURANT		✓		
RV FACILITIES			✓	
SHOPS / MALL		✓		
SHOWER				✓
SWIM POOL				✓
TAXI	✓			
TELEPHONE	✓			
TIDAL GRID				✓
TOILETS	✓			

CONVENIENT FOR WATER-SKIING AND SMALL
BOAT SAILING IN LAKE WASHINGTON.

HOURS SUMMER	NO	DIESEL	
HOURS WINTER	FUEL	GASOLINE	
	FLOAT	STOVE OIL	
TEL		PROPANE	
		AVIATION	

LOCALE

YOUNGQUIST MARINA
VHF:
TEL: 284-9004   CHART # 18447
FAX: 284-3070
Washington Area Codes 206, 360 & 509

2476 WESTLAKE AVE. N.
SEATTLE, WA.
98109

GENERAL

OFFICE HOURS
SUMMER:	10 AM - 5 PM DAILY
WINTER:	SAME

DAILY MOORAGE
SUMMER:	N/A
WINTER:	N/A

MONTHLY MOORAGE
SUMMER:	$5.50 - $6.50 / FT
WINTER:	SAME

VISA   MasterCard   [   ]   DISCOVER

ON THE DOCK SERVICES
POWER	✓	LIGHTING	✓
30 AMP	✓	CABLE	
WATER	✓	PHONE	✓
GARBAGE	✓	DERRICK	
WASTE OIL		LIVE ABRD	

WHARVES\FLOATS   UP TO 75 FT

Note: All marina information is subject to; change without notice, misinterpretation, misrepresentation and human error. In no way are the facilities mentioned in this book obligated to honor the rates and services listed. All information is given without guarantee. No part of this book is intended for navigation.

PUBLIC SERVICES

A: Located at Marina   B: Within Walking   C: Within 20 Miles   D: Not Available

	A	B	C	D
ACCOMMODATION			✓	
BAIT & TACKLE			✓	
BANK MACHINE	✓			
BOAT CHARTER	✓			
BOAT LAUNCH			✓	
BOAT RENTAL			✓	
CAMPING				✓
CAR RENTAL			✓	
CHARTS			✓	
DIVE SHOP			✓	
FISH LICENSE				✓

	A	B	C	D
GOLFING				✓
GROCERY		✓		
HARDWARE			✓	
HOSPITAL			✓	
ICE		✓		
LAUNDRY			✓	
BOAT LIFT			✓	
LIQUOR STORE			✓	
24 HR PARKING	✓			
POST OFFICE			✓	
PROPANE			✓	

	A	B	C	D
PUB	✓			
PUMPOUT STN	✓			
RESTAURANT	✓			
RV FACILITIES			✓	
SHOPS / MALL			✓	
SHOWER			✓	
SWIM POOL				
TAXI	✓			
TELEPHONE		✓		
TIDAL GRID				✓
TOILETS	✓			

50 AMP AVAILABLE.

HOURS SUMMER
HOURS WINTER
TEL

NO FUEL FLOAT

DIESEL [ ]
GASOLINE [ ]
STOVE OIL [ ]
PROPANE [ ]
AVIATION [ ]

156

SEQUIM BAY

LOCALE

JOHN WAYNE MARINA
VHF:
TEL: 417-3440   CHART # 18471
FAX: 417-3442   N 48 03.95 W 123 02.31
Washington Area Codes 206, 360 & 509

2577 WEST SEQUIM BAY RD.
SEQUIM BAY, WA.
98382

GENERAL

OFFICE HOURS

SUMMER:	8AM - 5PM
WINTER:	SAME

DAILY MOORAGE

SUMMER:	$15.00 - $23.00
WINTER:	PLUS $3 PWR

MONTHLY MOORAGE

SUMMER:	SEE
WINTER:	COMMENTS

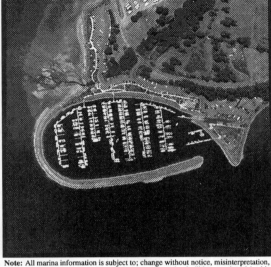

ON THE DOCK SERVICES

POWER	✓	LIGHTING	✓
30 AMP	✓	CABLE	
WATER	✓	PHONE	✓
GARBAGE	✓	DERRICK	
WASTE OIL	✓	LIVE ABRD	✓

WHARVES\FLOATS   10,500 FT

Note: All marina information is subject to; change without notice, misinterpretation, misrepresentation and human error. In no way are the facilities mentioned in this book obligated to honor the rates and services listed. All information is given without guarantee. No part of this book is intended for navigation.

PUBLIC SERVICES

A: Located at Marina   B: Within Walking   C: Within 20 Miles   D: Not Available

	A	B	C	D
ACCOMMODATION		✓		
BAIT & TACKLE	✓			
BANK MACHINE		✓		
BOAT CHARTER	✓			
BOAT LAUNCH	✓			
BOAT RENTAL	✓			
CAMPING		✓		
CAR RENTAL			✓	
CHARTS	✓			
DIVE SHOP			✓	
FISH LICENSE	✓			

	A	B	C	D
GOLFING			✓	
GROCERY	✓			
HARDWARE	✓			
HOSPITAL			✓	
ICE	✓			
LAUNDRY	✓			
BOAT LIFT			✓	
LIQUOR STORE		✓		
24 HR PARKING	✓			
POST OFFICE		✓		
PROPANE			✓	

	A	B	C	D
PUB	✓			
PUMPOUT STN	✓			
RESTAURANT	✓			
RV FACILITIES		✓		
SHOPS / MALL		✓		
SHOWER	✓			
SWIM POOL			✓	
TAXI	✓			
TELEPHONE	✓			
TIDAL GRID				✓
TOILETS	✓			

TEXACO

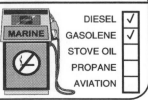

HOURS SUMMER		DIESEL	✓
8:30AM-4:30PM	MARINE	GASOLENE	✓
HOURS WINTER		STOVE OIL	
		PROPANE	
TEL 417-3440		AVIATION	

RESIDENT & NON-RESIDENT MOORAGE RATES. RATES VARY BY LENGTH. CONTACT MARINA FOR RATE SHEET.

RENTAL BOATS, PEDAL BOATS, GROCERIES, JOHN WAYNE MEMENTOS, MARINE AND FISHING SUPPLIES ALL AVAILABLE AT BOSUN'S LOCKER.

TACOMA

LOCALE

BREAKWATER MARINA INC
VHF: 13
TEL: 752-6663   CHART # 18445
FAX: 752-8291   N 47 15 W 122.23
Washington Area Codes 206, 360 & 509

5603 WATERFRONT DRIVE
TACOMA, WA.
98407

GENERAL

OFFICE HOURS
SUMMER:	8AM - 5PM M-F
WINTER:	SAME

DAILY MOORAGE
SUMMER:	$.50 PER FT
WINTER:	SAME

MONTHLY MOORAGE
SUMMER:	$4.25 - $5.00/FT
WINTER:	SAME

 YES   YES

ON THE DOCK SERVICES
POWER	✓	LIGHTING	✓
30 AMP		CABLE	
WATER	✓	PHONE	
GARBAGE	✓	DERRICK	
WASTE OIL	✓	LIVE ABRD	

WHARVES\FLOATS   UP TO 80 FT

Note: All marina information is subject to; change without notice, misinterpretation, misrepresentation and human error. In no way are the facilities mentioned in this book obligated to honor the rates and services listed. All information is given without guarantee. No part of this book is intended for navigation.

PUBLIC SERVICES

A: Located at Marina   B: Within Walking   C: Within 20 Miles   D: Not Available

	A	B	C	D
ACCOMMODATION			✓	
BAIT & TACKLE		✓		
BANK MACHINE			✓	
BOAT CHARTER			✓	
BOAT LAUNCH	✓			
BOAT RENTAL	✓			
CAMPING			✓	
CAR RENTAL	✓			
CHARTS	✓			
DIVE SHOP		✓		
FISH LICENSE		✓		

	A	B	C	D
GOLFING			✓	
GROCERY		✓		
HARDWARE			✓	
HOSPITAL			✓	
ICE	✓			
LAUNDRY		✓		
BOAT LIFT			✓	
LIQUOR STORE		✓		
24 HR PARKING	✓			
POST OFFICE		✓		
PROPANE	✓			

	A	B	C	D
PUB		✓		
PUMPOUT STN	✓			
RESTAURANT		✓		
RV FACILITIES				✓
SHOPS / MALL				✓
SHOWER	✓			
SWIM POOL			✓	
TAXI	✓			
TELEPHONE	✓			
TIDAL GRID	✓			
TOILETS	✓			

POINT DEFIANCE PARK AND ZOO.
CONVENIENCE STORE AND FULL SERVICE
MARINE REPAIRS.
LOCATED BESIDE VASHON ISLAND FERRY.

CHEVRON

HOURS SUMMER
9AM - 8PM

HOURS WINTER
9AM - 5PM

TEL   752-6663

DIESEL	✓
GASOLINE	✓
STOVE OIL	
PROPANE	✓
AVIATION	

TACOMA

LOCALE

CHINOOK LANDING MARINAS
VHF: 79
TEL: 627-7676   CHART # 18445
FAX: 383-2823   N 47 17 W 122 24
Washington Area Codes 206, 360 & 509

3702 MARINE VIEW DRIVE
SUITE 100
TACOMA ,WA.
98422

GENERAL

OFFICE HOURS
SUMMER:	8:30 - 5:30 M-SAT
WINTER:	SAME

DAILY MOORAGE
SUMMER:	$.75 PER FT
WINTER:	CALL

MONTHLY MOORAGE
SUMMER:	$5.67- $7.60 /FT*
WINTER:	SAME

ON THE DOCK SERVICES
POWER	✓	LIGHTING	✓
30 AMP	✓	CABLE	✓
WATER	✓	PHONE	✓
GARBAGE	✓	DERRICK	
WASTE OIL	✓	LIVE ABRD	

Note: All marina information is subject to; change without notice, misinterpretation, misrepresentation and human error. In no way are the facilities mentioned in this book obligated to honor the rates and services listed. All information is given without guarantee. No part of this book is intended for navigation.

PUBLIC SERVICES

A: Located at Marina   B: Within Walking   C: Within 20 Miles   D: Not Available

	A	B	C	D
ACCOMMODATION			✓	
BAIT & TACKLE	✓			
BANK MACHINE			✓	
BOAT CHARTER			✓	
BOAT LAUNCH		✓		
BOAT RENTAL			✓	
CAMPING			✓	
CAR RENTAL			✓	
CHARTS	✓			
DIVE SHOP			✓	
FISH LICENSE		✓		

	A	B	C	D
GOLFING			✓	
GROCERY	✓			
HARDWARE			✓	
HOSPITAL			✓	
ICE	✓			
LAUNDRY	✓			
BOAT LIFT			✓	
LIQUOR STORE		✓		
24 HR PARKING	✓			
POST OFFICE			✓	
PROPANE			✓	

	A	B	C	D
PUB			✓	
PUMPOUT STN	✓			
RESTAURANT			✓	
RV FACILITIES			✓	
SHOPS / MALL			✓	
SHOWER	✓			
SWIM POOL			✓	
TAXI	✓			
TELEPHONE	✓			
TIDAL GRID				✓
TOILETS	✓			

NO FUEL FLOAT
HOURS SUMMER		DIESEL	
		GASOLINE	
HOURS WINTER		STOVE OIL	
		PROPANE	
TEL		AVIATION	

LOCALE

CITY MARINA
VHF:
TEL: 272-8348   CHART # 18445
FAX: 572-3656   N 47 15 W 122 26
Washington Area Codes 206, 360 & 509

1616 EAST "D" ST.
TACOMA, WA.
98421

GENERAL

OFFICE HOURS

SUMMER:	9 AM - 5 PM M - F
WINTER:	SAME

DAILY MOORAGE

SUMMER:	N/A
WINTER:	N/A

MONTHLY MOORAGE

SUMMER:	$3.85 PER FT
WINTER:	PLUS POWER

VISA   MasterCard
[ ]   DISCOVER

ON THE DOCK SERVICES

POWER	✓	LIGHTING	✓
30 AMP	✓	CABLE	
WATER	✓	PHONE	✓
GARBAGE	✓	DERRICK	✓
WASTE OIL	✓	LIVE ABRD	✓

WHARVES\FLOATS   20' TO 60' SLIPS

Note: All marina information is subject to; change without notice, misinterpretation, misrepresentation and human error. In no way are the facilities mentioned in this book obligated to honor the rates and services listed. All information is given without guarantee. No part of this book is intended for navigation.

PUBLIC SERVICES

A: Located at Marina   B: Within Walking   C: Within 20 Miles   D: Not Available

	A	B	C	D
ACCOMMODATION		✓		
BAIT & TACKLE		✓		
BANK MACHINE		✓		
BOAT CHARTER		✓		
BOAT LAUNCH		✓		
BOAT RENTAL		✓		
CAMPING			✓	
CAR RENTAL		✓		
CHARTS		✓		
DIVE SHOP			✓	
FISH LICENSE		✓		

	A	B	C	D
GOLFING			✓	
GROCERY	✓			
HARDWARE		✓		
HOSPITAL		✓		
ICE	✓			
LAUNDRY	✓			
BOAT LIFT		✓		
LIQUOR STORE	✓			
24 HR PARKING	✓			
POST OFFICE	✓			
PROPANE		✓		

	A	B	C	D
PUB		✓		
PUMPOUT STN		✓		
RESTAURANT	✓			
RV FACILITIES			✓	
SHOPS / MALL		✓		
SHOWER	✓			
SWIM POOL			✓	
TAXI	✓			
TELEPHONE	✓			
TIDAL GRID				✓
TOILETS	✓			

HOURS SUMMER

HOURS WINTER

TEL

NO FUEL FLOAT

DIESEL	
GASOLINE	
STOVE OIL	
PROPANE	
AVIATION	

TACOMA

LOCALE

CITY VIEW MARINA
VHF:
TEL: 572-3120
FAX: 838-2280
Washington Area Codes 206, 360 & 509

CHART # 18445
N 47 15 W 122 26

1811 DOCK STREET
5628 MARINE VIEW DR.
TACOMA, WA.
98422

GENERAL

OFFICE HOURS
SUMMER:	BY APPOINTMENT
WINTER:	ONLY

DAILY MOORAGE
SUMMER:	N/A
WINTER:	N/A

MONTHLY MOORAGE
SUMMER:	$4.20- 4.50 PER FT
WINTER:	SAME

ON THE DOCK SERVICES
POWER	✓	LIGHTING	
30 AMP	✓	CABLE	
WATER	✓	PHONE	✓
GARBAGE	✓	DERRICK	
WASTE OIL		LIVE ABRD	✓

Note: All marina information is subject to; change without notice, misinterpretation, misrepresentation and human error. In no way are the facilities mentioned in this book obligated to honor the rates and services listed. All information is given without guarantee. No part of this book is intended for navigation.

PUBLIC SERVICES

A: Located at Marina   B: Within Walking   C: Within 20 Miles   D: Not Available

	A	B	C	D
ACCOMMODATION		✓		
BAIT & TACKLE		✓		
BANK MACHINE		✓		
BOAT CHARTER		✓		
BOAT LAUNCH		✓		
BOAT RENTAL			✓	
CAMPING			✓	
CAR RENTAL		✓		
CHARTS			✓	
DIVE SHOP			✓	
FISH LICENSE		✓		

	A	B	C	D
GOLFING			✓	
GROCERY		✓		
HARDWARE		✓		
HOSPITAL		✓		
ICE		✓		
LAUNDRY		✓		
BOAT LIFT		✓		
LIQUOR STORE		✓		
24 HR PARKING	✓			
POST OFFICE		✓		
PROPANE			✓	

	A	B	C	D
PUB		✓		
PUMPOUT STN		✓		
RESTAURANT		✓		
RV FACILITIES			✓	
SHOPS / MALL		✓		
SHOWER		✓		
SWIM POOL			✓	
TAXI		✓		
TELEPHONE		✓		
TIDAL GRID				✓
TOILETS	✓			

HOURS SUMMER	
HOURS WINTER	
TEL	

NO FUEL FLOAT

DIESEL	
GASOLINE	
STOVE OIL	
PROPANE	
AVIATION	

TACOMA

LOCALE

CROW'S NEST MARINA
VHF:
TEL: 272-2827   CHART # 18445
FAX: 954-3752   N 47 17 W 122 25
Washington Area Codes 206, 360 & 509

5410 MARINE VIEW DRIVE
TACOMA, WA.
98422

GENERAL

OFFICE HOURS

SUMMER:	M-F 9-5:30 SAT 10-2
WINTER:	M WF 9-5:30 S 10-2

DAILY MOORAGE

SUMMER:	< 32' $10, 36' >$15
WINTER:	SAME

MONTHLY MOORAGE

SUMMER:	$5.00 PER FT
WINTER:	PLUS SERVICES

VISA   MasterCard
    DISCOVER

ON THE DOCK SERVICES

POWER	✓	LIGHTING	✓
30 AMP	✓	CABLE	✓
WATER	✓	PHONE	✓
GARBAGE	✓	DERRICK	
WASTE OIL		LIVE ABRD	✓

WHARVES\FLOATS   28' - 70' SLIPS

Note: All marina information is subject to; change without notice, misinterpretation, misrepresentation and human error. In no way are the facilities mentioned in this book obligated to honor the rates and services listed. All information is given without guarantee. No part of this book is intended for navigation.

PUBLIC SERVICES

A: Located at Marina   B: Within Walking   C: Within 20 Miles   D: Not Available

	A	B	C	D
ACCOMMODATION			✓	
BAIT & TACKLE		✓		
BANK MACHINE			✓	
BOAT CHARTER	✓			
BOAT LAUNCH		✓		
BOAT RENTAL				
CAMPING			✓	
CAR RENTAL			✓	
CHARTS			✓	
DIVE SHOP			✓	
FISH LICENSE			✓	

	A	B	C	D
GOLFING			✓	
GROCERY			✓	
HARDWARE			✓	
HOSPITAL			✓	
ICE			✓	
LAUNDRY	✓			
BOAT LIFT	✓			
LIQUOR STORE			✓	
24 HR PARKING	✓			
POST OFFICE	✓			
PROPANE			✓	

	A	B	C	D
PUB			✓	
PUMPOUT STN	✓			
RESTAURANT			✓	
RV FACILITIES			✓	
SHOPS / MALL			✓	
SHOWER	✓			
SWIM POOL			✓	
TAXI	✓			
TELEPHONE	✓			
TIDAL GRID				✓
TOILETS	✓			

HOURS SUMMER

HOURS WINTER

TEL

NO FUEL FLOAT

DIESEL	
GASOLINE	
STOVE OIL	
PROPANE	
AVIATION	

162

TACOMA

LOCALE

DAY ISLAND MARINA INC.
VHF:
TEL: 564-0211   CHART # 18445
FAX: 565-2869   N 47 14 W 122 33
Washington Area Codes 206, 360 & 509

9023 W 19TH ST.
TACOMA, WA.
98466

GENERAL

OFFICE HOURS
SUMMER:	M-S 9-5, SUN 9-4
WINTER:	SAME

DAILY MOORAGE
SUMMER:	NO TRANSIENT
WINTER:	SAME

MONTHLY MOORAGE
SUMMER:	VARIES
WINTER:	WITH SLIP

VISA — YES   MasterCard — YES
DISCOVER

ON THE DOCK SERVICES
POWER	✓	LIGHTING	✓
30 AMP		CABLE	
WATER	✓	PHONE	
GARBAGE	✓	DERRICK	
WASTE OIL	✓	LIVE ABRD	

Note: All marina information is subject to; change without notice, misinterpretation, misrepresentation and human error. In no way are the facilities mentioned in this book obligated to honor the rates and services listed. All information is given without guarantee. No part of this book is intended for navigation.

PUBLIC SERVICES

A: Located at Marina   B: Within Walking   C: Within 20 Miles   D: Not Available

	A	B	C	D		A	B	C	D		A	B	C	D
ACCOMMODATION			✓		GOLFING			✓		PUB		✓		
BAIT & TACKLE		✓			GROCERY		✓			PUMPOUT STN			✓	
BANK MACHINE			✓		HARDWARE		✓			RESTAURANT		✓		
BOAT CHARTER			✓		HOSPITAL			✓		RV FACILITIES			✓	
BOAT LAUNCH		✓			ICE		✓			SHOPS / MALL			✓	
BOAT RENTAL			✓		LAUNDRY			✓		SHOWER			✓	
CAMPING			✓		BOAT LIFT	✓				SWIM POOL			✓	
CAR RENTAL			✓		LIQUOR STORE		✓			TAXI	✓			
CHARTS		✓			24 HR PARKING	✓				TELEPHONE	✓			
DIVE SHOP			✓		POST OFFICE			✓		TIDAL GRID			✓	
FISH LICENSE		✓			PROPANE					TOILETS	✓			

HOURS SUMMER		DIESEL
	NO FUEL FLOAT	GASOLINE
HOURS WINTER		STOVE OIL
		PROPANE
TEL		AVIATION

DRY AND WET STORAGE.
SEA RAY BOAT SALES , TRAILERS, SERVICE
FOR MERCRUISER STERN DRIVES.

TACOMA

LOCALE

DAY ISLAND YACHT HARBOR
VHF:
TEL: 565-4814   CHART # 18445
FAX: 565-1278   N 47 14 W 122 33
Washington Area Codes 206, 360 & 509

1855 DAY ISLAND BLVD. W
TACOMA, WA.
98466

GENERAL

OFFICE HOURS

SUMMER:	8:30-5 M-F 9:30-3 S T
WINTER:	8:30AM - 5PM M-F

DAILY MOORAGE

SUMMER:	NO TRANSIENT
WINTER:	SAME

MONTHLY MOORAGE

SUMMER:	LEASED
WINTER:	MOORAGE

VISA   MasterCard
[ ]   DISCOVER

ON THE DOCK SERVICES

POWER	✓	LIGHTING	✓
30 AMP	✓	CABLE	
WATER	✓	PHONE	
GARBAGE	✓	DERRICK	✓
WASTE OIL		LIVE ABRD	

Note: All marina information is subject to; change without notice, misinterpretation, misrepresentation and human error. In no way are the facilities mentioned in this book obligated to honor the rates and services listed. All information is given without guarantee. No part of this book is intended for navigation.

PUBLIC SERVICES

A: Located at Marina   B: Within Walking   C: Within 20 Miles   D: Not Available

	A	B	C	D
ACCOMMODATION			✓	
BAIT & TACKLE			✓	
BANK MACHINE			✓	
BOAT CHARTER			✓	
BOAT LAUNCH			✓	
BOAT RENTAL			✓	
CAMPING			✓	
CAR RENTAL			✓	
CHARTS			✓	
DIVE SHOP			✓	
FISH LICENSE			✓	

	A	B	C	D
GOLFING			✓	
GROCERY		✓		
HARDWARE	✓			
HOSPITAL			✓	
ICE			✓	
LAUNDRY			✓	
BOAT LIFT	✓			
LIQUOR STORE			✓	
24 HR PARKING	✓			
POST OFFICE			✓	
PROPANE			✓	

	A	B	C	D
PUB			✓	
PUMPOUT STN			✓	
RESTAURANT			✓	
RV FACILITIES			✓	
SHOPS / MALL			✓	
SHOWER			✓	
SWIM POOL			✓	
TAXI			✓	
TELEPHONE			✓	
TIDAL GRID			✓	
TOILETS			✓	

COVERED MOORAGE, PRIVATELY OWNED
BOATHOUSES.
PHONES, TOILETS ETC. AVAILABLE DURING
OFFICE HOURS.
SHALLOW HARBOR - SAILBOATS SHOULD
WATCH TIDES.

HOURS SUMMER
HOURS WINTER
TEL

NO FUEL FLOAT

DIESEL
GASOLINE
STOVE OIL
PROPANE
AVIATION

164

TACOMA

LOCALE

JOHNNY'S DOCK
VHF:
TEL: 627-3186   CHART # 18445
FAX: N 47 15 W 122 26
Washington Area Codes 206, 360 & 509

1900 EAST "D" ST.
TACOMA , WA.
98421

GENERAL

OFFICE HOURS
SUMMER:	10-9 M-F 10-10 S-S
WINTER:	SAME

DAILY MOORAGE
SUMMER:	$.75 PER FT
WINTER:	SAME

MONTHLY MOORAGE
SUMMER:	$4.25 PER FT
WINTER:	PLUS SERVICES

VISA	YES	MasterCard	YES
	YES	DISCOVER	YES

ON THE DOCK SERVICES
POWER	✓	LIGHTING	
30 AMP	✓	CABLE	
WATER	✓	PHONE	✓
GARBAGE	✓	DERRICK	
WASTE OIL		LIVE ABRD	✓

Note: All marina information is subject to; change without notice, misinterpretation, misrepresentation and human error. In no way are the facilities mentioned in this book obligated to honor the rates and services listed. All information is given without guarantee. No part of this book is intended for navigation.

PUBLIC SERVICES

A: Located at Marina   B: Within Walking   C: Within 20 Miles   D: Not Available

	A	B	C	D
ACCOMMODATION		✓		
BAIT & TACKLE		✓		
BANK MACHINE		✓		
BOAT CHARTER			✓	
BOAT LAUNCH	✓			
BOAT RENTAL	✓			
CAMPING			✓	
CAR RENTAL		✓		
CHARTS		✓		
DIVE SHOP			✓	
FISH LICENSE		✓		

	A	B	C	D
GOLFING			✓	
GROCERY		✓		
HARDWARE		✓		
HOSPITAL		✓		
ICE		✓		
LAUNDRY		✓		
BOAT LIFT		✓		
LIQUOR STORE		✓		
24 HR PARKING	✓			
POST OFFICE		✓		
PROPANE		✓		

	A	B	C	D
PUB	✓			
PUMPOUT STN		✓		
RESTAURANT	✓			
RV FACILITIES			✓	
SHOPS / MALL		✓		
SHOWER		✓		
SWIM POOL			✓	
TAXI	✓			
TELEPHONE	✓			
TIDAL GRID				✓
TOILETS	✓			

HOURS SUMMER	NO FUEL FLOAT	DIESEL	
		GASOLINE	
HOURS WINTER		STOVE OIL	
		PROPANE	
TEL		AVIATION	

"JOHNNY'S DOCK RESTAURANT " - TACOMA'S ORIGINAL WATERFRONT RESTAURANT EST. 1955 ON THE FOSS WATERWAY ACROSS FROM DOWNTOWN. BREAKFAST, LUNCH AND DINNER SERVED.

TACOMA

|---|---|
NARROWS MARINA	9007 S 19TH ST.
VHF:	1912 - 64TH AVE W
TEL: 565-9790 CHART # 18445	TACOMA, WA.
FAX: N 47 14 W 122 33	98466
Washington Area Codes 206, 360 & 509	

LOCALE

GENERAL

OFFICE HOURS
SUMMER:	5:30 AM - 7 PM
WINTER:	6 AM - 7 PM

DAILY MOORAGE
SUMMER:	NO TRANSIENT
WINTER:	SAME

MONTHLY MOORAGE
SUMMER:	SEE COMMENTS
WINTER:	THIS PAGE

VISA YES   MasterCard YES
          DISCOVER YES

ON THE DOCK SERVICES
POWER	✓	LIGHTING	✓
30 AMP	✓	CABLE	
WATER	✓	PHONE	✓
GARBAGE	✓	DERRICK	
WASTE OIL		LIVE ABRD	

Note: All marina information is subject to; change without notice, misinterpretation, misrepresentation and human error. In no way are the facilities mentioned in this book obligated to honor the rates and services listed. All information is given without guarantee. No part of this book is intended for navigation.

PUBLIC SERVICES

A: Located at Marina   B: Within Walking   C: Within 20 Miles   D: Not Available

	A	B	C	D
ACCOMMODATION		✓		
BAIT & TACKLE	✓			
BANK MACHINE		✓		
BOAT CHARTER		✓		
BOAT LAUNCH	✓			
BOAT RENTAL		✓		
CAMPING		✓		
CAR RENTAL		✓		
CHARTS	✓			
DIVE SHOP		✓		
FISH LICENSE	✓			

	A	B	C	D
GOLFING			✓	
GROCERY			✓	
HARDWARE	✓			
HOSPITAL			✓	
ICE	✓			
LAUNDRY			✓	
BOAT LIFT	✓			
LIQUOR STORE	✓			
24 HR PARKING	✓			
POST OFFICE			✓	
PROPANE			✓	

	A	B	C	D
PUB		✓		
PUMPOUT STN			✓	
RESTAURANT		✓		
RV FACILITIES			✓	
SHOPS / MALL			✓	
SHOWER			✓	
SWIM POOL			✓	
TAXI	✓			
TELEPHONE	✓			
TIDAL GRID	✓			
TOILETS	✓			

LAUNCH RAMP $6.00 WEEKDAYS
$10.00 WEEKENDS

STORAGE GARAGE $.50 PER SQ. FT.
WAREHOUSE $40 -$90 PER MONTH
BOATSHEDS $6.50 PER FT.
OWNER BOATHOUSES $5.50 PER FT.

CHEVRON
HOURS SUMMER		DIESEL	✓
5:30 AM - 7 PM	MARINE	GASOLINE	✓
HOURS WINTER		STOVE OIL	
6 AM - 7 PM		PROPANE	
TEL 564-4222		AVIATION	

TACOMA

OLE & CHARLIE'S MARINAS

VHF:
TEL: 272-1173
FAX:
Washington Area Codes 206, 360 & 509

CHART # 18445
N 47 17 W 122 24

4224 MARINE VIEW DRIVE
TACOMA, WA.
98422

GENERAL

OFFICE HOURS

SUMMER:	M - F 8-6, S - S 8-8
WINTER:	OCT-APR 9-5 7DAY

DAILY MOORAGE

SUMMER:	< 20' $7, 21'-26' $10
WINTER:	SAME

MONTHLY MOORAGE

SUMMER:	$100 - $140 OPEN
WINTER:	$140-415 COVERED

ON THE DOCK SERVICES

POWER	✓	LIGHTING	✓
30 AMP		CABLE	
WATER	✓	PHONE	
GARBAGE	✓	DERRICK	
WASTE OIL	✓	LIVE ABRD	

Note: All marina information is subject to; change without notice, misinterpretation, misrepresentation and human error. In no way are the facilities mentioned in this book obligated to honor the rates and services listed. All information is given without guarantee. No part of this book is intended for navigation.

A: Located at Marina   B: Within Walking   C: Within 20 Miles   D: Not Available

PUBLIC SERVICES

	A	B	C	D
ACCOMMODATION			✓	
BAIT & TACKLE	✓			
BANK MACHINE			✓	
BOAT CHARTER		✓		
BOAT LAUNCH	✓			
BOAT RENTAL		✓		
CAMPING			✓	
CAR RENTAL			✓	
CHARTS		✓		
DIVE SHOP			✓	
FISH LICENSE		✓		

	A	B	C	D
GOLFING			✓	
GROCERY	✓			
HARDWARE			✓	
HOSPITAL			✓	
ICE	✓			
LAUNDRY			✓	
BOAT LIFT		✓		
LIQUOR STORE			✓	
24 HR PARKING	✓			
POST OFFICE			✓	
PROPANE			✓	

	A	B	C	D
PUB		✓		
PUMPOUT STN		✓		
RESTAURANT		✓		
RV FACILITIES			✓	
SHOPS / MALL			✓	
SHOWER			✓	
SWIM POOL			✓	
TAXI	✓			
TELEPHONE	✓			
TIDAL GRID				✓
TOILETS	✓			

DRY STORAGE AND LOCKERS.

HOURS SUMMER	NO FUEL FLOAT	DIESEL
		GASOLINE
HOURS WINTER		STOVE OIL
		PROPANE
TEL		AVIATION

TACOMA

LOCALE

PICK'S COVE MARINE CENTER

VHF:

TEL: 572-3625   CHART # 18445

FAX: 572-0503   N 47 15 W 122 26

Washington Area Codes 206, 360 & 509

1940 E. "D" ST.
TACOMA, WA.
98421

GENERAL

OFFICE HOURS

SUMMER:	8AM - 6PM DAILY
WINTER:	SAME

DAILY MOORAGE

SUMMER:	LIMIITED $.75/FT
WINTER:	SAME

MONTHLY MOORAGE

SUMMER:	VARIES
WINTER:	VARIES

VISA	YES	MasterCard	YES
	YES	DISCOVER	YES

ON THE DOCK SERVICES

POWER	✓	LIGHTING	✓
30 AMP	✓	CABLE	
WATER	✓	PHONE	✓
GARBAGE	✓	DERRICK	✓
WASTE OIL	✓	LIVE ABRD	

WHARVES\FLOATS   34' TO 50' SLIPS

Note: All marina information is subject to; change without notice, misinterpretation, misrepresentation and human error. In no way are the facilities mentioned in this book obligated to honor the rates and services listed. All information is given without guarantee. No part of this book is intended for navigation.

PUBLIC SERVICES

A: Located at Marina   B: Within Walking   C: Within 20 Miles   D: Not Available

	A	B	C	D
ACCOMMODATION		✓		
BAIT & TACKLE		✓		
BANK MACHINE		✓		
BOAT CHARTER		✓		
BOAT LAUNCH	✓			
BOAT RENTAL			✓	
CAMPING			✓	
CAR RENTAL		✓		
CHARTS	✓			
DIVE SHOP			✓	
FISH LICENSE			✓	

	A	B	C	D
GOLFING			✓	
GROCERY		✓		
HARDWARE	✓			
HOSPITAL			✓	
ICE	✓			
LAUNDRY	✓			
BOAT LIFT	✓			
LIQUOR STORE			✓	
24 HR PARKING	✓			
POST OFFICE		✓		
PROPANE	✓			

	A	B	C	D
PUB		✓		
PUMPOUT STN	✓			
RESTAURANT		✓		
RV FACILITIES			✓	
SHOPS / MALL		✓		
SHOWER	✓			
SWIM POOL			✓	
TAXI	✓			
TELEPHONE	✓			
TIDAL GRID				✓
TOILETS	✓			

HOURS SUMMER	**NO FUEL FLOAT**	DIESEL	
HOURS WINTER		GASOLINE	
		STOVE OIL	
		PROPANE	
TEL		AVIATION	

168

TACOMA

LOCALE

POINT DEFIANCE BOATHOUSE MARINA
VHF:
TEL: 591-5325   CHART # 18445
FAX: N 47 18 W 122 30
Washington Area Codes 206, 360 & 509

5912 N WATERFRONT DR.
5400 N PEARL DR. BOX 8
TACOMA, WA.
98407

GENERAL

OFFICE HOURS

SUMMER:	5AM - 9PM
WINTER:	6AM - 6PM

DAILY MOORAGE

SUMMER:	$6.00 - $10.00
WINTER:	SAME

MONTHLY MOORAGE

SUMMER:	N/A
WINTER:	N/A

 YES   YES

ON THE DOCK SERVICES

POWER		LIGHTING	
30 AMP		CABLE	
WATER	✓	PHONE	
GARBAGE		DERRICK	
WASTE OIL		LIVE ABRD	

WHARVES\FLOATS   60' OVERNIGHT

Note: All marina information is subject to; change without notice, misinterpretation, misrepresentation and human error. In no way are the facilities mentioned in this book obligated to honor the rates and services listed. All information is given without guarantee. No part of this book is intended for navigation.

PUBLIC SERVICES

A: Located at Marina   B: Within Walking   C: Within 20 Miles   D: Not Available

	A	B	C	D		A	B	C	D		A	B	C	D
ACCOMMODATION			✓		GOLFING			✓		PUB		✓		
BAIT & TACKLE	✓				GROCERY	✓				PUMPOUT STN	✓			
BANK MACHINE			✓		HARDWARE			✓		RESTAURANT	✓			
BOAT CHARTER			✓		HOSPITAL			✓		RV FACILITIES			✓	
BOAT LAUNCH	✓				ICE	✓				SHOPS / MALL			✓	
BOAT RENTAL	✓				LAUNDRY		✓			SHOWER			✓	
CAMPING			✓		BOAT LIFT			✓		SWIM POOL			✓	
CAR RENTAL			✓		LIQUOR STORE			✓		TAXI	✓			
CHARTS	✓				24 HR PARKING	✓				TELEPHONE	✓			
DIVE SHOP			✓		POST OFFICE			✓		TIDAL GRID				✓
FISH LICENSE	✓				PROPANE			✓		TOILETS	✓			

CHEVRON

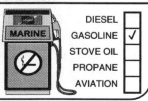

HOURS SUMMER
5AM - 9PM

HOURS WINTER
6AM - 6PM

TEL   591-5325

DIESEL	
GASOLINE	✓
STOVE OIL	
PROPANE	
AVIATION	

TOURIST DESTINATION IN POINT DEFIANCE PARK. FIFTY FREE MOORING BUOYS ALONG SHORELINE. LIMITED OVERNIGHT - MAX 72 HOURS. PUBLIC FISHING PIER. DRY BOAT STORAGE FOR 320 BOATS UP TO 17'.

PRE MIX AVAILABLE.

LOCALE

TOTEM MARINA

VHF:

TEL: 272-4404   CHART # 18445

FAX: N 47 15 W 122 26

Washington Area Codes 206, 360 & 509

821 DOCK STREET
TACOMA, WA.
98402

GENERAL

OFFICE HOURS

| SUMMER: | 9AM- 5PM M-F |
| WINTER: | SAME |

DAILY MOORAGE

| SUMMER: | $.50 PER FT |
| WINTER: | SAME |

MONTHLY MOORAGE

| SUMMER: | VARIES BY LENGTH |
| WINTER: | SAME |

VISA ☐   MasterCard ☐

☐   DISCOVER ☐

ON THE DOCK SERVICES

POWER	✓	LIGHTING	✓
30 AMP	✓	CABLE	
WATER	✓	PHONE	✓
GARBAGE	✓	DERRICK	
WASTE OIL	✓	LIVE ABRD	✓

WHARVES\FLOATS   460 SLIPS

Note: All marina information is subject to; change without notice, misinterpretation, misrepresentation and human error. In no way are the facilities mentioned in this book obligated to honor the rates and services listed. All information is given without guarantee. No part of this book is intended for navigation.

PUBLIC SERVICES

A: Located at Marina   B: Within Walking   C: Within 20 Miles   D: Not Available

	A	B	C	D		A	B	C	D		A	B	C	D
ACCOMMODATION		✓			GOLFING			✓		PUB	✓			
BAIT & TACKLE	✓				GROCERY	✓				PUMPOUT STN	✓			
BANK MACHINE		✓			HARDWARE		✓			RESTAURANT	✓			
BOAT CHARTER	✓				HOSPITAL		✓			RV FACILITIES			✓	
BOAT LAUNCH	✓				ICE	✓				SHOPS / MALL		✓		
BOAT RENTAL			✓		LAUNDRY	✓				SHOWER	✓			
CAMPING			✓		BOAT LIFT	✓				SWIM POOL			✓	
CAR RENTAL			✓		LIQUOR STORE	✓				TAXI	✓			
CHARTS	✓				24 HR PARKING	✓				TELEPHONE	✓			
DIVE SHOP		✓			POST OFFICE	✓				TIDAL GRID				✓
FISH LICENSE	✓				PROPANE		✓			TOILETS	✓			

WALKING DISTANCE TO TACOMA DOME AND DOWNTOWN.
STORE OPEN 7 DAYS 6 AM - 6 PM DURING THE SUMMER - SHORTER WINTER HOURS.

HOURS SUMMER	**NO**	DIESEL	☐
	FUEL	GASOLINE	☐
HOURS WINTER	**FLOAT**	STOVE OIL	☐
		PROPANE	☐
TEL		AVIATION	☐

TACOMA

LOCALE

TYEE MARINA
VHF:
TEL: 383-5321   CHART # 18445
FAX: 838-2280   N 47 17 W 122 25
Washington Area Codes 206, 360 & 509

5618 MARINE VIEW DRIVE
TACOMA, WA.
98422

GENERAL

OFFICE HOURS
SUMMER:	T - SAT 10 - 4:30
WINTER:	SAME

DAILY MOORAGE
SUMMER:	NO VISITOR
WINTER:	MOORAGE

MONTHLY MOORAGE
SUMMER:	$4.10 - $5.35 /FT
WINTER:	SAME

ON THE DOCK SERVICES
POWER	✓	LIGHTING	✓
30 AMP	✓	CABLE	✓
WATER	✓	PHONE	✓
GARBAGE	✓	DERRICK	
WASTE OIL		LIVE ABRD	

WHARVES\FLOATS   20' UP TO 60'

Note: All marina information is subject to; change without notice, misinterpretation, misrepresentation and human error. In no way are the facilities mentioned in this book obligated to honor the rates and services listed. All information is given without guarantee. No part of this book is intended for navigation.

PUBLIC SERVICES

A: Located at Marina   B: Within Walking   C: Within 20 Miles   D: Not Available

	A	B	C	D
ACCOMMODATION			✓	
BAIT & TACKLE			✓	
BANK MACHINE			✓	
BOAT CHARTER			✓	
BOAT LAUNCH			✓	
BOAT RENTAL			✓	
CAMPING			✓	
CAR RENTAL			✓	
CHARTS			✓	
DIVE SHOP			✓	
FISH LICENSE			✓	

	A	B	C	D
GOLFING			✓	
GROCERY			✓	
HARDWARE			✓	
HOSPITAL			✓	
ICE			✓	
LAUNDRY			✓	
BOAT LIFT			✓	
LIQUOR STORE			✓	
24 HR PARKING	✓			
POST OFFICE			✓	
PROPANE			✓	

	A	B	C	D
PUB			✓	
PUMPOUT STN	✓			
RESTAURANT			✓	
RV FACILITIES			✓	
SHOPS / MALL			✓	
SHOWER	✓			
SWIM POOL			✓	
TAXI	✓			
TELEPHONE	✓			
TIDAL GRID				✓
TOILETS	✓			

HOURS SUMMER	NO FUEL FLOAT	DIESEL	
		GASOLINE	
HOURS WINTER		STOVE OIL	
		PROPANE	
TEL		AVIATION	

VASHON ISLAND

QUARTERMASTER MARINA

VHF:
TEL: 463-3624
FAX:
Washington Area Codes 206, 360 & 509

CHART # 18445
N 47 22.50 W 122 28

23824 VASHON HWY S.W.
P.O. BOX 13097
BURTON, WA.
98013

LOCALE

GENERAL

OFFICE HOURS

SUMMER:	9AM - 5PM M - SAT
WINTER:	SAME

DAILY MOORAGE

SUMMER:	$15.00 PER DAY
WINTER:	SAME

MONTHLY MOORAGE

SUMMER:	$6.00 PER FT
WINTER:	SAME

VISA   MasterCard

DISCOVER

ON THE DOCK SERVICES

POWER	✓	LIGHTING	✓
30 AMP		CABLE	
WATER	✓	PHONE	✓
GARBAGE	✓	DERRICK	
WASTE OIL		LIVE ABRD	✓

Note: All marina information is subject to; change without notice, misinterpretation, misrepresentation and human error. In no way are the facilities mentioned in this book obligated to honor the rates and services listed. All information is given without guarantee. No part of this book is intended for navigation.

PUBLIC SERVICES

A: Located at Marina   B: Within Walking   C: Within 20 Miles   D: Not Available

	A	B	C	D
ACCOMMODATION		✓		
BAIT & TACKLE		✓		
BANK MACHINE			✓	
BOAT CHARTER			✓	
BOAT LAUNCH	✓			
BOAT RENTAL			✓	
CAMPING			✓	
CAR RENTAL			✓	
CHARTS			✓	
DIVE SHOP			✓	
FISH LICENSE			✓	

	A	B	C	D
GOLFING			✓	
GROCERY		✓		
HARDWARE		✓		
HOSPITAL			✓	
ICE		✓		
LAUNDRY			✓	
BOAT LIFT	✓			
LIQUOR STORE			✓	
24 HR PARKING	✓			
POST OFFICE		✓		
PROPANE			✓	

	A	B	C	D
PUB			✓	
PUMPOUT STN			✓	
RESTAURANT		✓		
RV FACILITIES				✓
SHOPS / MALL			✓	
SHOWER			✓	
SWIM POOL			✓	
TAXI	✓			
TELEPHONE		✓		
TIDAL GRID				✓
TOILETS		✓		

MARINA IS CURRENTLY UNDERGOING UPGRADES. NEW FACILITIES SHOULD INCLUDE SHOWERS, BATHROOMS, CHARTERS, RENTALS, ETC.

HOURS SUMMER

HOURS WINTER

TEL

NO FUEL FLOAT

DIESEL	
GASOLINE	
STOVE OIL	
PROPANE	
AVIATION	

WHIDBEY ISLAND

CORNET BAY MARINA AT DECEPTION PASS

VHF: 16
TEL: 675-5411   CHART # 18423
FAX: 679-4783   N 48 24 W 122 38
Washington Area Codes 206, 360 & 509

5191 CORNET BAY RD.
OAK HARBOUR, WA.
98277

GENERAL

OFFICE HOURS

SUMMER:	8AM - 6PM DAILY
WINTER:	9AM - 4PM DAILY

DAILY MOORAGE

SUMMER:	$.65 PER FT
WINTER:	SAME

MONTHLY MOORAGE

SUMMER:	VARIES
WINTER:	SAME

VISA	YES	MasterCard	YES
	YES	DISCOVER	YES

ON THE DOCK SERVICES

POWER	✓	LIGHTING	✓
30 AMP	✓	CABLE	
WATER	✓	PHONE	
GARBAGE	✓	DERRICK	
WASTE OIL	✓	LIVE ABRD	

Note: All marina information is subject to; change without notice, misrepresentation, misrepresentation and human error. In no way are the facilities mentioned in this book obligated to honor the rates and services listed. All information is given without guarantee. No part of this book is intended for navigation.

PUBLIC SERVICES

A: Located at Marina   B: Within Walking   C: Within 20 Miles   D: Not Available

	A	B	C	D
ACCOMMODATION			✓	
BAIT & TACKLE	✓			
BANK MACHINE			✓	
BOAT CHARTER			✓	
BOAT LAUNCH		✓		
BOAT RENTAL		✓		
CAMPING		✓		
CAR RENTAL			✓	
CHARTS	✓			
DIVE SHOP		✓		
FISH LICENSE	✓			

	A	B	C	D
GOLFING		✓		
GROCERY	✓			
HARDWARE	✓			
HOSPITAL			✓	
ICE	✓			
LAUNDRY		✓		
BOAT LIFT	✓			
LIQUOR STORE			✓	
24 HR PARKING	✓			
POST OFFICE			✓	
PROPANE	✓			

	A	B	C	D
PUB		✓		
PUMPOUT STN	✓			
RESTAURANT	✓			
RV FACILITIES	✓			
SHOPS / MALL			✓	
SHOWER	✓			
SWIM POOL			✓	
TAXI	✓			
TELEPHONE	✓			
TIDAL GRID				✓
TOILETS	✓			

TEXACO

HOURS SUMMER
8AM-6PM DAILY
HOURS WINTER
9AM-4PM DAILY
TEL   675-5411

DIESEL	✓
GASOLENE	✓
STOVE OIL	
PROPANE	✓
AVIATION	

WHIDBEY ISLAND

LOCALE

DECEPTION PASS STATE PARK

VHF:
TEL: 675-2417   CHART # 18423
FAX: N 48 24 W 122 38
Washington Area Codes 206, 360 & 509

5175 N. CORNET RD.
OAK HARBOR, WA.
98277

GENERAL

OFFICE HOURS
SUMMER:
WINTER:

DAILY MOORAGE
SUMMER:
WINTER:

MONTHLY MOORAGE
SUMMER:
WINTER:

VISA   *MasterCard*

   DISCOVER

ON THE DOCK SERVICES
POWER   LIGHTING
30 AMP   CABLE
WATER   PHONE
GARBAGE   DERRICK
WASTE OIL   LiVE ABRD

WHARVES\FLOATS   300 FT +

Note: All marina information is subject to; change without notice, misinterpretation, misrepresentation and human error. In no way are the facilities mentioned in this book obligated to honor the rates and services listed. All information is given without guarantee. No part of this book is intended for navigation.

PUBLIC SERVICES

A: Located at Marina   B: Within Walking   C: Within 20 Miles   D: Not Available

	A	B	C	D		A	B	C	D		A	B	C	D
ACCOMMODATION			✓		GOLFING	✓				PUB		✓		
BAIT & TACKLE		✓			GROCERY	✓				PUMPOUT STN	✓			
BANK MACHINE			✓		HARDWARE	✓				RESTAURANT		✓		
BOAT CHARTER			✓		HOSPITAL			✓		RV FACILITIES		✓		
BOAT LAUNCH	✓				ICE	✓				SHOPS / MALL			✓	
BOAT RENTAL		✓			LAUNDRY	✓				SHOWER	✓			
CAMPING		✓			BOAT LIFT	✓				SWIM POOL			✓	
CAR RENTAL			✓		LIQUOR STORE			✓		TAXI		✓		
CHARTS		✓			24 HR PARKING	✓				TELEPHONE		✓		
DIVE SHOP		✓			POST OFFICE			✓		TIDAL GRID				✓
FISH LICENSE		✓			PROPANE	✓				TOILETS	✓			

LARGE BOAT LAUNCH AREA WITH PLENTY OF
PARKING FOR BOAT TRAILERS.

LOCATED NEXT TO CORNET BAY MARINA.

HOURS SUMMER

HOURS WINTER

TEL

NO FUEL FLOAT

DIESEL
GASOLINE
STOVE OIL
PROPANE
AVIATION

WHIDBEY ISLAND

OAK HARBOR MARINA

VHF: 16
TEL: 679-2628
FAX: 240-0603
Washington Area Codes 206, 360 & 509

CHART # 18423
N 48 17.12 W 122 38.03

8075 CATALINA DR
3075 300 AVE W
OAK HARBOR, WA.
98277

LOCALE

GENERAL

OFFICE HOURS

SUMMER:	8-6SU-TH 8-7F&ST
WINTER:	8AM - 5PM DAILY

DAILY MOORAGE

SUMMER:	$11.00-$40.00
WINTER:	SAME

MONTHLY MOORAGE

SUMMER:	$3.84-$4.47
WINTER:	SAME

VISA	YES	MasterCard	YES
	YES	DISCOVER	YES

ON THE DOCK SERVICES

POWER	✓	LIGHTING	✓
30 AMP	✓	CABLE	
WATER	✓	PHONE	
GARBAGE	✓	DERRICK	
WASTE OIL	✓	LIVE ABRD	✓

WHARVES\FLOATS   2000' PLUS GUEST

Note: All marina information is subject to; change without notice, misinterpretation, misrepresentation and human error. In no way are the facilities mentioned in this book obligated to honor the rates and services listed. All information is given without guarantee. No part of this book is intended for navigation.

PUBLIC SERVICES

A: Located at Marina   B: Within Walking   C: Within 20 Miles   D: Not Available

	A	B	C	D
ACCOMMODATION		✓		
BAIT & TACKLE		✓		
BANK MACHINE		✓		
BOAT CHARTER	✓			
BOAT LAUNCH	✓			
BOAT RENTAL				✓
CAMPING		✓		
CAR RENTAL		✓		
CHARTS	✓			
DIVE SHOP		✓		
FISH LICENSE	✓			

	A	B	C	D
GOLFING			✓	
GROCERY		✓		
HARDWARE	✓			
HOSPITAL			✓	
ICE	✓			
LAUNDRY		✓		
BOAT LIFT				✓
LIQUOR STORE			✓	
24 HR PARKING	✓			
POST OFFICE	✓			
PROPANE	✓			

	A	B	C	D
PUB		✓		
PUMPOUT STN	✓			
RESTAURANT		✓		
RV FACILITIES		✓		
SHOPS / MALL		✓		
SHOWER	✓			
SWIM POOL			✓	
TAXI	✓			
TELEPHONE	✓			
TIDAL GRID	✓			
TOILETS	✓			

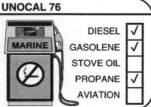

UNOCAL 76

HOURS SUMMER
8-5:3S-TH8-6:30F&S

HOURS WINTER
8-4:30 DAILY

TEL   679-4609

DIESEL	✓
GASOLENE	✓
STOVE OIL	
PROPANE	✓
AVIATION	

ANNUAL WHIDBEY ISLAND RACE WEEK IN JULY
NATIONAL / REGATTA.

BRITISH COLUMBIA WATERS

A selection of B. C. marinas, taken from
The Marina Handbook S.W. British Columbia Edition

This is but a small number of the many fine marinas and marine facilities located on British Columbia waters. From Victoria's inner harbour to uninhabited islands up north and the rugged west coast of Vancouver Island. These waters offer boaters the natural beauty, wildlife and marine facilities to enjoy safe boating adventures ***again and again.....***

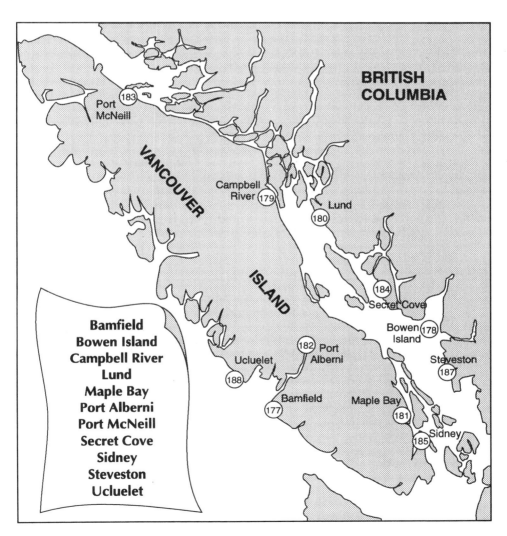

BRITISH
COLUMBIA

Port
McNeill (183)

VANCOUVER

Campbell
River (179)

Lund
(180)

ISLAND

(184)
Secret Cove

Bowen (178)
Island

Steveston
(187)

(182) Port
Alberni

Ucluelet
(188)

Bamfield
(177)

Maple Bay
(181)

(185) Sidney

Bamfield
Bowen Island
Campbell River
Lund
Maple Bay
Port Alberni
Port McNeill
Secret Cove
Sidney
Steveston
Ucluelet

BAMFIELD

LOCALE

FISHERIES & OCEANS SMALL CRAFT HRBS

VHF:
TEL: 728-3450   CHART # 3671, 3602
FAX: N 48 51 W 125 08
British Columbia Area Code: 604

BOX 31
BAMFIELD, B.C.
V0R 1B0

GENERAL

OFFICE HOURS

SUMMER:	ATTENDED
WINTER:	ATTENDED

DAILY MOORAGE

SUMMER:	$1.45 PER METRE
WINTER:	$1.45 PER METRE

MONTHLY MOORAGE

SUMMER:	$7.95 PER METRE
WINTER:	$7.95 PER METRE

ON THE DOCK SERVICES

POWER		LIGHTING	
30 AMP		CABLE	
WATER		PHONE	
GARBAGE		DERRICK	
WASTE OIL		LIVE ABRD	

Note: All marina information is subject to; change without notice, misinterpretation, misrepresentation and human error. In no way are the facilities mentioned in this book obligated to honor the rates and services listed. All information is given without guarantee. No part of this book is intended for navigation.

PUBLIC SERVICES

A: Located at Marina   B: Within Walking   C: Within 30 Km   D: Not Available

	A	B	C	D
ACCOMMODATION		✓		
BAIT & TACKLE		✓		
BANK MACHINE		✓		
BOAT CHARTER	✓			
BOAT LAUNCH		✓		
BOAT RENTAL				✓
CAMPING		✓		
CAR RENTAL				✓
CHARTS			✓	
DIVE SHOP		✓		
FISH LICENSE		✓		

	A	B	C	D
GOLFING				✓
GROCERY		✓		
HARDWARE			✓	
HOSPITAL		✓		
ICE		✓		
LAUNDRY			✓	
BOAT LIFT			✓	
LIQUOR STORE		✓		
24 HR PARKING		✓		
POST OFFICE		✓		
PROPANE		✓		

	A	B	C	D
PUB		✓		
PUMPOUT STN			✓	
RESTAURANT		✓		
RV FACILITIES			✓	
SHOPS / MALL			✓	
SHOWER		✓		
SWIM POOL				✓
TAXI	✓			
TELEPHONE	✓			
TIDAL GRID				✓
TOILETS				✓

ESSO - OSTROMS

HOURS SUMMER
6 AM - 10 PM
HOURS WINTER
9 AM - 6 PM
TEL   728-2050

DIESEL	✓
GASOLENE	✓
STOVE OIL	✓
PROPANE	
AVIATION	

CAUTION !

MARKED REEF LOCATED SOUTH EAST CORNER OF FACILITY, NOT VISIBLE AT HIGH TIDE. USE GOOD JUDGEMENT.

BOWEN ISLAND

LOCALE

UNION STEAMSHIP CO. MARINA

VHF: 68
TEL: 947-0707
FAX: 947-0708
British Columbia Area Code: 604

CHART # 3526, 3311
N 49 23 W 123 19

#1 GOVERNMENT ROAD
P.O. BOX 250
BOWEN ISLAND, B.C.
VON 1GO

GENERAL

OFFICE HOURS

SUMMER:	9 AM - 9 PM
WINTER:	10 AM - 5 PM

DAILY MOORAGE

SUMMER:	$.90 PER FT
WINTER:	$.40 PER FT

MONTHLY MOORAGE

SUMMER:	ON REQUEST
WINTER:	ON REQUEST

VISA	YES	MasterCard	YES
(ATM)	YES	DISCOVER	

ON THE DOCK SERVICES

POWER	✓	LIGHTING	✓
30 AMP	✓	CABLE	
WATER	✓	PHONE	
GARBAGE	✓	DERRICK	
WASTE OIL		LIVE ABRD	

Note: All marina information is subject to; change without notice, misinterpretation, misrepresentation and human error. In no way are the facilities mentioned in this book obligated to honor the rates and services listed. All information is given without guarantee. No part of this book is intended for navigation.

PUBLIC SERVICES

A: Located at Marina   B: Within Walking   C: Within 30 Km   D: Not Available

	A	B	C	D
ACCOMMODATION	✓			
BAIT & TACKLE	✓			
BANK MACHINE			✓	
BOAT CHARTER				✓
BOAT LAUNCH	✓			
BOAT RENTAL			✓	
CAMPING				✓
CAR RENTAL			✓	
CHARTS	✓			
DIVE SHOP			✓	
FISH LICENSE	✓			

	A	B	C	D
GOLFING			✓	
GROCERY		✓		
HARDWARE	✓			
HOSPITAL			✓	
ICE	✓			
LAUNDRY	✓			
BOAT LIFT			✓	
LIQUOR STORE		✓		
24 HR PARKING	✓			
POST OFFICE		✓		
PROPANE			✓	

	A	B	C	D
PUB	✓			
PUMPOUT STN	✓			
RESTAURANT	✓			
RV FACILITIES				✓
SHOPS / MALL			✓	
SHOWER	✓			
SWIM POOL			✓	
TAXI		✓		
TELEPHONE	✓			
TIDAL GRID			✓	
TOILETS	✓			

UNION STEAMSHIP CO. MARINA
SNUG COVE
BOWEN ISLAND, B.C.
ORIGINALLY ESTABLISHED 1889

HOURS SUMMER	DIESEL
	NO FUEL FLOAT GASOLINE
HOURS WINTER	STOVE OIL
	PROPANE
TEL	AVIATION

CAMPBELL RIVER

LOCALE

DISCOVERY HARBOUR MARINA
VHF: 73
TEL: 287-2614   CHART # 3312
FAX: 287-8939   N 50 2.11 W 125 14.63
British Columbia Area Code: 604

1400 WEIWAIKUM RD.
CAMPBELL RIVER, B.C.
V9W 5W8

GENERAL

OFFICE HOURS
SUMMER:	7 AM - 9 PM
WINTER:	8 AM - 4 PM

DAILY MOORAGE
SUMMER:	$.68 / FT
WINTER:	$.34 / FT

MONTHLY MOORAGE
SUMMER:	$.37 PER FT
WINTER:	1/12 OF YEARLY

VISA	YES	MasterCard	YES
		DISCOVER	

ON THE DOCK SERVICES
POWER	✓	LIGHTING	✓
30 AMP	✓	CABLE	
WATER	✓	PHONE	✓
GARBAGE	✓	DERRICK	
WASTE OIL		LIVE ABRD	

Note: All marina information is subject to; change without notice, misinterpretation, misrepresentation and human error. In no way are the facilities mentioned in this book obligated to honor the rates and services listed. All information is given without guarantee. No part of this book is intended for navigation.

PUBLIC SERVICES

A: Located at Marina   B: Within Walking   C: Within 30 Km   D: Not Available

	A	B	C	D		A	B	C	D		A	B	C	D
ACCOMMODATION		✓			GOLFING			✓		PUB		✓		
BAIT & TACKLE	✓				GROCERY		✓			PUMPOUT STN				✓
BANK MACHINE		✓			HARDWARE		✓			RESTAURANT		✓		
BOAT CHARTER	✓				HOSPITAL			✓		RV FACILITIES		✓		
BOAT LAUNCH		✓			ICE	✓				SHOPS / MALL		✓		
BOAT RENTAL	✓				LAUNDRY	✓				SHOWER	✓			
CAMPING		✓			BOAT LIFT			✓		SWIM POOL			✓	
CAR RENTAL	✓				LIQUOR STORE		✓			TAXI	✓			
CHARTS		✓			24 HR PARKING	✓				TELEPHONE	✓			
DIVE SHOP		✓			POST OFFICE		✓			TIDAL GRID		✓		
FISH LICENSE	✓				PROPANE		✓			TOILETS	✓			

ESSO

HOURS SUMMER
4:30 AM - 12:00 PM

HOURS WINTER
7:00 AM - 5:00 PM

TEL   287-3456

DIESEL	✓
GASOLENE	✓
STOVE OIL	✓
PROPANE	
AVIATION	

B.C. WATERS 🍁

GENERAL

OFFICE HOURS

SUMMER:	LEAVE MOORAGE
WINTER:	IN ENVELOPE

DAILY MOORAGE

SUMMER:	$1.28 PER METRE
WINTER:	$1.28 PER METRE

MONTHLY MOORAGE

SUMMER:	$9.45 PER METRE
WINTER:	$9.45 PER METRE

ON THE DOCK SERVICES

POWER		LIGHTING	
30 AMP		CABLE	
WATER	✓	PHONE	
GARBAGE		DERRICK	
WASTE OIL		LIVE ABRD	

Note: All marina information is subject to; change without notice, misinterpretation, misrepresentation and human error. In no way are the facilities mentioned in this book obligated to honor the rates and services listed. All information is given without guarantee. No part of this book is intended for navigation.

PUBLIC SERVICES

A: Located at Marina   B: Within Walking   C: Within 30 Km   D: Not Available

	A	B	C	D
ACCOMMODATION			✓	
BAIT & TACKLE			✓	
BANK MACHINE				✓
BOAT CHARTER			✓	
BOAT LAUNCH			✓	
BOAT RENTAL			✓	
CAMPING			✓	
CAR RENTAL				✓
CHARTS			✓	
DIVE SHOP			✓	
FISH LICENSE			✓	

	A	B	C	D
GOLFING				✓
GROCERY			✓	
HARDWARE			✓	
HOSPITAL			✓	
ICE			✓	
LAUNDRY			✓	
BOAT LIFT			✓	
LIQUOR STORE			✓	
24 HR PARKING			✓	
POST OFFICE			✓	
PROPANE			✓	

	A	B	C	D
PUB			✓	
PUMPOUT STN				✓
RESTAURANT			✓	
RV FACILITIES			✓	
SHOPS / MALL			✓	
SHOWER			✓	
SWIM POOL			✓	
TAXI			✓	
TELEPHONE			✓	
TIDAL GRID				✓
TOILETS			✓	

CAUTION !

BOATERS DROPPING ANCHOR BETWEEN THE HEAD OF FINN BAY AND LUND SHOULD BE CAUTIONED OF SEWER LINES LAID IN THE SEA BED.

USE OF FACILITIES IS ENCOURAGED.

ESSO

HOURS SUMMER
8 AM - 8 PM
HOURS WINTER
8 AM - 4 PM
TEL   483-3199

Esso

DIESEL	✓
GASOLENE	✓
STOVE OIL	
PROPANE	✓
AVIATION	

MAPLE BAY

LOCALE

MAPLE BAY MARINA
VHF: 68
TEL: 746-8482 CHART # 3313
FAX: 746-8490 N 48 47.75 W 123 35.95
British Columbia Area Code: 604

6145 GENOA BAY
DUNCAN, B.C.
V9L 1M3

GENERAL

OFFICE HOURS
SUMMER:	8 AM - 8 PM
WINTER:	9 AM - 5 PM

DAILY MOORAGE
SUMMER:	$.55 PER FT
WINTER:	$.55 PER FT

MONTHLY MOORAGE
SUMMER:	$3.75 PER SLIP FT
WINTER:	$3.75 PER SLIP FT

VISA	YES	MasterCard	YES
[logo]	YES	DISCOVER	

ON THE DOCK SERVICES
POWER	✓	LIGHTING	✓
30 AMP		CABLE	
WATER	✓	PHONE	
GARBAGE	✓	DERRICK	
WASTE OIL	✓	LIVE ABRD	✓

Note: All marina information is subject to; change without notice, misinterpretation, misrepresentation and human error. In no way are the facilities mentioned in this book obligated to honor the rates and services listed. All information is given without guarantee. No part of this book is intended for navigation.

PUBLIC SERVICES

A: Located at Marina B: Within Walking C: Within 30 Km D: Not Available

	A	B	C	D		A	B	C	D		A	B	C	D
ACCOMMODATION			✓		GOLFING			✓		PUB	✓			
BAIT & TACKLE	✓				GROCERY	✓				PUMPOUT STN				✓
BANK MACHINE	✓				HARDWARE	✓				RESTAURANT	✓			
BOAT CHARTER	✓				HOSPITAL			✓		RV FACILITIES			✓	
BOAT LAUNCH			✓		ICE	✓				SHOPS / MALL	✓			
BOAT RENTAL		✓			LAUNDRY	✓				SHOWER	✓			
CAMPING			✓		BOAT LIFT		✓			SWIM POOL				✓
CAR RENTAL		✓			LIQUOR STORE			✓		TAXI	✓			
CHARTS	✓				24 HR PARKING	✓				TELEPHONE	✓			
DIVE SHOP			✓		POST OFFICE			✓		TIDAL GRID			✓	
FISH LICENSE	✓				PROPANE	✓				TOILETS	✓			

INDEPENDENT

HOURS SUMMER	DIESEL	✓
8 AM - 8 PM	GASOLINE	✓
HOURS WINTER	STOVE OIL	
9 AM - 5 PM	PROPANE	✓
TEL 746-8482	AVIATION	

PORT ALBERNI

LOCALE

CHINA CREEK MARINA
VHF: 16
TEL: 723-9812   CHART # 3668
FAX: N 49 09 W 124 38
British Columbia Area Code: 604

C/O PORT ALBERNI HRB COM.
2750 HARBOUR RD.
PORT ALBERNI, B.C.
V9Y 7X2

GENERAL

OFFICE HOURS

SUMMER:	8 AM - 8 PM
WINTER:	8 AM - 4PM

DAILY MOORAGE

SUMMER:	VARIES BY
WINTER:	VESSEL LENGTH

MONTHLY MOORAGE

SUMMER:	$3.25 PER FT
WINTER:	$2.20 PER FT *

VISA   MasterCard
DISCOVER

ON THE DOCK SERVICES

POWER	✓	LIGHTING	✓
30 AMP		CABLE	
WATER	✓	PHONE	
GARBAGE	✓	DERRICK	
WASTE OIL	✓	LIVE ABRD	

Note: All marina information is subject to; change without notice, misinterpretation, misrepresentation and human error. In no way are the facilities mentioned in this book obligated to honor the rates and services listed. All information is given without guarantee. No part of this book is intended for navigation.

PUBLIC SERVICES

A: Located at Marina   B: Within Walking   C: Within 30 Km   D: Not Available

	A	B	C	D
ACCOMMODATION			✓	
BAIT & TACKLE	✓			
BANK MACHINE			✓	
BOAT CHARTER	✓			
BOAT LAUNCH	✓			
BOAT RENTAL	✓			
CAMPING	✓			
CAR RENTAL			✓	
CHARTS		✓		
DIVE SHOP		✓		
FISH LICENSE	✓			

	A	B	C	D
GOLFING			✓	
GROCERY	✓			
HARDWARE		✓		
HOSPITAL			✓	
ICE	✓			
LAUNDRY	✓			
BOAT LIFT			✓	
LIQUOR STORE			✓	
24 HR PARKING	✓			
POST OFFICE			✓	
PROPANE			✓	

	A	B	C	D
PUB			✓	
PUMPOUT STN				✓
RESTAURANT	✓			
RV FACILITIES	✓			
SHOPS / MALL				✓
SHOWER	✓			
SWIM POOL				✓
TAXI			✓	
TELEPHONE	✓			
TIDAL GRID				✓
TOILETS	✓			

LOCATED 10 MILES SOUTH OF PORT ALBERNI ON ALBERNI INLET. DESTINATION FISHING RESORT AND RV PARK.
ALL THE AMENITIES FOR THE TRAILER BOATER.

CHINA CREEK MARINA

HOURS SUMMER
8 AM - 8 PM
HOURS WINTER
8 AM - 4 PM
TEL   723-9812

MARINE

DIESEL	✓
GASOLINE	✓
STOVE OIL	
PROPANE	
AVIATION	

PORT MCNEILL

LOCALE

TOWN OF PORT MCNEILL HARBOUR
VHF: 73
TEL: 956-3881   CHART # 3546, 3548
FAX: 956-2897   N 50 35 W 127 05
British Columbia Area Code: 604

1626 BEACH DRIVE
BOX 1389
PORT MCNEILL, B.C.
VON 2RO

GENERAL

OFFICE HOURS
SUMMER:	8 AM - 7 PM DAILY
WINTER:	SEE COMMENTS

DAILY MOORAGE
SUMMER:	$.52 PER FT
WINTER:	$.52 PER FT

MONTHLY MOORAGE
SUMMER:	$5.61 PER FT
WINTER:	$2.81 PER FT

VISA — YES   MasterCard — YES
DISCOVER —

ON THE DOCK SERVICES
POWER	✓	LIGHTING	✓
30 AMP	✓	CABLE	
WATER	✓	PHONE	
GARBAGE	✓	DERRICK	
WASTE OIL	✓	LIVE ABRD	

Note: All marina information is subject to; change without notice, misinterpretation, misrepresentation and human error. In no way are the facilities mentioned in this book obligated to honor the rates and services listed. All information is given without guarantee. No part of this book is intended for navigation.

PUBLIC SERVICES

A: Located at Marina   B: Within Walking   C: Within 30 Km   D: Not Available

	A	B	C	D
ACCOMMODATION		✓		
BAIT & TACKLE		✓		
BANK MACHINE		✓		
BOAT CHARTER	✓			
BOAT LAUNCH	✓			
BOAT RENTAL			✓	
CAMPING		✓		
CAR RENTAL	✓			
CHARTS		✓		
DIVE SHOP	✓			
FISH LICENSE		✓		

	A	B	C	D
GOLFING			✓	
GROCERY		✓		
HARDWARE		✓		
HOSPITAL		✓		
ICE	✓			
LAUNDRY	✓			
BOAT LIFT		✓		
LIQUOR STORE		✓		
24 HR PARKING	✓			
POST OFFICE		✓		
PROPANE	✓			

	A	B	C	D
PUB	✓			
PUMPOUT STN				✓
RESTAURANT		✓		
RV FACILITIES		✓		
SHOPS / MALL		✓		
SHOWER		✓		
SWIM POOL		✓		
TAXI		✓		
TELEPHONE	✓			
TIDAL GRID	✓			
TOILETS	✓			

SHELL

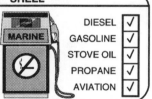

HOURS SUMMER
8 AM - 8 PM
HOURS WINTER
8 AM - 5 PM
TEL 956-4044

DIESEL	✓
GASOLINE	✓
STOVE OIL	✓
PROPANE	✓
AVIATION	✓

WINTER OFFICE HOURS:
8:30 AM - 4:30 PM MONDAY - FRIDAY
8:30 AM - 12:00 PM WEEKENDS.

SECRET COVE

LOCALE

SECRET COVE MARINA
VHF:
TEL: 885-3533
FAX:
British Columbia Area Code: 604

CHART # 3311
N 49 32 W 123 58

BOX 1118
SECHELT, B.C.
V0N 3A0

GENERAL

OFFICE HOURS

SUMMER:	MARCH - OCT
WINTER:	CLOSED

DAILY MOORAGE

SUMMER:	$.80 PER FT
WINTER:	$.50 PER FT

MONTHLY MOORAGE

SUMMER:	VARIES*
WINTER:	VARIES*

VISA	YES	MasterCard	YES
	YES	DISCOVER	

ON THE DOCK SERVICES

POWER	✓	LIGHTING	✓
30 AMP	✓	CABLE	
WATER	✓	PHONE	
GARBAGE	✓	DERRICK	
WASTE OIL		LIVE ABRD	

Note: All marina information is subject to; change without notice, misinterpretation, misrepresentation and human error. In no way are the facilities mentioned in this book obligated to honor the rates and services listed. All information is given without guarantee. No part of this book is intended for navigation.

PUBLIC SERVICES

A: Located at Marina   B: Within Walking   C: Within 30 Km   D: Not Available

	A	B	C	D
ACCOMMODATION		✓		
BAIT & TACKLE	✓			
BANK MACHINE			✓	
BOAT CHARTER		✓		
BOAT LAUNCH		✓		
BOAT RENTAL		✓		
CAMPING			✓	
CAR RENTAL			✓	
CHARTS	✓			
DIVE SHOP			✓	
FISH LICENSE	✓			

	A	B	C	D
GOLFING			✓	
GROCERY	✓			
HARDWARE			✓	
HOSPITAL			✓	
ICE	✓			
LAUNDRY			✓	
BOAT LIFT		✓		
LIQUOR STORE	✓			
24 HR PARKING	✓			
POST OFFICE	✓			
PROPANE	✓			

	A	B	C	D
PUB		✓		
PUMPOUT STN				✓
RESTAURANT		✓		
RV FACILITIES			✓	
SHOPS / MALL			✓	
SHOWER	✓			
SWIM POOL			✓	
TAXI			✓	
TELEPHONE	✓			
TIDAL GRID			✓	
TOILETS	✓			

ON ENTRY TO SECRET COVE STAY TO PORT OF MARKER.

EXCELLENT SWIMMING AND BEACH ACTIVITIES AT BUCCANEER BAY. GREAT DINNING NEAR BY.

ESSO

HOURS SUMMER
6 AM - 10 PM
HOURS WINTER
CLOSED
TEL   885-3533

DIESEL	✓
GASOLENE	✓
STOVE OIL	
PROPANE	
AVIATION	

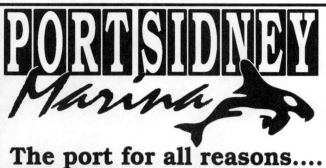
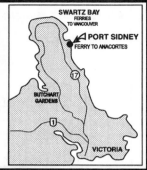

185

SIDNEY

LOCALE

PORT SIDNEY MARINA

VHF: 68

TEL: 655-3711 CHART # 3313

FAX: 655-3771 N 48 39 W 123 23.5

British Columbia Area Code: 604

9835 SEAPORT PLACE
SIDNEY, B.C.
V8L 4X3

GENERAL

OFFICE HOURS

SUMMER:	8 AM - 8 PM
WINTER:	8 AM - 5 PM

DAILY MOORAGE

SUMMER:	<40'$.90 >40' $.95
WINTER:	$.50 PER FT.

MONTHLY MOORAGE

SUMMER:	$6.00 PER FOOT
WINTER:	$6.00 PER FOOT

VISA	YES	MasterCard	YES
	YES	DISCOVER	

ON THE DOCK SERVICES

POWER	✓	LIGHTING	✓
30 AMP	✓	CABLE	✓
WATER	✓	PHONE	✓
GARBAGE	✓	DERRICK	
WASTE OIL		LIVE ABRD	✓

FIRST CLASS FACILITY, ALL CONCRETE DOCKS WITH MAIN DOCK 16' WIDE. FIREWORKS ON JULY LONG WEEKEND. FLOWER POTS ON ALL PILINGS. DOCKOMIINIUMS FOR SALE. LIMITED ANNUAL MOORAGE AVAILABLE, INQUIRE ABOUT REBATE OFFER. 30 & 50 AMP POWER.

PUBLIC SERVICES

A: Located at Marina   B: Within Walking   C: Within 30 Km   D: Not Available

	A	B	C	D		A	B	C	D		A	B	C	D
ACCOMMODATION		✓			GOLFING			✓		PUB	✓			
BAIT & TACKLE		✓			GROCERY		✓			PUMPOUT STN	✓			
BANK MACHINE		✓			HARDWARE		✓			RESTAURANT	✓			
BOAT CHARTER	✓				HOSPITAL			✓		RV FACILITIES			✓	
BOAT LAUNCH		✓			ICE	✓				SHOPS / MALL	✓			
BOAT RENTAL			✓		LAUNDRY	✓				SHOWER	✓			
CAMPING			✓		BOAT LIFT			✓		SWIM POOL			✓	
CAR RENTAL		✓			LIQUOR STORE		✓			TAXI	✓			
CHARTS	✓				24 HR PARKING		✓			TELEPHONE	✓			
DIVE SHOP		✓			POST OFFICE		✓			TIDAL GRID				✓
FISH LICENSE	✓				PROPANE		✓			TOILETS	✓			

STEVESTON

LOCALE

STEVESTON HARBOUR AUTHORITY
VHF:
TEL: 272-5539
FAX: 271-6142
CHART # 3313
N 49 07.14 W 123 09.45
British Columbia Area Code: 604

12740 TRITES ROAD
RICHMOND, B.C.
V7E 3R8

GENERAL

OFFICE HOURS
SUMMER:	24 HRS. 272-5539
WINTER:	24 HRS. 272-5539

DAILY MOORAGE
SUMMER:	SEE COMMENTS
WINTER:	SEE COMMENTS

MONTHLY MOORAGE
SUMMER:	SEE COMMENTS
WINTER:	SEE COMMENTS

VISA | YES | MasterCard | ☐
☐ | | DISCOVER | ☐

ON THE DOCK SERVICES
POWER	✓	LIGHTING	✓
30 AMP	✓	CABLE	
WATER	✓	PHONE	
GARBAGE	✓	DERRICK	✓
WASTE OIL	✓	LIVE ABRD	

Note: All marina information is subject to; change without notice, misinterpretation, misrepresentation and human error. In no way are the facilities mentioned in this book obligated to honor the rates and services listed. All information is given without guarantee. No part of this book is intended for navigation.

PUBLIC SERVICES

A: Located at Marina B: Within Walking C: Within 30 Km D: Not Available

	A	B	C	D
ACCOMMODATION		✓		
BAIT & TACKLE		✓		
BANK MACHINE		✓		
BOAT CHARTER				✓
BOAT LAUNCH	✓			
BOAT RENTAL				✓
CAMPING				✓
CAR RENTAL			✓	
CHARTS		✓		
DIVE SHOP		✓		
FISH LICENSE		✓		

	A	B	C	D
GOLFING			✓	
GROCERY		✓		
HARDWARE		✓		
HOSPITAL			✓	
ICE		✓		
LAUNDRY		✓		
BOAT LIFT	✓			
LIQUOR STORE			✓	
24 HR PARKING	✓			
POST OFFICE		✓		
PROPANE			✓	

	A	B	C	D
PUB		✓		
PUMPOUT STN				✓
RESTAURANT		✓		
RV FACILITIES			✓	
SHOPS / MALL		✓		
SHOWER	✓			
SWIM POOL			✓	
TAXI		✓		
TELEPHONE	✓			
TIDAL GRID	✓			
TOILETS	✓			

SEE COMMENTS

HOURS SUMMER

HOURS WINTER

TEL   SEE COMMENTS

DIESEL	✓
GASOLINE	✓
STOVE OIL	✓
PROPANE	
AVIATION	

STEVESTON HARBOUR AUTHORITY FOCUSES ON SERVICING THE COMMERCIAL FISHING FLEET. PLEASURE CRAFT ARE INVITED TO CONTACT 272-5539 TO INQUIRE ABOUT MOORAGE AVAILABLITY.
FUEL IS AVAILABLE AT THREE BARGES.
PETRO CANADA 277-7744, ESSO 277-5211, CHEVRON 277-4712.

B.C. WATERS

UCLUELET

LOCALE	**UCLUELET SMALL CRAFT HARBOURS**		P.O. BOX 910
	VHF:		HEMLOCK ST.
	TEL: 726-4241	CHART # 3602	UCLUELET, B.C.
	FAX:	N 48 56 W 125 33	VOR 3AO
	British Columbia Area Code: 604		

OFFICE HOURS

SUMMER:	ATTENDED
WINTER:	ATTENDED

DAILY MOORAGE

SUMMER:	$1.49 PER METRE
WINTER:	$1.49 PER METRE

MONTHLY MOORAGE

SUMMER:	$11.99 PER METRE
WINTER:	$11.99 PER METRE

VISA   MasterCard   [card]   DISCOVER

ON THE DOCK SERVICES

POWER	√	LIGHTING	√
30 AMP	√	CABLE	
WATER	√	PHONE	
GARBAGE	√	DERRICK	
WASTE OIL	√	LIVE ABRD	

Note: All marina information is subject to; change without notice, misinterpretation, misrepresentation and human error. In no way are the facilities mentioned in this book obligated to honor the rates and services listed. All information is given without guarantee. No part of this book is intended for navigation.

PUBLIC SERVICES

A: Located at Marina   B: Within Walking   C: Within 30 Km   D: Not Available

	A	B	C	D
ACCOMMODATION	√			
BAIT & TACKLE	√			
BANK MACHINE	√			
BOAT CHARTER	√			
BOAT LAUNCH	√			
BOAT RENTAL	√			
CAMPING	√			
CAR RENTAL	√			
CHARTS	√			
DIVE SHOP	√			
FISH LICENSE	√			

	A	B	C	D
GOLFING			√	
GROCERY	√			
HARDWARE	√			
HOSPITAL			√	
ICE	√			
LAUNDRY	√			
BOAT LIFT	√			
LIQUOR STORE	√			
24 HR PARKING	√			
POST OFFICE	√			
PROPANE	√			

	A	B	C	D
PUB	√			
PUMPOUT STN	√			
RESTAURANT	√			
RV FACILITIES	√			
SHOPS / MALL	√			
SHOWER	√			
SWIM POOL	√			
TAXI	√			
TELEPHONE	√			
TIDAL GRID	√			
TOILETS	√			

UCLUELET FUEL FLOATS
CHEVRON - 726-4472
ESSO - 726-4368
PETRO CANADA - 726-4262

HOURS SUMMER		DIESEL	
	NO	GASOLINE	
HOURS WINTER	FUEL	STOVE OIL	
	FLOAT	PROPANE	
TEL		AVIATION	

FUEL FLOATS

Each number on this map represents a *marina* that has indicated a fuel float at or near their facility. Look to the corresponding map numbers on the following page to reference names and telephone numbers. Fuel types and other information can be accessed by looking up the appropriate marina page.

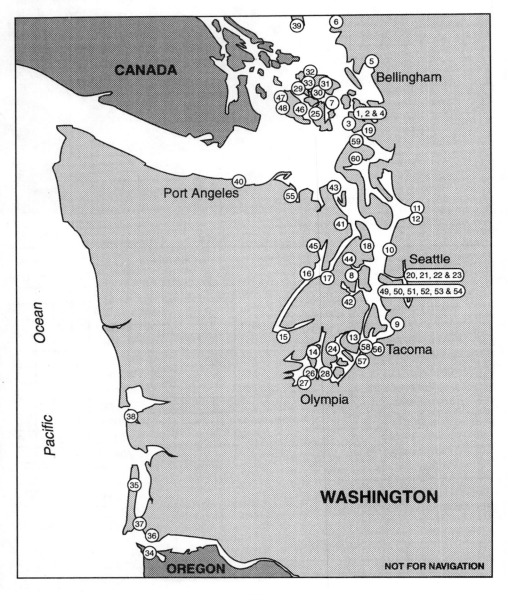

FUEL FLOATS

1 - **ANACORTES** *Anacortes Marina*
Chevron Tel: 293-8200
2 - **ANACORTES** *Cap Sante Boat Haven*
Shell Tel: 293-3145
3 - **ANACORTES** *Skyline Marina*
Unocal 76 Tel: 293-5134
4 - **ANACORTES** *Wyman's Marina*
Independent Tel: 293-4606
5 - **BELLINGHAM** *Port Of Bellingham*
Shell Tel: 734-1710
6 - **BLAINE** *Blaine Harbor*
Blaine Marina Tel: 332-8425
7 - **BLAKELY ISLAND** *Blakely I. Marina*
Independent Tel: 375-6121
8 - **BREMERTON** *Port Of Brownsville*
Texaco Tel: 692-5498
9 - **DES MOINES** *City Of Des Moines*
Texaco Tel: 824-5700
10 - **EDMONDS** *Port Of Edmonds*
Unocal 76 Tel: 775-4588
11 - **EVERETT** *Dagmars Marina*
Chevron Tel: 259-6124
12 - **EVERETT** *Port Of Everett Marina*
Unocal 76 Tel: 388-0689
13 - **GIG HARBOR** *Tides Tavern*
Shell Tel: 858-9131
14 - **HARTSTENE ISLAND** *Jarrell's Cove*
Chevron Tel: n/a
15 - **HOOD CANAL** *Hood Canal Marina*
Unocal 76 Tel: 898-2252
16 - **HOOD CANAL** *Pleasant Hbr Marina*
Chevron Tel: 796-4611
17 - **HOOD CANAL** *Seabeck Marina*
Texaco Tel: 830-5129
18 - **KINGSTON**
TexacoTel: 297-3545
19 - **LA CONNER** *La Conner Marina*
Chevron Tel: 466-4478
20 - **LAKE WASHINGTON** *Davidson's*
Chevron Tel: n/a
21 - **LAKE WASHINGTON** *Kenmore Air*
Texaco Tel: 486-1257
22 - **LAKE WASHINGTON** *Leschi*
Chevron Tel: 324-4100
23 - **LAKE WASHINGTON** *Yarrow Bay*
Texaco Tel: 822-8081
24 - **LONGBRANCH** *Lakebay Marina*
Unbranded Tel: 844-3350
25 - **LOPEZ ISLAND** *The Islander Lopez*
Chevron Tel: 468-3383
26 - **OLYMPIA** *Boston Harbor Marina*
Chevron Tel: 357-5670
27 - **OLYMPIA** *West Bay Marina*
West Bay Marina Tel: 943-2080
28 - **OLYMPIA** *Zittel's Marina*
Texaco Tel: 459-1950
29 - **ORCAS ISLAND** *Deer Harbor Resort*
Shell Tel: 376-4420
30 - **ORCAS ISLAND** *Island Petro Service*
Texaco Tel: 376-3883

31 - **ORCAS ISLAND** *Rosario Resort*
Independent Tel: 376-2222
32 - **ORCAS ISLAND** *West Beach Marina*
Texaco Tel: 376-2240
33 - **ORCAS ISLAND** *West Sound Marina*
Independent Tel: 376-2314
34 - **OREGON** *Hammond Marina*
Unbranded Tel: 325-5701
35 - **PACIFIC COAST** *Nahcotta*
Unbranded Tel: 665-4541
36 - **PACIFIC COAST** *Port Of Chinook*
Unocal 76 Tel: n/a
37 - **PACIFIC COAST** *Port Of Ilwaco*
Nichol's Fuel Dock Tel: 642-4159
38 - **PACIFIC COAST** *Westport Marina*
Chevron Tel: 268-0076
39 - **POINT ROBERTS**
TEXACO Tel: 945-2255
40 - **PORT ANGELES**
CHEVRON Tel: 457-4505
41 - **PORT LUDLOW** *Port Ludlow Marina*
Texaco Tel: 437-0513
42 - **PORT ORCHARD**
Texaco Tel: 876-5535
43 - **PORT TOWNSEND**
Unbranded Tel: 385-7031
44 - **POULSBO**
Texaco Tel: 779-9905
45 - **QUILCENE BAY**
Unbranded Tel: n/a
46 - **SAN JUAN ISLAND** *Friday Harbor*
Chevron Tel: 378-2464
47 - **SAN JUAN ISLAND** *Roche Harbor*
Texaco Tel: 378-2155
48 - **SAN JUAN ISLAND** *Snug Harbor*
Snug Gas Tel: 378-4762
49 - **SEATTLE** *Chris Berg Inc.*
Unocal 76 Tel: 284-6600
50 - **SEATTLE** *Elliot Bay Marina*
Chevron Tel: 282-8424
51 - **SEATTLE** *Harbor Island Marina*
Texaco Tel: n/a
52 - **SEATTLE** *Port Of Seattle*
Delta Western Tel: 282-1567
53 - **SEATTLE** *Shilshole Bay Marina*
Texaco Tel: 783-7555
54 - **SEATTLE** *Stimson Marina*
Chevron Tel: 784-0171
55 - **SEQUIM BAY** *John Wayne Marina*
Texaco Tel: 417-3440
56 - **TACOMA** *Breakwater Marina Inc.*
Chevron Tel: 752-6663
57 - **TACOMA** *Narrows Marina*
Chevron Tel: 564-4222
58 - **TACOMA** *Pt Defiance Boathouse*
Chevron Tel: 591-5325
59 - **WHIDBEY ISLAND** *Cornet Bay Marina*
Texaco Tel: 675-5411
60 - **WHIDBEY ISLAND** *Oak Harbor Marina*
Unocal 76 Tel: 679-4609

Each number on this map represents a *State Marine Park* or *Recreation Area*. Look to the corresponding map number on the following page to access information for each park.

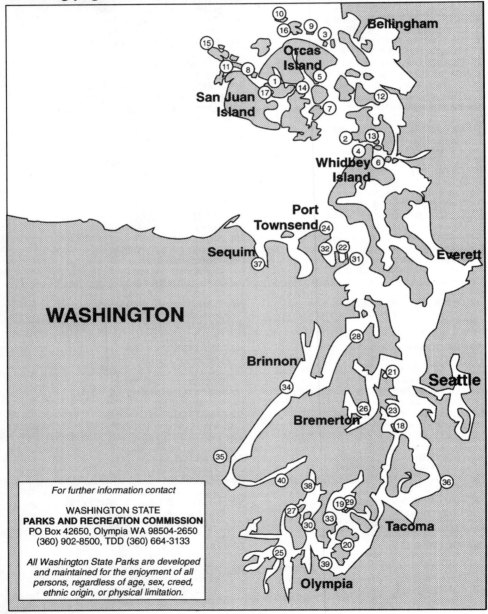

For further information contact

WASHINGTON STATE
PARKS AND RECREATION COMMISSION
PO Box 42650, Olympia WA 98504-2650
(360) 902-8500, TDD (360) 664-3133

All Washington State Parks are developed and maintained for the enjoyment of all persons, regardless of age, sex, creed, ethnic origin, or physical limitation.

STATE MARINE PARKS
San Juan Islands & Puget Sound

* Moorage / boat launch, floats removed during winter.

Map #	Park Name	Number of moorage buoys	Moorage float space footage	Accessible by boat only	Underwater park for divers	Boat launch	Sewage pump-out station	Porta-potty dump station	Fees	Campsites (primitive)
1	Blind Island	4		●						●
2	Bowman Bay								●	
	Sharps Cove*	5	128			●		●	●	
3	Clark Island	9		●						●
4	Cornet Bay		1140			●	●	●	●	
5	Doe Island*		60	●						●
6	Hope Island	4		●						
7	James Island	5	134	●					●	●
8	Jones Island*	7	264	●					●	●
9	Matia Island*	2	144	●			●	●	●	●
10	Patos Island	2		●						●
11	Posey Island			●						●
12	Saddlebag Island			●						●
13	Skagit Island	2		●						
14	Spencer Spit	16								●
15	Stuart Island			●					●	●
	Reid Harbor	15	621	●		●	●	●	●	●
	Prevost Harbor	7	256	●					●	●
16	Sucia Island			●					●	●
	Echo Bay	14							●	●
	Fox Cove	4							●	●
	Shallow Bay	8							●	●
	Ewing Cove	4		●					●	●
	Snoring Bay	2							●	●
	Fossil Bay	16	778						●	●
17	Turn Island	3		●						●
18	Blake Island	23	1744	●	●		●	●	●	●
19	Cutts Island	9		●						
20	Eagle Island	3		●						
21	Fay Bainbridge	3				●				●
22	Fort Flagler*	7	244		●		●	●	●	●
23	Fort Ward	2			●	●				●
24	Fort Worden*	8	128		●	●			●	●
25	Hope Island	1		●						
26	Illahee	5	356			●		●	●	●
27	Jarrell Cove	14	682				●	●	●	●
28	Kitsap Memorial	2								●
29	Kopachuck	2			●					
30	McMicken Island	5			●					
31	Mystery Bay	7	683				●	●	●	
32	Old Ft. Townsend	4								
33	Penrose Point	8	304				●	●	●	
34	Pleasant Harbor		218				●	●	●	
35	Potlatch	5								
36	Saltwater	2			●					●
37	Sequim Bay*	6	424			●		●		●
38	Stretch Point	5							●	
39	Tolmie	5			●					
40	Twanoh	7	192			●	●	●		●

FEES
Floats, Docks and Floating Islands

Boats under 26 feet:	$8 a night
Annual Permit:	$50 a year
Boats more than 26 feet:	$11 a night
Annual Permit:	$80 a year
Moorage buoys:	$5 a night

RULES

1) Overnight boaters must self-register and pay the fees where posted.
2) Facility use is first come, first served.
3) Leaving a dinghy at a buoy or dock does not reserve moorage space.
4) Annual permits must be displayed as directed.
5) Continuous moorage at a facility is limited to three consecutive nights.
6) Rafting is permitted within posted limits. A vessel rafted to another vessel will be charged a moorage fee based on its own length.
7) Open flames, live coals, and combustibles must be placed on a fireproof base, away from fuel tanks and vents.
8) Commercial vessels are restricted to loading and unloading passengers from May 1 through September 15.
9) Pets must be kept on leashes.

Note: Fees and participating parks are subject to change.

Washington State Parks and Recreation Commission Guide

PUMPOUT STATIONS

This map index represents page numbers of the marinas included in *The Marina Handbook* that indicated a pumpout station at their facility. Look to the list (right) to see names of the marinas depicted or look them up by page number to reference further information.

It is illegal to discharge untreated sewage into Washington State waters.

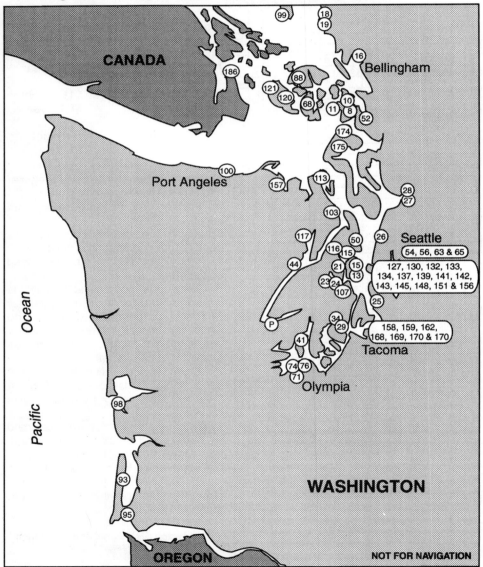

PUMPOUT STATIONS

This is a list of the marinas included in *The Marina Handbook* that indicated a pumpout station at their facility. Look to map index (left) to see locations. Page numbers indicated beside names & on map.

HAULOUTS AND SHIPYARDS

Haulout Facilities	Type of lift	Weight (up to)	Length (up to)	Haulout (per ft)	Power Wash	Lay-over charge	Shipwright on duty (rate)	Boat owners may perform work	Boat owners may bring in shipwright
American Marine Contractors Inc Seattle	Railway	100 Ton	100 ft	$4/ft @ 50'	$1.50/ft	None	$50/hr	No	No
Bayside Marine Everett	Sling	6000 lb	26 ft	$30 @ 26'	$1/ft	$.30/ft/day	$58/hr	Yes	Yes
Blaine Marine Service	Hydraulic Trailer	18 Ton	38 ft	$3.95/ft	$1/ft	$10/day*	Onsite	Yes	Yes
Block & Tackle Boat Yard Des Moines	Travel Lift	37 Ton	50 ft	$6/ft @ 50'	$1.50/ft	$.75/ft/day	$50/hr	Yes	No*
C.S.R. Marine Inc. Seattle	Crane	20 Ton	50 ft	$4/ft	$1/ft*	$.50/ft/day	$52/hr	Yes*	No
Canal Boat Yard Seattle	Travel Lift	70,000 lb	65 ft	$5/ft @ 50'	$1.50/ft	$.55/ft/day	$35/hr	Yes	Yes
Deer Harbor Boatworks	Hydraulic Trailer	18 Ton	50 ft	$3.50/ft@50'	$35	$.30/ft/day	$40/hr	Yes	Yes
Delta Marine Seattle	Crane	100 Ton	100 ft	$5/ft	$39/hr	None	$39/hr	Yes*	No
Dockside Sales & Service Port Orchard	Travel Lift	30 Ton	55 ft	$5.76/ft@50'	$1.76/ft	$.66/ft/day	$45/hr	Yes	No
Dunato's Seattle	Sling	60 Ton	65 ft	$5/ft @ 50'	$1.50/ft	$.50/ft/day*	$48/hr	Yes	No
Fidalgo Boat Yard Anacortes	Travel Lift	55 Ton	80 ft	$5.75/ft	$1.50/ft*	$.50/ft/day	$40 - $55/hr	Yes	Yes*
Fleet Marine Inc. Port Townsend	Travel Lift	30 Ton	50 ft	$5/ft @ 50'	$.50/ft	$.22/ft/day	$40/hr	Yes	Yes*
Gig Harbor Marina	Travel Lift	25 Ton	50 ft	$5.50/ft@50'	$60/hr	$1/ft/day*	$44/hr	Yes	Yes*
Lieb Marine Industries Seattle	Crane	15 Ton	40 ft	$4/ft	$1.75/ft	None	$48/hr	No	No
Lovric's Sea-Craft Anacortes	Railway	1000 Ton	130 ft	$7/ft @ 50'	$44/hr	None	$44/hr	No	No
Modutech Marine Tacoma	Railway	100 Ton	70 ft	$4/ft	$60/hr	None	$48/hr	No	No
Padden Creek Marine Inc. Bellingham	Travel Lift	30 Ton	Inquire	$5/ft	$1.50/ft	$.50/ft/day*	$44/hr	Yes	Yes*
Penmar Marine Co. Skyline Marina, Anacortes	Travel Lift	35 Ton	65 ft	$4.25/ft	$1.25/ft	$.45/ft/day*	$48/hr	Yes	Yes*

HAULOUTS AND SHIPYARDS

Haulout Facilities	Type of lift	Weight (up to)	Length (up to)	Haulout (per ft)	Power Wash	Lay-over charge	Shipwright on duty (rate)	Boat owners may perform work	Boat owners may bring in shipwright
Port Angeles Marine	Marine Ways	200 Ton	100 ft	$6/ft	$.70/ft	$2/ft/day	Onsite	Yes	Yes
Port of Edmonds	Travel Lift	35 Ton	55 ft	$5/ft*	Included	$20/day	Onsite	Yes	Yes*
Port of Port Angeles	Travel Lift	70 Ton	65 ft	$3.25/ft	$.70/ft	$.40/ft/day	Onsite	Yes	Yes
Port of Port Townsend	Travel Lift	70 Ton	70 ft	$285 @ 50'	Included	$.17/ft/day	Nearby	Yes	Yes
Salmon Bay Boat Yard Inc. Seattle	Sling	25 Ton	50 ft	$5/ft	$30	$.50/ft/day	$25/hr	Yes	Yes
Seaview Boatyard East Seattle	Travel Lift	88 Ton	80 ft	$5/ft	$1.50/ft	$.60/ft/day	$48/hr	Yes	Yes*
Seaview Boatyard West Seattle	Travel Lift	35 Ton	60 ft	$5/ft	$1.50/ft	$.60/ft/day	$48/hr	Yes	Yes*
Skagit Bay Boatyard La Conner	Sling	100 Ton	100 ft	$4.25/ft	$1.50/ft*	$.30/ft/day*	$40/hr	Yes	No
South Park Marina Seattle	Crane	15 Ton	40 ft	$5/ft	$35	$.25/ft/day	Nearby	Yes	Yes
Sunnfjord Boats Inc. Tacoma	Railway	70 Ton	65 ft	$5.50/ft	$60/hr	$60/day*	$48/hr	Yes	No
Warrenton Boatyard Warrenton, Or.	Railway	100 Ton+	90 ft	$3.50/ft	$36/hr	Varies*	$36/hr	No	No*
West Bay Marine Services LLC Olympia	Travel Lift	35 Ton	55 ft	$6/ft @ 50'	$1.45/ft*	$.65/ft/day	$46.50/hr	Yes	Yes*
Westman Marine Inc. Blaine	Travel Lift	30 Ton	50 ft	$4.75/ft	$2/ft*	$25/day@50'	$42.50/hr	Yes	Yes*

The above table lists some of the areas haulout facilities giving comparable information from Blaine to Olympia to Warrenton Oregon. When gathering these weights and rates, many of the boatyards did not have a set price per foot and used a graduated scale, or had more than one lift. For ease of comparison in most cases we took the largest lift and then calculated a price per foot from the 50 foot quote. Any information designated by an "*" has details that could not be mentioned on this type of table.

NOTE: The rates and weights listed above were gathered by a non-scientific telephone survey March 1996. All information is subject to change without notice, misinterpretation, misrepresentation and human error. In no way are the above mentioned haulout facilities under any obligation to honor these rates.

TRAFFIC SEPARATION SCHEME (TSS)

TSS - Traffic Separation Schemes are designed to place a "Separation Zone" between opposing vessel traffic lanes similar to the "median" between the lanes of the Interstate highway system. Think of the TSS as a two lane waterborne highway with each lane being 1000 yards wide separated by a 500 yard separation zone. Traffic Separation Schemes add predictability to waterway traffic flows just like the interstate. You can rely on the fact that large vessels will more than likely be in the traffic lanes. *Sample below (as indicated on chart)*

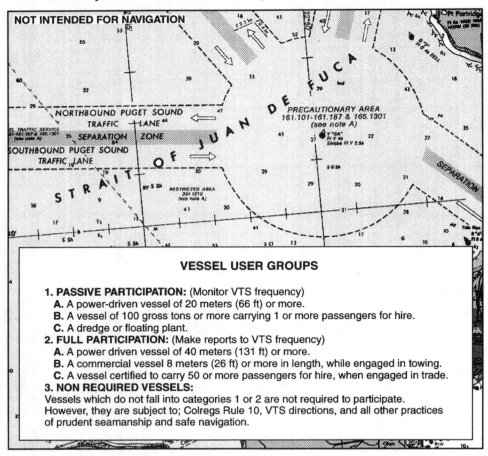

NOT INTENDED FOR NAVIGATION

NORTHBOUND PUGET SOUND TRAFFIC LANE

SEPARATION ZONE

SOUTHBOUND PUGET SOUND TRAFFIC LANE

PRECAUTIONARY AREA 161.101-161.187 & 165.1301 (see note A)

STRAIT OF JUAN DE FUCA

VESSEL USER GROUPS

1. PASSIVE PARTICIPATION: (Monitor VTS frequency)
   A. A power-driven vessel of 20 meters (66 ft) or more.
   B. A vessel of 100 gross tons or more carrying 1 or more passengers for hire.
   C. A dredge or floating plant.

2. FULL PARTICIPATION: (Make reports to VTS frequency)
   A. A power driven vessel of 40 meters (131 ft) or more.
   B. A commercial vessel 8 meters (26 ft) or more in length, while engaged in towing.
   C. A vessel certified to carry 50 or more passengers for hire, when engaged in trade.

3. NON REQUIRED VESSELS:
Vessels which do not fall into categories 1 or 2 are not required to participate.
However, they are subject to; Colregs Rule 10, VTS directions, and all other practices of prudent seamanship and safe navigation.

If you operate in the TSS you are bound by the TSS rules. Rule 10 of the Navigation Rules details a vessels conduct when operating within a TSS. These rules are designed to enhance safety in U.S. waters and reduce conflicts between the many users of local waters (i.e. freighter / tanker vs. recreational boaters).

TSS NAVIGATION RULES
(COLREGS RULE 10)

1. A vessel shall, so far as practicable, avoid crossing traffic lanes but, if obliged to do so, shall cross on a heading as nearly as practicable at right angles to the general direction of traffic flow. See e.g. 2-1

WHY Do This? Not only will this practice result in a faster crossing of the traffic lanes, but will reduce the amount of time of exposure to large vessels operating in the traffic lanes. More importantly however, crossing at right angles will also make you much more easily detectable both visually and by radar by providing a beam aspect of your vessel. Hence, the safer you and your vessel will be.

2. A vessel other than a crossing vessel or vessel joining or leaving a lane shall not normally enter a separation zone.

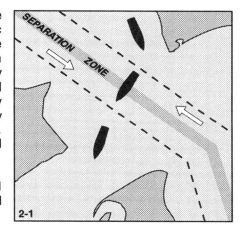

WHY? Separation Zones provide areas where a vessel can "bail out" in the event of an emergency. Furthermore, fishing vessels, particularly in the Strait of Juan de Fuca have a tendency to fish in these "medians".

3. A vessel not using a TSS shall avoid it by as wide a margin as possible.

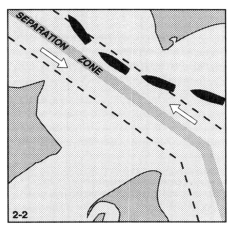

WHY? Recreational boaters are more maneuverable than a large vessel or a tug and tow. These vessels rely on the predictability of the traffic flow when following the traffic lanes. Recreational boaters that congest the TSS tend to reduce the predictability and therefore safety of vessel traffic.

4. Vessels, when leaving or joining traffic lanes, shall do so at as small an angle to the general direction of traffic flow as practicable. See e.g. 2-2

WHY? This allows vessels to safely "merge" with existing traffic in the lanes and minimizes disruptions to existing traffic flow. Merging in this manner is similar to using a highway on / off ramp.

TSS NAVIGATION RULES
(COLREGS RULE 10)

5. A vessel of less than 20 meters (66 feet) or a **sailing vessel,** shall not impede the safe passage of a power-driven vessel following a traffic lane. **A vessel engaged in fishing** shall not impede the passage of a vessel following a traffic lane.

NOTE: "Shall not impede" means a vessel MUST NOT navigate in such a way as to risk the development of a collision with another vessel (i.e. when a vessel following a TSS is forced to make an unusual or dangerous maneuver in order to avoid one of the vessels listed above, than the vessel following the TSS has been impeded.

WHY? The larger the vessel, the more room and time it takes for that ship to maneuver or stop. A 900 foot container ship or a tug with a cumbersome tow can't turn or stop on a dime! **Stay well clear!** The master or pilot must anticipate rudder commands or speed changes miles in advance. Remember, the master of a large vessel or tug and tow doesn't always know what you are going to do!

6. All vessels are required to keep the center of the precautionary area to port. NOTE: A precautionary area is usually marked by a yellow lighted buoy and is clearly marked on all nautical charts.

WHY? This is an area where vessels following the TSS are negotiating course changes and where other vessels join or depart the TSS, therefore, all mariners must exercise caution in these areas. If you are in the TSS and encounter a large vessel, or tug & tow in a precautionary area, BEWARE, for the vessel is most likely changing course and may be less able to avoid you.

NOTE: Failure to comply with these regulations could create an unsafe navigational situation and may result in a civil penalty of up to $5000.

Ships and tugs using the TSS use VHF channels 13, 14 and 5A (U.S., NOT INTERNATIONAL). The PSVT's call sign is "Seattle Traffic" or simply "Traffic".

EMERGENCY PROCEDURES, IMPORTANT RADIO FREQUENCIES & FLAGS

Emergency Procedures

In case of grave and imminent danger, on one of the VHF radio distress channels (listed below) repeat **"MAYDAY"** three times, then give name of vessel and position, and nature of distress and assistance requested.

When no grave and imminent danger exists but assistance of some nature is required, use the urgency signal. On one of the VHF radio distress channels repeat **"PAN PAN"** three times, then give name of vessel and position, and nature of urgency and assistance requested. Complete instructions are available upon request by contacting the *DEPARTMENT OF TRANSPORTATION UNITED STATES COAST GUARD.*

Important Radio Frequencies

156.8 MHz - Ch. 16 - International Distress, Safety and Calling
2182 kHz - International Distress
Ship to Ship or Ship to Shore - 9, 68, 69, 71, 78
Ship to Ship only - 67, 72

162.550 MHz - VHF Ch. WX1 - Weather
162.400 MHz - VHF Ch. WX2 - Weather
162.475 MHz - VHF Ch. WX3 - Weather

Flags

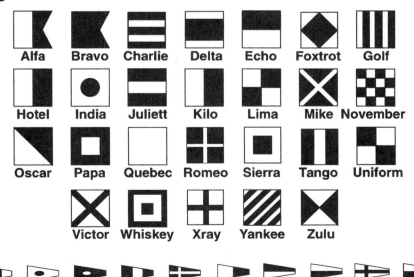

CUSTOMS REPORTING REQUIREMENTS & PROCEDURES FOR PLEASURE BOATS AND YACHTS

DESIGNATED PORTS OF ENTRY

CUSTOMS TELEPHONE NUMBERS: To report your arrival, call the telephone numbers listed below.

WASHINGTON

Aberdeen	532-2030
Anacortes	293-2331
Bellingham	734-5463
Blaine	332-6318
Everett	259-0246
Friday/Roche Harbour	378-2080
Neah Bay (see Port Angeles)	457-4311
Olympia (see Tacoma)	593-6338
Point Roberts	945-2314
Port Angeles (Neah Bay)	457-4311
Port Townsend	385-3777
Seattle	553-4678
Tacoma (Services Olympia)	593-6338

ALASKA

Anchorage	243-4312
Haines	767-5511
Juneau	586-7211
Ketchikan	225-2254
Sitka	747-3374
Skagway	983-2325
Valdez	835-2355
Wrangell	847-3415

AFTER HOURS

For Washington ports, call **1-800-562-5943** toll-free, after 5:00 p.m. and before 8:00 a.m. on weekdays-or anytime on holidays or Sundays. If you can't reach the toll-free number, contact the local telephone operator for appropriate local access code. NOTE: Vessels licensed for fisheries and trade may **not** use the 1-800 number. Call the local number.
Saturday 8:00 AM - 5:00 PM - Call Designated Port of Entry to Report Your Arrival.

PLEASURE VESSELS ARRIVING AT PUGET SOUND AND ALASKAN PORTS

Who Reports: The master or person in charge of the boat, or his designated representative, must report to Customs in person or by telephone from a designated Port of Entry. For the purpose of these instructions, the term "boat" means any vessel not engaged in trade or documented for trade (not carrying merchandise or passengers for hire) such as pleasure boats and yachts regardless of size.

When Report is Required: Masters of boats arriving in U.S. waters having been at any foreign port or place, or having had contact with any hovering vessel (i.e. lying off the coast apparently for illegal purposes) are required to report their arrival to Customs.

Time of Reporting: The report of arrival must be made **immediately** after the boat has come to rest. Leaving the boat for any other purpose other than reporting is a violation of the Customs Law.

Where to Report: The report of arrival must be made from one of the designated Customs Ports of Entry (see left). The boat must be made available for possible boarding at the time of report.

Reporting Procedure: The master or designee may go ashore only to report the arrival to Customs either in person, or by telephone. No other person may leave the boat and no baggage or merchandise may be removed until the report of arrival is made and release granted by Customs.

Failure to Report: If upon arrival in United States, any person leaves the boat for any purpose other than to report arrival to Customs, such action will constitute a violation of failure to report arrival of a boat, and/or unloading passengers, baggage or

CUSTOMS REPORTING REQUIREMENTS & PROCEDURES FOR PLEASURE BOATS AND YACHTS

merchandise without Customs permission. The penalty for failure to report is $5,000 for the first violation and $10,000 for each subsequent violation. The boat may become subject to seizure and forfeiture. (19USC1433,1436,1453, and 1454).

Processing Fees: In some circumstances pleasure boats will have to pay an annual processing (user) fee of $25 (e.g., pleasure vessels 30' in length are not subject to the fee, provided the vessel has nothing to declare. The payment is required at or before the time of the first arrival each calendar year for the vessel. If you report your arrival by telephone, a fee application will be mailed (if applicable). A nontransferable decal will be issued upon payment.

Reporting to U.S. Customs: To avoid delays, please have the following information available at the time you report your arrival:

1. **VESSEL NUMBER** Be sure to use the same number that you use when you report to Canadian Customs.
2. **VESSEL NAME AND LENGTH**
3. **USER FEE DECAL NUMBER** if applicable.
4. **CANADIAN CLEARANCE NUMBER** Required for U.S. moored boats
5. **ESTIMATED DATE OF DEPARTURE** Required for Canadian moored boats.

Release Number: You will receive a release number upon completion of the arrival report to Customs. This number should be recorded in the vessel log and kept available for use in case of future inquiry. With the release number, please record the date, time and place where the vessel reported. It is strongly recommended that you retain the release number for at least one year.

GOODS & SERVICES TAX (GST)

Under the GST, most goods and services sold or provided in Canada are taxed at the rate of 7%. Non-residents of Canada may apply for a rebate of the 7% GST. The following guidelines for qualifying for the rebate are taken from the GST Rebate for Visitors pamphlet, published and distributed by Revenue Canada Customs and Excise.

In order to qualify for the GST rebate:
1. Consumer goods and short-term accommodation must total a minimum of $100 Cdn.
2. GST was paid on goods
3. Goods were purchased for use outside Canada.
4. Goods were removed from Canada within 60 days of purchase.
5. Original receipts and supporting documents must be attached.

Application must be mailed to: **Revenue Canada Customs & Excise GST Visitors**

Rebate, Ottawa, Canada K1A 1J5 or presented at a participating Duty Free Shop if your rebate is $500 Cdn or less

The claim period is one year from the date you purchased the goods and/or short term accommodations. If the seller ships your purchase outside Canada directly, you will not have to pay the GST. There is no GST rebate for alcoholic beverages, tobacco products, automotive fuels, and certain used goods that tend to increase in value, such as paintings, jewelry, rare books and coins.

If you require further information or assistance, please write to: Revenue Canada's Visitor Rebate Program (address above) or call, toll-free from anywhere in Canada, 1-300-66VISIT. If you are outside Canada, please call (613) 991-3346.

CUSTOMS REPORTING
CANPASS - Private Boats Program
FOR PLEASURE BOATS AND YACHTS

CANPASS - Private Boats Program

**Marine Customs Reporting Center
Victoria 1-800-222-4919**

If you enter Canada from the United States using pleasure craft, a new program in British Columbia called CANPASS - Private Boats may be for you.

As a traveler on a Canadian or U.S. registered pleasure craft, you can apply to participate in the program.

If you are accepted, you will receive a CANPASS - Private Boats permit holders package which includes a letter of authority, a decal for the boat's windshield, and a burgee.

As a permit holder, you can:

- report by telephone **up to four hours before arriving in Canada** using a 1-800 number; and
- make a declaration by telephone of goods you are importing for personal use.

If you are not a permit holder, you have to follow the procedures described in the section, "What if you do not have a permit?"

Do you qualify for the program?

You, your spouse, and any dependent children you list on your CANPASS - Private Boats application form will qualify for the program if all of you are:

- citizens or permanent residents of Canada;
- citizens or resident aliens of the U.S. who meet the normal visitor requirements, i.e., good health, no criminal or narcotic record, and the ability to financially support your self and your dependents while in Canada;
- citizens or resident of the U.S. entering Canada to work or study, who meet all Canadian immigration requirements, which may include possession of valid written authorization from an immigration officer.

You, your spouse, and any dependent children you list on your CANPASS - Private Boats application will not qualify for the program if any of you:

- do not meet the above qualifications;
- provide false or incomplete information on your application;
- have a criminal record for which a pardon has not been granted;
- had a customs seizure within the past five years;
- have contravened the customs or immigration legislation;
- are inadmissible to Canada under the *Immigration Act.*

How do you apply?

Complete an application form, and send it and CAN$25 (*non-refundable*) to:
CANPASS Processing Centre
28 - 176th Street
Surrey, B.C. V4P 1M7
Phone (604) 535-9346

What are your responsibilities?
- You cannot transfer your CANPASS privileges to anyone else, or let anyone not listed on your letter of authority use your CANPASS - Private Boats permit, windshield decal, or burgee.
- You have to comply with the *Customs Act* and regulations, the *Immigration Act* and regulations, and any other laws or regulations enforced by either

department. If you violate these laws, you can be severely penalized.

- When requested by a customs or immigration officer, you have to show your CANPASS - Private Boats letter of authority, personal identification, and any required immigration documents.
- You must comply with the CANPASS - Private Boats telephone reporting procedures.
- If there are any changes in your personal information, residence, or conveyance as listed on your application, you must immediately report them to Revenue Canada.

How do permit holders use the program?

These are the steps to follow:
- Call customs at 1-800-222-4919 up to four hours before arriving in Canada from the U.S.
- Inform a customs officer of your intended arrival time and destination in Canada, and for each person on board, provide the following information: full name, date of birth, citizenship, and CANPASS - Private Boats permit number.
- If you are a returning resident, we need to know how long you were away from Canada.
- If you are a U.S. resident, we need to know how long you intend to stay in Canada, and the purpose of your visit.
- All travelers on board have to declare all personal goods they are importing. If duties and taxes are payable, the customs officer will require your VISA or MasterCard number and expiry date.
- Once you dock in Canada, you can enter Canada, unless a customs or immigration officer is there to conduct an examination.

Are there penalties if you misuse your permit?

Your acceptance in the CANPASS program is a privilege. We will periodically examine boats to ensure participants are using their CANPASS privileges properly. **We will strictly enforce the law.**

What if you do not have a permit?

You use the following steps:
1. You have to report to a designated telephone reporting station on arrival in Canada.
2. You have to contact Revenue Canada by calling the 1-800 number posted at the telephone reporting station.
3. You will be asked to provide the following information: full name, birth date, and citizenship for each person on board; purpose and length of stay in Canada, if travelers are not returning residents; and passport and visa details, if applicable.
4. You have to declare all goods being imported. If duties and taxes are payable, you have to provide customs with your VISA or MasterCard number and expiry date.
5. The customs officer receiving the telephone report will advise you whether you are free to leave the area and enter Canada, or that you must await the arrival of customs and immigration officers for a routine inspection or to complete documents.

What if there are permit holders and non-permit holders on the same vessel?

If any person on board your vessel is not a CANPASS - Private Boats permit holder, you must use the procedures outlined

CUSTOMS REPORTING REQUIREMENTS & PROCEDURES FOR PLEASURE BOATS AND YACHTS

earlier in the section, "What if you do not have a permit?"

Designated Reporting Stations

Metro Vancouver
Crescent Beach Marina
False Creek Government Dock
Steveston Government Dock
White Rock Government Dock

Victoria
Victoria Customs Dock
Oak Bay Marina
Royal Victoria Yacht Club (Cadboro Bay)

Sidney
Angler's Anchorage
Bedwell Hbr (Summer Only)
Canoe Cove
Port Sidney
Royal Victoria Yacht Club (Tseum Hbr)
Van Isle Marina

Nanaimo
Brechin Point Marina
Nanaimo Harbour Commission

Campbell River
Discovery Chevron
Discovery Marina

Port Alberni
Government Dock

Powell River
Government Dock

Prince Rupert
Fairview Petrocan
Government Dock (Rushbrook)
Prince Rupert Yacht Club

Rushbrook
Government Dock

Reports will also be accepted from:

Bamfield
Fisherman's Dock West
Kingfisher Marina (Chevron)

Ucluelet
Small Craft Harbour

Customs Regulations On Control Of Goods Entering Canada

Live Animals: Check with your local Veterinarian on transporting animals across international borders.

Fresh Fruit and Vegetables: Certain fruits or vegetables are prohibited. Contact the Department of Agriculture at the number provided:

*Victoria ....(604) 363-3421
*Vancouver ....(604) 666-7073

Plants and Plant Material: There are numerous restrictions on plants. Please contact the Department of Agriculture.

Liquor or Wine, After 48 Hours: 1.14 litres of liquor or wine per person or Beer or Ale 24 x 355 ml bottles per person. Legal age for B.C. is 19 years old.

Tobacco Products per Person, After 48 Hours: Cigarettes, 200; Cigars, 50; Tobacco Sticks, 400; Manufactured Tobacco, 400 grams.

Foodstuffs: An amount related to the purpose and length of stay.

Prohibited and Restricted Weapons: All automatic weapons, handguns and mace. Items mentioned are not all inclusive. Please contact Canada Customs for further information.

Regulated Firearms: Long rifles and shotguns. Please contact Canada Customs for information on importation of regulated firearms.

Personal Exemptions

As a Canadian resident returning from a trip abroad, you may qualify for a personal exemption and be able to bring to Canada goods up to a certain value, free of duties! These exemptions are also available to former residents of Canada who are returning to live in this country, temporary residents, and even babes in arms. In the case of infants or small children, the parent or guardian must make the customs declaration, and the goods being declared in the child's name must be for his or her use.

It is important that your personal exemptions have limitations and these are determined by the length of your stay abroad, how often you use your personal exemption entitlements, your age (in the case of tobacco and alcohol), and the nature of the goods. In general, the goods brought in under a personal exemption must be for personal or household use, as souvenirs of your trip or as gifts. Goods brought in for commercial use, or on behalf of another person, do not qualify and are subject to full duties.

Remember, your personal exemption is "personal" and cannot be pooled with other peoples' or transferred to someone else.

After 24 Hours' Absence Or More

Any number of times per year, you may bring in goods to the value of $50 (except tobacco products and alcoholic beverages). **A written declaration may be required.**

- If the total value of all goods brought in exceeds $50, this exemption may not be claimed. Rather, you must pay duties on the full value.

After 48 Hours' Absence Or More

Any number of time per years, you may bring in goods to the value of $200. **A written declaration may be required.**

After 7 Days' Absence Or More

Any number of times per year, you may bring in goods to the value of $500. **A written declaration will be required.**

- It is **dates** that matter, not times, for example leave Friday the 7th, return Friday 14th.

If you are claiming an exemption after a 48 hour absence, in addition to your $200 or $500 duty free goods, you are also entitled to claim goods valued at up to $300 Cdn. at a preferred rate of duty:
- Goods made in the U.S. or Canada: 2.1% duty +7% GST
- Goods made in other countries: 7.1% duty +7% GST

Be Prepared

Here are a few hints that will help to reduce the amount of time you spend at Canada Customs:

- Call ahead for duty rates on items you are considering buying.
- Prepare a detailed list of all items that you have purchased or acquired outside Canada.
- Keep your receipts and be prepared to present them to a Customs Inspector.

Have proper identification available for all persons traveling with you.

INFORMATION SOURCES

Both experienced and novice boaters should ensure that they have complete information on conditions before they embark on their trip. The following list of publications and administrative offices should provide you with the information you need for safe boating in Washington State.

For nautical charts, sailing directions and tide and current tables, contact
National Oceanic & Atmospheric Administration (NOAA)

Coast Pilot 7
National Oceanic & Atmospheric Administration (NOAA)

Special Notice To Mariners
Department of Transportation
United States Coast Guard
Thirteenth Coast Guard District

Washington Boater's Guide
Washington State Parks and Recreation Commission

Administrative Offices

For more information about Washington State Parks and their facilities contact:
Washington State Parks
PO box 42650
Olympia, WA.
98504-2650
(206) 753-2027

Hunting and fishing licensees may obtained at most sporting goods stores. For more information contact:
Washington Wildlife Department licensing Office
Olympia (206) 753-5700

For general boating information, boating safety instruction and information, and boater environmental information, contact:
Washington State Parks and Recreation Commission
7150 Cleanwater Lane (KY-11)
Olympia, WA
98504
Boater Environmental Education Program,
(206) 586-8592
Boating Safety Program,
(206) 586-2166

Coast Guard - 13th District
Marine Safety Office Puget Sound
1519 Alaskan Way S. Seattle, WA
98134-1192
Capt. of the Port OCMI (206) 217-6200
Pollution Reports (206) 217-6232
Puget Sound Vessel Traffic Service VTS
(206) 217-6050
Group Offices Seattle (Southern Puget Sound) (206) 217-6000
Port Angeles (Northern Puget Sound)
(360) 457-2226
Astir /Grays Harbor (503) 861-2213

National Oceanic & Atmospheric Administration (NOAA)
7600 Sand Point Way N.E.,
Bin C-15700, Seattle 98115
Western Administrative Support Center
(206) 526-6026
National Fisheries Service (206) 526-6150
Pacific Marine Center
1801 Fairview Ave. E., Seattle 98102
(206) 553-4548
National Weather Service (Public Service Unit) (206) 526-6087
(Port Meteorologist) (206) 526-6100

HANDY REFERENCE NUMBERS

Directory

Amtrak.. 1-800-872-7245
Department of Ecology Recycling Hotline...................... 1-800-732-9253
Department of Ecology Hazardous Waste Hotline........... 1-800-633-7585
Department of Ecology Litter Hotline............................. 1-800-548-8377
Forest Fire reports only 1-800-562-6010
National Weather Service (NOAA) - Weather Reports ..... (206) 526-6087
Office of Marine Safety (OMS) .... (360) 664-9110
Red Tide Hotline.. 1-800-562-5632
Report a spill 1-800-258-5990
Report vandalism of public lands.................................. 1-800-527-3305

United States Coast Guard:
Group Offices Seattle... (206) 217-6000
Port Angeles (Northern Puget Sound) .... (360)457-2226
Astir/Grays Harbor... (503) 861-2213
Pollution Reports .... (206) 217-6232
Vessel Traffic Service... (206) 217-6050

United States Customs... (see pg. 201)
United States Power Squadrons'................................... 1-800-336-2628
Washington State Ferries.. 1-800-843-3779

MARINA INDEX

MARINA INDEX

WEIGHTS & MEASURES

CONVERSIONS

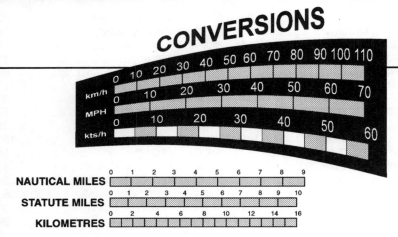

NAUTICAL MILES 0 1 2 3 4 5 6 7 8 9

STATUTE MILES 0 1 2 3 4 5 6 7 8 9 10

KILOMETRES 0 2 4 6 8 10 12 14 16

Miles x 1.6 = Kilometres
Kilometres x .6 = Miles

CELSIUS   FAHRENHEIT

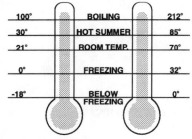

100°	BOILING	212°
30°	HOT SUMMER	85°
21°	ROOM TEMP.	70°
0°	FREEZING	32°
-18°	BELOW FREEZING	0°

Celsius x 9/5 then + 32 = Fahrenheit
Fahrenheit - 32 then x 5/9 = Celsius

Miles (Statute) x 66/76 = Miles (Nautical)
Miles (Nautical) x 76/66 = Miles (Statute)
Miles (Nautical) x 1.853249 = Kilometres
1 Fathom = 6 Feet
1 League = 3 Miles
Feet x 0.30481 = Metres
Litres x 1.58 = Pounds (Fuel)
Kilograms x 2.2 = Pounds

WIND WARNINGS

SMALL CRAFT WARNING = Wind to exceed 20 knots
GALE WARNING = Wind to exceed 34 knots but remain less than 48 knots
STORM WARNING = Wind to exceed 47 knots

U.S. GALLON   CANADIAN IMPERIAL GALLON

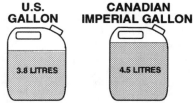

3.8 LITRES   4.5 LITRES

Imperial Gallons x 4.5 = Litres
Litres x .22 = Imperial Gallons
5 Imperial Gallons = 6 U.S. Gallons
231 Cubic inches = 1 U.S. Gallon

IMPORTANT: For ease of use conversions have been approximated.

NOTES

NOTES